HANDBOOK OF RADIATION THERAPY PHYSICS

John L. Horton, Ph.D.

prentice-hall, inc., englewood cliffs, n.j. 07632

Prentice-Hall International, Inc., *London*
Prentice-Hall of Australia, Pty. Ltd., *Sydney*
Prentice-Hall Canada, Inc., *Toronto*
Prentice-Hall of India Private Ltd., *New Delhi*
Prentice-Hall of Japan, Inc., *Tokyo*
Prentice-Hall of Southeast Asia Pte. Ltd., *Singapore*
Editora Prentice-Hall do Brasil Ltda., *Rio de Janeiro*
Prentice-Hall Hispanoamericana, S.A., *Mexico*

© 1987 *by*

PRENTICE-HALL, INC.

Englewood Cliffs, N.J.

Library of Congress Cataloging-in-Publication Data

Horton, John L.
　Handbook of radiation therapy physics.

　1. Radiotherapy.　2. Medical physics.
I. Title. [DNLM: 1. Health Physics.
2. Radiotherapy. WN 110 H823h]
RM849.H66 1987　　　615.8′42　　　86–25180

ISBN 0-13-379272-2

Printed in the United States of America

To Jennifer and Meredith

Acknowledgments

I would like to thank my colleagues of the Cleveland Clinic and M. D. Anderson Hospital for their support and suggestions during the preparation of this book. Also I must express my gratitude to the administrations of these two institutions for providing outstanding working environments. I appreciate the helpful nudges and encouragement of my executive editor at Prentice-Hall, George Parker, and his editorial assistant Jo-Anne Kern. Finally I must thank Pearl Lutcher and Barbara Keenan for transforming my sometimes enigmatic scribble into a final manuscript, a taxing process involving many drafts and revisions.

Preface

Medical physics as a discipline is difficult to define. It is neither pure science, nor purely clinical. For want of a better term, "applied clinical physics" is the closest approximation of a good definition. To complicate matters even further, medical physicists have diverse educational backgrounds. Many enter the profession from other physics disciplines, some are trained on the job and have no formal instruction; others attend seminars and workshops, and still others spend one or two years in a clinical training program. It is accurate to state that even two years of formal training is insufficient to prepare a medical physicist for all the possible problems and complex tasks he or she is likely to encounter in daily clinical practice.

One aspect of medical physics that needs no definition or explanation is the scope of responsibility. There is no ambiguity there. A physicist is involved, directly or indirectly in every aspect of patient treatment, with the exception of dose prescription. The tasks range from changing light bulbs to commissioning therapy units. Between these two extremes lie the countless daily tasks, which a physicist may perform himself or delegate to others, but for which the responsibility lies squarely on his or her shoulders.

To acquire the necessary knowledge and information, a physicist has to consider the dual nature of medical physics. One can approach it as a science and turn to textbooks, which deal with medical physics in broad general terms, but provide little in terms of applicability; or one can approach it as clinical and read publications from the ICRU, NCRP, NBS, and the AAPM. These reports usually deal with one topic or protocol in great depth and detail. Regardless of which approach is chosen, the problem is time. The information is there, but in routine clinical work one is rarely afforded the luxury of perusing textbooks and reports for a pressing practical task.

This book will bridge the gap between general textbooks and specific protocols. It is a distillation of appropriate useful publications and years of clinical experience with the specific intent of providing guidance in solving an immediate problem. Each chapter focuses on a specific practical subject. A list of references is provided in each chapter to allow for a more complete understanding of the subject. This material may also lead the reader into personal research in a particular area if he or she desires, although no attempt has been made to make this book a broad review of recent research.

Equipment selection is an important decision, involving the expenditure of over one million dollars for a large linear accelerator and perhaps one-fourth that for a treatment planning computer. The personnel who make these decisions vary from institution to institution. In some institutions, a therapist may make the decisions, in others, a physicist, a technologist, or an administrator. Because the personnel in the department will live with these decisions for a long time, an orderly approach to evaluation of equipment is essential.

Three chapters are devoted to equipment selection. The first chapter examines therapy units, the second, dosimetry equipment, and the third, treatment planning computers. Equipment manufacturers are listed, but models, specifications, and prices are not given as these are in a constant state of flux. Rather, a general approach to equipment selection is discussed. These chapters will be useful to whomever makes these decisions, be it therapist, physicist, technologist, or administrator.

After the decision on what equipment to purchase is made and the equipment is received, the physicist is responsible for its acceptance and commissioning. Whether the equipment is a therapy unit, electrometer, or treatment-planning computer, the acceptance and commissioning tests must be accomplished in a timely fashion. A well-organized approach is essential during these tests.

Very few physicists are prepared in a training program for these tasks because most institutions do not purchase new equipment every year. There is one chapter devoted to acceptance tests and one devoted to commissioning tests. A generalized protocol of acceptance tests is provided that may be modified easily for each specific task. By using this format, a physicist should be able to complete the acceptance tests in a reasonable amount of time with a great deal of confidence that the equipment will perform as expected. The drafting of specifications and acceptance tests has the additional advantage of solidifying one's thoughts on the characteristics desired for the equipment.

After the equipment is commissioned, it is employed in clinical practice. If the equipment is a therapy unit, it is used for patient treatment. One important component is clinical dosimetry, which includes both treatment planning and central axis calculations.

A chapter is devoted to clinical dosimetry for external beam and another to brachytherapy. A general system is presented and calculation sheets are reproduced. The system is straightforward and the terminology employed is widely used. A physicist or dosimetrist should find these chapters useful. This clinical dosimetry system can be adopted as presented, or it can be modified easily to an institution's particular needs. Additionally, because of the general nature of the system, a therapist will be able to benefit from these chapters and gain an understanding of all the aspects involved in the calculations.

There are several chapters on physical dosimetry covering the calibration of photon beams from 10 kV to 50 MV, electron beams from 1 MeV to 50 MeV, and fast neutron beams up to 70 MV. There is also a chapter on radiation protection discussing barrier design and personnel monitoring.

In summary, this book will serve as a ready reference to the practicing medical physicist and provide useful information to the radiation therapist, dosimetrist, and hospital administrator. The chapters on equipment selection will help in the decision-making process; the chapters on calibration, in the accuracy of dose measurement; and the chapters on clinical dosimetry, in the accuracy of dose delivery. When these goals are fulfilled, and result in the improved care of even one patient, then the effort will have indeed been worthwhile.

Contents

ONE | SELECTION OF TELETHERAPY EQUIPMENT

1.1 INTRODUCTION

The major capital expenditure of a Radiation Therapy Department involves the purchase of a treatment unit or a simulator. The total value of all dosimetry equipment in a department generally will be less than one-tenth and treatment planning computer less than one quarter, the cost of a single medium energy linear accelerator. The magnitude of these costs makes it imperative that the selection of the machine is decided for sound reasons.

In considering the purchase, personnel must answer the age-old question, "Why are we here?" Is the department a private or a university practice? A private practice may want to maximize throughput, while a university group may want something to enhance its research capabilities.

Another question to be answered is the importance of service. If the department has qualified service personnel, the service reputation of the vendor and the location of the nearest service office may not be important, however for a department without in-house service, these become essential points.

Allied with this question is the amount of physics support in the department. A small department without a full-time physicist should certainly consider a smaller universe of machines than the department with a full complement of physicists.

Is this to be the only machine or does the department have other treatment equipment? If this is the only machine and physics and service support are not problems, the department may want to consider a sophisticated, multimodality, multienergy unit. However, in a large department with several units, a machine to fulfill a single purpose may be appropriate.

Does the department have a residency training program? If so, this must weigh in the decision. Should the department purchase a machine used at a large number of institutions to ease the residents' transition to the "real world" or should the department buy a more sophisticated and complex unit to teach residents innovative techniques?

Let's not forget the financial aspects. How much money is in the budget? What is the payback period? What about service costs and reliability?

To address all these aspects, a team of individuals should be assembled. This group should include as a minimum a radiation therapist, a physicist, a technologist, and an administrator. If the department has service technicians one should be included in the group as well. If the department has an educational program then it is incumbent upon the therapist to consider that aspect of the decision. Preliminary meetings of these individuals should answer the questions just proposed and determine the needs of the department. Once this problem is resolved the group should draft specifications and solicit proposals from all vendors who can meet these needs. Following receipt of these proposals, one individual, the most appropriate being the physicist or service technician, should distill the appropriate information into a chart as illustrated in Table 1–1. This chart summarizes a comparison of four therapy machines, a betatron and three accelerators. In this example I have included machines that are no longer available because the table is intended as an illustration of the technique and not as a synopsis of the latest machine specifications.

I cannot overemphasize the importance of this step. The vendors will supply an enormous amount of data. This data from each vendor must be compared to the appropriate data from other vendors. Table 1–1 is an easy way to compare the data. After the data has been abstracted into the chart, the working party should meet to consider it. The individual who compiled the chart should carefully explain the data and provide his or her insight. If possible the group should narrow down the number of units considered. The person responsible for making the chart should then begin contacting users of the equipment for their opinions. Upon completion of this survey the group should reconvene to consider the information and further winnow the number of units considered. Then site visits by the working group should be made to institutions that have the units which are under consideration. This allows the group to observe the machines in use and determine the advantages and disadvantages of the unit. Frequently problems will be seen that the group would not have imagined. Following these site visits, the group should list the machines in order of preference. If the machine is to be placed in an existing room, the group should meet with their institution's architect and vendor to determine if any installation problems exist. If no problems are encountered the purchase order can then be placed.

1.2 COBALT MACHINES

A cobalt machine is the simplest, most reliable piece of teletherapy equipment. This unit probably would be the unit of choice in a small department in a remote location without a full-time physicist. A part-time consulting physicist can easily provide the required calibrations and the need for factory service should be rare. For most cases, treatment planning can be done with published central axis percent depth dose values. For the cases that require more sophistication, a department can subscribe to one of the national services offering computerized planning. These organizations have a large central computer that may be accessed through telephone lines from any location in the country.

The above discussion should not be construed to mean that a cobalt unit has no place in a large department in a metropolitan area with a full staff of engineering technicians and physicists supported with a large treatment planning computer. On the contrary, some therapists prefer a cobalt unit for head and neck, lymphoma, breast, and certain palliative treatments. A large department should have a range of photon energies and cobalt may be a logical choice

TABLE 1-1. Comparison of Clinical Characteristics of Three Linear Accelerators and a Betatron

Machine	RF source	X-ray beam Energy	Dose rate	Field size	Flatness	Symmetry	Target axis distance	Electron beam Energy	Dose rate	Field size	Flatness	Symmetry	X-ray contaminations	Space requirements
BETATRON		Variable 6 to 25 MV	55 cGy/min at 25 MV at 100 cm	Variable to 20 × 20 cm at 100 cm	±3% over the central 80% of a 14 × 14 cm field at 25 MV measured at d_{max} at 100 cm SSD		Not isocentric	Variable 6 to 25 MeV in accelerator	400 cGy/min at 100 cm for 25 MeV	Variable to 15 × 15 cm at 100 cm	±5% across central 80% of any scan through the center of an 8 × 10 cm field		Not specified	15 × 15 ft. + maze entrance
LINAC	Magnetron	10 MV	300 cGy/min at 100 cm	Variable 0.5 × 0.5 cm to 35 × 35 cm at 100 cm	±3% over central 28 × 28 cm of 35 × 35 cm field at 10 cm depth at 100 cm SSD	±1% over central 28 cm of 35 × 35 cm field at 10 cm depth at 100 cm SSD	100 cm ± .5 cm	3, 7, 11 MeV at isocenter	300 cGy/min at d_{max} at isocenter	5 × 5 cm, 10 × 10 cm, 15 × 15 cm, 20 × 20 cm, 25 × 25 cm at isocenter	< ±5% over the area of applicator at isocenter	±2% over a 20 × 20 area centered in a 25 × 25 cm field at 100 cm SSD	< 3% of electron dose at maximum buildup at 11 MeV	SIZE OF MACHINE: Height 102 in. Length 109 in. Width 48 in. Weight 14,000 lbs

L I N A C B	Klystron	10 MV	100 to 500 cGy/min at 100 cm	Variable 0 to 35 × 35 cm at 100 cm	±3% over central 80% of a 10 × 10 cm field at depth of 10 cm at 100 cm SSD	The integrated doses of longitudinal or transverse halves of a field at 100 cm SSD and measured at a depth of 10 cm will not differ more than ± 2% for all fields from 10 × 10 cm to 35 × 35 cm	100 cm ± .5 cm	6, 7, 12, 15, 18 MeV at the scattering foil	100 to 500 cGy/min in four steps for a 15 × 15 cm field at 100 cm SSD	4 × 4 cm to 25 × 25 cm at 100 cm (not continuously variable)	±5% over central 80% of a scan along a longitudinal or transverse axis of 15 × 15 cm field at 100 cm at d_{max}	The integrated dose of the longitudinal & transverse halves of a field will not differ more than ±2% for all fields from 10 × 10 cm to 25 × 25 cm, measured at 100 cm SSD at depth d_{max}	<5% of central axis intensity for 15 × 15 cm field at a depth of 10 cm below depth of 10% isodose	20 ft × 20 ft × 9 ft Weight 18,000 lbs
L I N A C C	Klystron	18 MV	100 to 400 cGy/min in steps of 100 cGy/min at 100 cm	2 × 2 cm to 40 × 40 cm at 100 cm	±3% over central 80% of a 30 × 30 cm field at depth of 5 cm at 100 cm SSD	±2% of total dose over the central 80% of each half field	100 cm ± .2 cm	5, 9, 13, 17, 20 MeV (point of measurement not specified)	6 MeV 150 cGy/min 9 MeV 150 cGy/min 13 MeV 400 cGy/min 17 MeV 400 cGy/min 20 MeV 400 cGy/min	2 × 2 cm to 30 × 30 cm, continuously variable, at isocenter	±3% for 13, 17, & 20 MeV, ±5% for 6 & 9 MeV over central 80% of 15 × 15 cm & 30 × 30 cm fields at d_{max} at 100 cm, measured along transverse & longitudinal axis.	Not specified	20 ft × 19 ft × 9 ft

for the low energy end. Also, it is an excellent unit in a department with a residency program because it is probable that when the residents graduate they will work with cobalt at some point in their careers.

These advantages must be balanced against the disadvantages of having to change treatment times monthly because of decay, a relatively large penumbra, and poor penetration compared to high energy X-ray beams.

1.3 LINEAR ACCELERATORS

Linear accelerators are an omnibus subject. Linear accelerators may provide low energy X-rays only, low energy X-rays and electrons, medium energy X-rays and electrons, or high energy X-rays and electrons. They may have a single X-ray energy or dual energies. They may have a bending magnet for energy analysis or they may not. They may have a selection of electron energies in one, two, or four MeV steps. The electron beam may be flattened with scattering foils and cones or with scanning magnets and "trimmers." They may or may not be isocentrically mounted. The monitoring of the unit may be performed with computer control or with conventional hardwired techniques.

The first decision a department must make is the X-ray energy of interest. Then, decisions on whether electron capabilities are desired and, if so, what electron energies, scattered or scanned electrons, single or dual X-ray energies, isocentrically mounted or not, follow.

1.3.1 Low Energy X-ray Units

A small department may opt for a low energy X-ray unit as an alternative to cobalt-60. Some low energy units, notably the Varian Clinac 4, have a reputation for reliability that almost equals cobalt. The lowest energy X-ray accelerators do not have electron capabilities because the applications for electrons below 5 MeV are limited.

1.3.2 Low Energy Units with X-ray and Electron Capabilities

Linear accelerators with photon energies of 6 MV and above may be purchased with electron capabilities. Some of the lowest energy units in this category, 6 MV, have electrons up to approximately

9 MeV. If a somewhat higher X-ray energy is desirable electron energies of 12 MeV are available. An institution that wants a higher electron energy should consider either a single X-ray energy machine of 10 MV and above or a dual energy machine.

1.3.3 Medium Energy Accelerators

For a department that needs an X-ray beam of 10 to 18 MV, machines are available with electron energies of 4 or 5 MeV up to 20 MeV. Machines in this energy range may also offer two photon energies. One of these might be in the 6 to 10 MV range and the other in the 15 to 20 MV area. For many years, a popular unit in this energy range was the Varian Clinac 18. This machine had electron energies up to 18 MeV with a photon beam of 10 MV. One of the reasons the X-ray energy was liminted to 10 MV was to avoid problems with neutrons.

The neutron separation energy of many nuclei is 6 to 8 MeV. The cross section for this reaction generally increases with the atomic number of the material. The cross section also increases with photon energy, reaching a maximum at 20 MeV to 25 MeV for low atomic number nuclei and 10 to 15 MeV for high atomic number nuclei. Consequently for X-ray beams above 10 MV, neutron production in the target and shielding materials starts to become a problem. Neutrons are produced in the primary beam as well as outside the beam. While most studies demonstrate this is not an undue hazard to the patient, radiation protection of departmental personnel presents problems in shielding for these neutrons. Depending upon the treatment room, it may be necessary to include some hydrogenous material, such as borated polyethylene in the design of the shielding door. The polyethylene serves to thermalize the neutrons, which are then captured in the boron as well as the hydrogen of the polyethylene. Further details of shielding design are included in Chapter 13.

More recently, as people developed confidence in dealing with these problems, the trend has been to increased X-ray energies of 15 to 20 MV. Siemens has designed its linear accelerators using a thin target technique. This target consists of a layer of tungsten backed by a layer of carbon. The electrons strike the tungsten first, pass through and stop in the carbon. This design produces a higher average energy X-ray spectrum than the conventional thick target approach because the bremsstrahlung cross section increases with the atomic number of the material and the energy of the electron. Since the electrons "see" the tungsten first they have higher energy and can produce higher energy X-rays. The electrons that pass through the tungsten are degraded in energy and then interact in the carbon to produce lower energy X-rays. These are fewer in number than would be produced by the same energy electrons in tungsten. Consequently, more high energy X-rays are produced relative to the low energy X-rays than in thick tungsten targets. This concept has allowed Siemens to offer linear accelerators of 15 MV with X-ray beam characteristics similar to those of 18 MV of some other manufacturers. An additional benefit of this design is the concomitant reduction in the neutron production because of the reduction in the peak energy of the X-ray beam.

If a department is considering a medium energy accelerator it should very carefully consider the characteristics of electron beams. Many accelerators have been purchased based on the electron energies available on a particular machine. Unfortunately electron beam energy is an ill-defined term. The term may refer to either the *mean energy* or the *most probable energy*. The mean energy, Ea, is the energy equal to the arithmetical mean of the energies of the electrons in the spectrum. The most probable energy, Ep, is the energy that occurs most frequently; more electrons have this energy than any other.

In addition to this ambiguity in energy specification, the problem of the point of energy specification arises. Is the energy specified at the point the electron beam enters the bending magnet, exits the accelerator, or encounters the surface of the patient? These energies are all different, because the electrons lose energy in passing through the vacuum windows in the accelerator, scattering foils, and air. One must be careful to determine which electron energy a vendor specifies.

But in reality even knowledge of electron energy specification still yields an incomplete knowledge of electron beam characteristics because the same electron energy from different machines may have quite different characteristics. For this reason, Brahme and Svensson[1] have proposed several additional factors measured on the central axis that should be considered. These quantities include:

1. surface dose (measured at .5mm)
2. depth of maximum dose
3. depth of 85% dose (therapeutic range)
4. depth of 50% dose (half-value-depth)

5. practical range

6. dose gradient

7. photon background

These factors are reasonable to consider because electrons are chosen to uniformly irradiate a volume to a relatively shallow depth and spare the distal tissue as much trauma as possible. The amount of skin sparing is an important factor for electron therapy as skin tolerance is frequently the limiting factor with this modality. The depth of 0.5 mm was taken as the depth of the radiation sensitive layer of the skin and therefore the appropriate depth to state entrance dose. The depth of d_{max} and its distance from the depth of the 85% dose are important factors indicating the size of the volume to be uniformly irradiated. The therapeutic range was defined to be the depth of the 85% level. Although a dose uniformity of ±5% in the target is the stated aim, Brahme and Svensson thought it was unrealistic to take the 90% level as the therapeutic range. The depth of the 50% dose, the practical range and the dose gradient are all measures of how quickly the dose decreases past the treatment volume. Finally, the photon background indicates the amount of radiation received by tissues beyond the range of the electrons.

As a general rule for the same practical range, scanned electron beams have a lower surface dose, deeper depth of maximum dose, greater depth of 85% dose, higher dose gradient, and lower photon background than electrons flattened with scattering foils. However, improved design of scattering foils and collimating cones have reduced this difference in recent years. Scanned electron beams may present other problems to a department. For instance, if a department primarily treats irregularly shaped electron fields, it may be more convenient to attach beam shaping materials to the end of a collimating cone than to devise a method to attach them to electron "trimmers." If the machine is to be used for intraoperative radiation therapy, a unit that had collimating cones could be a definite benefit. For electron arc therapy neither machine demonstrates a clear advantage.

1.3.4 High Energy Accelerators

At the high energy end, accelerators offer X-ray energies of 20 to 25 MV and electron energies from 4 or 5 MeV up to 40 MeV. These machines frequently have dual X-ray energies and some manufacturers offer collimators that may be opened asymmetrically about the central axis.

1.4 BETATRONS

A betatron is an alternative to a linear accelerator. The betatron and the linear accelerator perform the same basic task: the production of high energy X-rays and electrons. A betatron provides higher energy electrons and X-rays than the linacs used in radiation therapy. X-ray energies up to 45 MV and electron energies up to 45 MeV are offered on betatrons. The disadvantages of betatrons are lack of isocentric mounting, lower dose rate, and narrow range of field sizes. Because of the large size of betatrons, they are not isocentrically mounted and therefore are not quite as versatile as linear accelerators. In a betatron, space charge limits the number of electrons that may circulate in an equilibrium orbit and therefore restricts the dose rate. This is usually not a problem with electrons but the X-ray dose rate may be a factor of 2 to 4 lower than that of a linear accelerator.

1.5 MICROTRONS

There are two basic types of microtrons, circular and racetrack. These are illustrated in Figure 1–1. The circular microtron consists of one radiofrequency (rf) cavity operated in the S band and a magnetic field oriented perpendicular to the plane in which the electrons travel. This magnetic field constrains the electrons to move in circular orbits. On each pass through the rf cavity, the electrons increase their energy. This increase in energy increases the magnetic rigidity of the electrons. Their increased magnetic rigidity forces the electrons into larger orbits which increases the travel time around the orbit. This difference in transit time is made equal to an integral multiple of microwave periods; this means the electrons arrive at the cavity at the correct time for acceleration. The total energy spread of the electron beam of a circular microtron is quoted as approximately 50 keV and the full width at half maximum as 35 keV. The maximum electron energy of this machine is 22 MeV.

A higher energy microtron has been christened the racetrack microtron. In this machine the electrons follow a path that resem-

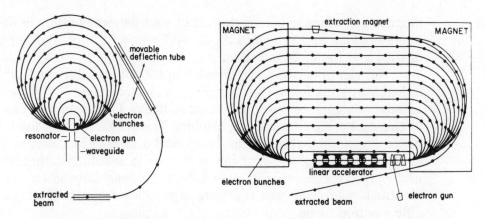

Figure 1–1 Schematic representation of a circular and a racetrack microtron. From A. Brahme and D. Reistad, "Microtrons for Electron and Photon Radiotherapy," *IEEE Transactions on Nuclear Science*, NS-28, 1880, 1981, © IEEE. Used with permission.

bles a racetrack. This machine operates on a principle similar to the circular microtron except several rf cavities are used for acceleration. The magnet must be divided into two halves which are separated by some distance to accommodate the additional cavities. The maximum electron energy of this machine is 50 MeV with a total energy spread of 500 keV.

The narrow energy spread of microtron beams produces an electron beam with very good emittance characteristics, which permit beam transport over long distances. Because of this property a single microtron may supply multiple therapy rooms or a therapy room and a surgical suite expressly designed for intraoperative radiation therapy. A further advantage of the circular microtron for intraoperative radiation therapy is its wide selection of electron energies from 2 MeV to 22 MeV in steps of approximately 2 MeV. Other unique features of the microtrons are technqiues used for flattening X-ray beams. The circular microtron has a composite flattening filter constructed with a high atomic number material in the center and a low atomic number material in the periphery. This design creates a photon beam with less change in mean energy across the face of the beam than is possible with a conventionally designed flattening filter.

The flattening of the racetrack microtron X-ray beam is accomplished by scanning the incident electron beam across the tungsten target. This results in a scanned X-ray beam because of the forward peaked production of 50 MV X-rays. This technique avoids the degradation in mean energy typical of lead flattening filters in this energy regime and produces an X-ray beam with a greater depth of d_{max} and better penetration.

The electrons from the circular microtron are flattened with a dual scattering foil system resulting in electron beams with characteristics similar to those of a scanned beam. This system consists of two scattering foils used in tandem. The primary scattering foil nearer the source spreads the beam and a second foil, placed 10 cm downstream of the first foil is thicker in the middle than the periphery. This design serves to flatten the dose distribution. The racetrack microtron uses scanning to produce a clinically acceptable electron beam.

Other features, such as range of field sizes and dose rates, are comparable to those available from linear accelerators. The microtron is not isocentrically mounted but the electron beam may be transported to an isocentric gantry. As previously mentioned, a microtron can supply beams to several treatment rooms, but do not be deceived into thinking one can get two or three treatment rooms for the price of one machine. The isocentric gantries and beam transport systems can become quite expensive. Also remember that if one machine serves two treatment rooms, when that machine is down two rooms and not one are down. This means one has to deal with twice as many upset patients.

1.6 CLINICAL ASPECTS OF THERAPY EQUIPMENT

Till now we have examined cobalt units, linear accelerators, betatrons, and microtrons individually. We have primarily looked at aspects that can be described easily in a list of specifications. Table 1–2 lists some reasonable specifications for an accelerator. A cobalt unit, betatron, or microtron will have a slightly different set of specifications. This table should only be used for initial consideration of various linear accelerators. It must not be considered all-inclusive and should not be used to draft specifications for a purchase order. Further discussion of this subject appears in Chapter 5.

If the specifications were the sum total of concern about therapy equipment, site visits would be unnecessary. But site visits are useful for investigating certain matters related to patient handling.

These concerns begin with the table. Most therapy tables come

TABLE 1–2. Typical Specifications for Medical Linear Accelerators

Mechanical specification for isocentric units

Target-Axis Distance   100 cm

Isocenter Accuracy   ± 1 mm

Gantry Rotation
 Range   ± 185°
 Speed   Continuously variable from 0 to 1 rpm

Collimator Rotation
 Range   ±185°
 Speed   Continuously variable from 0 to 1 rpm

Optical Distance Indicator
 Range   80 cm to 120 cm
 Accuracy   ± 2 mm

Field Defining Light   1)   Cross hair shall be within 2 mm of the central axis
                                    of the radiation beam
                            2)   The edges of the light field shall correspond to the
                                    50% decrement line of the radiation field to within
                                    2 mm

Accuracy of Gantry Angle Indicators   0.5°

Accuracy of Collimator Angle Indicators   0.5°

Radiation performance specifications

Photon Beam

Field Size   The field size shall be continuously variable from
                    2 cm × 2 cm to 40 cm × 40 cm

Flatness   The dose shall be within 3% of the average value over
                    the central 80% of the irradiated area for all fields larger
                    than 10 cm × 10 cm. This specification shall be measured
                    at a depth of 10 cm in a water phantom positioned with
                    its surface at the source-axis-distance

Symmetry   The integrated dose for any half of the field shall not
                    differ by more than 2% from the integrated dose of the
                    other half of the field

Electron Beam

Field Size   Variable from 5 cm × 5 cm to 25 cm × 25 cm

Flatness   The dose shall be within 5% of average value over the
                    central 80% of the irradiated volume for all fields larger
                    than 10 cm × 10 cm. This specification shall be measured
                    at the depth of d_{max} in a phantom positioned with its
                    surface at the source-axis-distance

Symmetry   Same as photon specifications

X-ray   The X-ray contamination shall be less than 5% of the
 Contamination   maximum dose on the central axis for all electron
                    energies

TABLE 1-2. (Continued)

Radiation performance specifications

Arc Therapy

Dose Rate	Continuously variable from 0.5 to 10 mu per degree
Direction	It shall be possible to perform arc therapy in a clockwise or counterclockwise direction
Accuracy	The system shall terminate within 2 mu or 1 degree of the set values. The mu per degree delivered during rotation shall be within 3% of the prescribed value

Mechanical specifications for treatment couch

Range of Motion	
Longitudinal	80 cm
Lateral	±25 cm
Vertical	60 cm with uppermost position at least 1 cm above isocenter height
Couch Rotation	±100°
Turntable Rotation	±100°
Accuracy of Motion	The table shall move in true horizontal and vertical planes to within ±1 mm over the entire range of motion
Accuracy of Position Indicators	All angle readouts shall be accurate to within 1° and all distance indicators shall be accurate to within 2 mm
Load Bearing Capabilities	The table shall support at least 150 kg. The table shall not deflect more than 5 mm under this load

equipped with an insert, usually in a tennis racquet-like configuration or of a thin mylar construction, through which the beam is directed when a posterior port is treated. One should investigate the amount this insert sags with an obese patient. A related question is the deflection of the entire table under a large patient's weight. One should also see how convenient it is to transfer a patient from a stretcher to the treatment table. Does this maneuver require lifting the patient or may the patient be slid from cart to table? Are the motions of the table sufficiently versatile to accommodate any imaginable treatment? How easy is it to position cassettes for verification films?

Next, the hand controls in the treatment room should be examined. Can personnel work on either side of the table? Are the table and the gantry motion controls on separate hand control pendants or are they on a single pendant? Are the gantry controls on a hand pendant and the table controls on the table? Does the table have a "free float" option or does it offer only motorized movement? How effective are the locks on the table? Where are the emergency off switches? Can they be accidentally activated or are they too remote?

After this aspect has been examined, turn to questions involving motion of the unit. Is it possible to treat oblique ports from under the table? If there is a beamstopper, how much does it interfere? Don't forget blocks and wedges. Are these easy to position individually as well as together? What are the interlocks? What is the design of the blocking tray? Is it versatile enough?

Then go outside the treatment room. How easy is it to initiate treatments? Is it too easy from a safety standpoint or too difficult from the patient throughput aspect? What are the verification techniques? What happens in case of a power failure in the midst of a treatment? What is the procedure for verification films? What is the warmup time? What are the start-up procedures? Ask to see the Operator's Manual. Talk with the technologists to determine their overall feelings about the machine. What do they love about it? What do they hate?

If possible discuss with the physician his or her impressions. How was the decision made to purchase the machine? What factors were considered? Which were most important? What is the quality of service? What are his or her feelings about working with the company?

Talk with the physicists and service technicians. Was the installation difficult or did it go smoothly? Have there been any catastrophic breakdowns with extended periods of downtime? If so, why? Was it a common problem or a quirk? How were the acceptance tests handled? Did the vendor's representatives know what they were doing? What do the users think are the machine's strong points and weak links?

1.7 TREATMENT SIMULATORS

The original task of a treatment simulator was as an alternative to using a therapy unit to take verification films. The simulator became popular because it increased the efficient use of treatment machines and provided images superior to the therapy unit. The simulator has outgrown its original job and today its use as a verification tool is a tertiary task. Its two primary uses today are for localization and treatment planning.

First, the area to be treated is localized. This job is greatly aided if the simulator has fluoroscopic capabilities. Although computed tomography (CT) scanners are widely used to aid in localization, the simulator remains as the workhorse for this task. Once the volume to be irradiated is determined, decisions are made on the best technique to treat this volume. The simulator is used to set up the desired radiation ports and appropriate marks placed on the patient. Today the use of the simulator for verification is much less important than these two tasks. We have returned to taking verification films mainly on the treatment unit.

The simulator must be a machine with a diagnostic X-ray tube that can reproduce exactly the geometry of a treatment unit. Since many departments have more than one therapy machine, the simulator should be versatile enough to mimic all the treatment units. This requirement demands that a simulator be an isocentrically mounted unit with a wide enough range of target-axis-distances (TAD) to reproduce extended fixed source-skin-distance (SSD) treatments as well as isocentric treatments. The simulator should maintain its isocenter over the entire range of TADs to ±1 mm.

There should be field defining wires, a cross hair to indicate the central axis of the beam and a diaphragm system in the X-ray head. The diaphragm assembly is used to limit the X-ray beam and the field defining wires are used to delineate the treatment area. The range of movement for the diaphragm and cross wires should be greater than the largest field size available on a treatment unit. One should be able to set the cross wire asymmetrically about the central axis; some accelerators currently offer this option. There should be a light field that corresponds to the X-ray field within 2 mm over the range of TADs.

The couch should have all the movements of any couch on a therapy unit. These movements include vertical, longitudinal, lateral, and rotational. The couch should be constructed to have minimal deflection under a 150 kilogram load but also it must be transparent to X-rays. The couch must be wide enough so that treatments, such as tangential breast fields may be simulated.

The X-ray tube and generator must be adequate to yield satisfactory images of views, such as a lateral pelvis, which may exceed 50 cm in thickness. Also, imaging on a simulator is performed at greater target-film-distances than most diagnostic radiology procedures. The focal spots for fluoroscopy and films should coincide to yield the same views in both modalities. One might think that a larger focal spot is permissible with a simulator than a regular diagnostic unit because typically one is not required to image very small structures. However, a large focal spot will degrade the sharpness of the field defining wires.

Simulators are offered with and without a fluoroscopy option. Although it is true that localization can be done with films, fluoroscopy greatly enhances the efficiency of this operation. The image intensifier (II) should be the largest available because it will be frequently necessary to image techniques such as mantle fields that may exceed 55 cm at the II. These cases will demand even the largest II be moved during exposure to image the entire field. Of course, the larger IIs can image more fields without moving and more effectively image the largest fields than smaller IIs. Because some fields are larger than even the largest II, it must have a wide range of movement in the vertical, longitudinal, and lateral directions. The movement of the II must not displace the axis of rotation of the gantry. The II is coupled into a TV chain that must be of sufficient quality to present a clear image.

Because most treatment fields require auxiliary shielding, the simulator should have a shadow tray attachment that duplicates the source-tray-distance on all the therapy machines in a department. Several alternatives are available to mimic shielding blocks. One might simply outline the area to be shielded with solder placed on the block tray. Another technique is the use of aluminum sheets approximately one HVL thick, cut in the shape of blocks on the therapy unit to shadow the desired area. A third method is the use of low density blocks the same shape and size as the shielding blocks. This allows one to visualize the differential absorption across blocks whose edges are parallel to the central axis. Finally, one could use the shielding blocks from the therapy unit if the shadow tray is designed to support the weight. Of course, if the simulator is consigned to the task for which it was originally conceived, verification of treatment fields, it would be essential to have a shielding tray capable of supporting the actual blocks.

A simulator should have an optical distance indicator (ODI) with the same accuracy as the ODI on the therapy units. Readouts for target-film-distance, target-axis-distance, and target-table-top-distance are very convenient. Of course, readout of field size, gantry angle, collimator angle, and couch angle are essential. If available as an option, an optical backpointer is an attractive feature to include in the purchase.

Two sets of controls are required for a simulator. One set should be located in the machine room for ease in patient positioning. A duplicate set must be located in the operators room to be used during fluoroscopy.

Table 1–3 is offered as an aid to determine reasonable specifications for a simulator. This table, like Table 1–2, should only be used for initial consideration of various simulators. It should not be considered all-inclusive or be used to write specifications for a purchase order.

1.8 CT SCANNERS

The application of CT scanners to tumor localization and treatment planning is widespread. Nevertheless, seldom does a radiation therapy department have a great deal of input to the selection process. This decision is generally made by the diagnostic radiology department and radiation therapy must abide by their decision and share the use of the equipment with them. For this reason I will not address questions involved in choosing a CT scanner but discuss details necessary for its successful implementation in a therapy department as the needs of the two departments are somewhat different.

To effectively use a CT scanner for treatment planning, the patient must be scanned in treatment position. However, tables on therapy machines are almost universally flat, whereas tables on CT scanners are sector shaped. This difference in the shape of table changes the patient's anatomy. It is essential the patient be scanned on a flat table. A plastic or wooden insert for the CT table facilitates this procedure. The insert fits into the "dished" area of the CT table and presents a flat surface for patient positioning. This insert may be easily moved off and on the table.

To insure that the patient is scanned in treatment position, all treatment aids, such as headrests and immobilization casts used during treatment, should be used during the scanning procedure. For this reason it is important these be fabricated from low density, low atomic number materials and are small enough to fit through the scanner's aperture. The treatment fields and their central axes should be outlined with radioopaque catheters, such as Angiocath, to image the treatment field. If lasers are used in the treatment room for patient positioning, it is helpful if an identical set is present in the CT room.

Diagnostic radiology is not concerned with the absolute value of Hounsfield (CT) numbers or with the constancy of these numbers. However, if these numbers are used in treatment planning for heterogeneity corrections, it is essential that they be accurately correla-

TABLE 1–3. Typical Specifications for Radiation Therapy Simulators

Mechanical specification for gantry

Target-Axis Distance	60 to 140 cm
Isocentric Accuracy	±1 mm over range of motion of image intensifier and X-ray tube
Optical Distance Indicator	
Range	60 cm to 160 cm
Accuracy	±1 mm
Gantry Rotation	
Range	± 185°
Speed	Continuously variable from 0 to 1 rpm
Collimator Rotation	
Range	± 185°
Speed	Continuously variable from 0 to 1 rpm
Field Defining Light	1) Cross hair shall indicate center of X-ray field to within 2 mm
	2) Edges of light field shall correspond with edges of X-ray field within 2 mm
Accuracy of Gantry Angle Indicator	0.5°
Accuracy of Collimator Angle Indicators	0.5°

Mechanical specifications for table

Range of Motion	
Longitudinal	80 cm
Lateral	±25 cm
Vertical	60 cm with uppermost position at least 1 cm above isocenter height
Couch Rotation	±100°
Turntable Rotation	±100°
Accuracy of Motion	The table shall move in true vertical and horizontal planes to within ±1 mm over the entire range of motion
Accuracy of Position Indicators	All angle readouts shall be accurate to within 1° and all position readouts shall be accurate to within 2 mm
Load Bearing Capabilities	The table shall support at least 150 kg and it shall not deflect more than 5 mm under this load

Mechanical specifications for image intensifier

Image Intensifier-Axis-Distance	10 cm to 70 cm
Range of Motion	
Longitudinal	±25 cm
Lateral	±15 cm

ted to electron densities. On occasion CT manufacturers may change the software on a particular unit to upgrade its capabilities. These changes may change the correspondence between electron densities and CT numbers. Also, CT numbers may be somewhat dependent on the scan diameter, therefore separate tables of CT number versus electron density are needed for each scan diameter. Occasionally, the image may be somewhat distorted. For example, a circle may appear as an ellipse with a small eccentricity. A quality assurance program should be instituted to address these problems.

1.9 SUMMARY

In this chapter I have formulated a strategy to assist one in choosing teletherapy equipment. I have described various treatment units and the likely applications of these units. I have also discussed simulators and CT scanners. Finally, the reader will find in Table 1–4 the names and addresses of manufacturers of teletherapy equipment and simulators.

TABLE 1–4. Suppliers of Therapy Equipment and Simulators

Linear accelerator	Linear accelerator
Mitsubishi International Corporation 1700 Market Street, Suite 2608 Philadelphia, Pennsylvania 19103	Toshiba Medical Systems 2441 Michelle Drive Tustin, California 92680
ATC Medical Group One Factory Row Geneva, Ohio 44041	Varian Associates, Inc. Radiation Division 611 Hansen Way Palo Alto, California 94303
Atomic Energy of Canada Limited 413 March Road P.O. Box 13140 Kanata, Canada K2K 1X8	**Microtron**
CGR Medical Corporation 10150 Old Columbia Road Columbia, Maryland 21046	Scanditronix, Inc. 106 Western Avenue P.O. Box 987 Essex, Massachusetts 01929
Philips Medical Systems, Inc. 710 Bridgeport Avenue Shelton, Connecticut 06484	**Betatrons**
Siemens Medical Systems, Inc. 186 Wood Avenue South Iselin, New Jersey 08830	ATC Medical Group ATC Betatron Corporation P.O. Box 2639 West Allis, Wisconsin 53214

TABLE 1–4. (Continued)

Betatrons	Simulators
BBC—Brown, Boveri and Company, Limited CH-5401 Baden, Switzerland Division E. Sales Office EKB-V	Cascade X-ray P.O. Box 1605 Yakima, Washington 98907
Cobalt-60 units	CGR Medical Corporation 10150 Old Columbia Road Columbia, Maryland 21046
ATC Medical Group Advanced Medical Systems, Inc. 121 North Eagle Street Geneva, Ohio 44041	Kermath Manufacturing Corporation 2251 Dabney Road Richmond, Virginia 23230
Atomic Energy of Canada Limited 413 March Road P.O. Box 13140 Kanata, Canada K2K 1X8	Oldelft 2735 Dorr Avenue Fairfax, Virginia 22031
CGR Medical Corporation 10150 Old Columbia Road Columbia, Maryland 21046	Philips Medical Systems, Inc. 710 Bridgeport Avenue Shelton, Connecticut 06484
Simulators	Siemens Medical Systems, Inc. 186 Wood Avenue South Iselin, New Jersey 08830
ATC Medical Group One Factory Row Geneva, Ohio 44041	Toshiba Medical Systems 2441 Michelle Drive Tustin, California 92680
Atomic Energy of Canada Limited 413 March Road P.O. Box 13140 Kanata, Canada K2K 1X8	Varian Associates, Inc. Radiation Division 611 Hansen Way Palo Alto, California 94303

Note

1. Anders Brahme and Hans Svensson, "Specification of Electron Beam Quality from the Central-Axis Depth Absorbed-Dose Distribution," *Med. Phys.* 3(1976), 95–102.

Additional Reading

C. J. KARZMARK AND ROBERT J. MORTON, *A Primer on Theory and Operation of Linear Accelerators in Radiation Therapy*, FDA 82–8181 (Washington, D. C.: U. S. Department of Health and Human Services, 1981).

The Use of Electron Linear Accelerators in Medical Radiation Therapy: Physical Characteristics (Overview Report No. 1), FDA 76–8027 (Washington, D. C.: U. S. Department of Health, Education, and Welfare, 1976).

C. J. KARZMARK AND NEIL C. PERING, "Electron Linear Accelerators for Radiation Therapy: History, Principles, and Contemporary Developments," *Phys. Med. Biol.*, 18(1973), pp. 321–54.

C. J. KARZMARK, "Advances in Linear Accelerator Design for Radiotherapy," *Med. Phys.*, 11(1984), pp. 105–28.

C. K. BOMFORD, and others, *Treatment Simulators*, *British Journal of Radiology Supplement 16*, (London, British Institute of Radiology, 1981).

EDWIN C. MCCULLOUGH and JOHN D. EARLE, "The Selection, Acceptance Testing, and Quality Control of Radiotherapy Treatment Simulators," *Radiol.* 131(1979), pp. 221–30.

ANGELA GARDNER M. A. BAGSHAW, VERA PAGE, AND C. J. KARZMARK, "Tumor Localization, Dosimetry, Simulation and Treatment Procedures in Radiotherapy: The Isocentric Technique," *Amer. J. Roentgenol. Rad. Ther. Nucl. Med.* 114(1972), pp. 163–71.

JAMES M. GALVIN, "The Physics of Radiation Therapy Equipment," *Seminars in Oncology*, 8(1981), pp. 18–37.

TWO | DOSIMETRY EQUIPMENT SELECTION

2.1 INTRODUCTION

A number of materials and techniques have been applied in radiation dosimetry. These systems include glass, polycarbonates, lyoluminescence, photoluminescence, radiophotoluminescence, and calorimetry. However, I will not discuss these systems in this chapter because they are rarely used in radiation therapy physics. I will, instead, concentrate the discussion in this chapter on ionometric and film dosimetry with limited discussion of TLD, Fricke dosimetry, and silicon diodes. If the reader desires further details of the other techniques, many references exist that address the practical aspects of their use. Also, because of the almost "classical" nature of the Victoreen R-meter copious references exist on its application. Accordingly, it will receive little attention in the section on ionometric dosimetry. Rather the focus of that section will be on the practical aspects of cable connected ion chamber-electrometer systems.

2.2 IONOMETRIC DOSIMETRY SYSTEMS

The term "ion chamber" is often used to describe an ionometric dosimetry system, but actually the ion chamber is only one component. Besides the ion chamber, an electrometer, readout device, and a coaxial or triaxial cable to connect the ion chamber to the electrometer are necessary. For precise dosimetry, each of these components must be carefully selected and scrupulously maintained. I will discuss each in turn.

2.2.1 Ion Chambers

The selection of an ion chamber must be carefully matched to its intended application. For instance, the buildup region cannot be measured with a 1cc spherical chamber, nor is it wise to perform megavoltage photon calibrations routinely with an extrapolation chamber. However, general characteristics may be enumerated which are desirable for an ion chamber.

Characteristics of an ideal ion chamber

Our ideal ion chamber should have:

1. an infinitesimally small volume.
2. a response independent of beam energy, bias polarity, orientation in the radiation beam, and fraction of stem irradiated.
3. homogeneous construction of walls and electrode.
4. no transient electrical effects.
5. a collection efficiency of 100%.
6. total indestructibility.

In the non-ideal world we inhabit this ion chamber is not available, but let's examine each of the desired characteristics individually so we may make judicious choices.

Infinitesimally small volume   An ion chamber must occupy a finite volume. When this ion chamber is placed in a water phantom it displaces an equivalent water volume. This displacement changes the absorption and scattering of the radiation beam that we are measuring. Also, the reading of the ion chamber is representative of some value averaged over the volume. In regions with a rapid change in dose gradient, such as the penumbra, the effective point of measurement becomes questionable. For these reasons the ion chamber must be as small as practicable. It must be remembered, however, that the signal from the ion chamber is proportional to its active volume and a large signal is a desirable characteristic. The magnitude of the signal may be estimated as .333 nanocoulomb per Roentgen $\left(\dfrac{nC}{R}\right)$ per cubic centimeter of active volume. This relation is a direct result of the definition of the Roentgen and is exact only if air is the gas in the active volume and the walls are air equivalent.

Response independent of energy   Ion chambers intended to measure isodose distributions in phantom should have a response independent of energy because at depth an appreciable amount of radiation may be scattered and have a lower energy than the primary beam. The Farmer Chamber was designed to have a relatively flat response in the orthovoltage region. This was accomplished by using a graphite thimble and an aluminum electrode to achieve a balance between wall attenuation and increased photoelectric absorption. Also, conducting plastics have been developed which are "air" or "tissue" equivalent.[1] Manufacturers have developed ion chambers that have both thimble and central electrode constructed of these plastics, making a homogeneous system. However, the "air" or "tissue" equivalence of these plastics is applicable over a certain limited range of energy for photons and these plastics should be used with caution outside this range. The energy dependence of a Capintec Farmer type chamber constructed with walls and central electrode of "air equivalent" plastic is shown in Figure 2–1.

Response independent of bias polarity   The ionization collected may depend on the polarity of the collecting electrode. The reasons for this effect are varied but depend upon the number of charged secondaries stopped in the collecting electrode and insulators. These problems may be particularly severe for measurements in electron beams and in the buildup region of photon beams. However, this effect should be checked for any measurement situation with a particular chamber. If a difference exists between the readings measured with positive and negative polarities, the average value should be used as the true value.[2]

Response independent of orientation in the beam   Ion chambers can be classified generally into three design geometries: parallel plate, cylindrical, and spherical. The chamber's geometry determines its orientation in the beam. A parallel plate chamber should

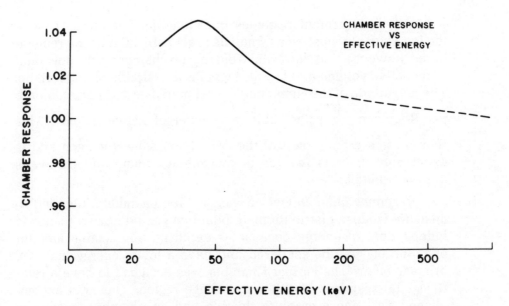

Figure 2–1 Energy dependence of a Capintec Farmer-type chamber. This curve is normalized to unity for cobalt-60 radiation.

be used with the plates perpendicular to the central axis of the radiation beam. Cylindrical chambers should be oriented with the major axis of the cylinder perpendicular to the beam's central axis. A spherical chamber with supporting stem should have its stem perpendicular to the beam axis. The angular dependence of the response of a Farmer chamber in a plane containing the central electrode is shown in Figure 2–2.

A cylindrical or spherical chamber may exhibit angular dependence also because of bent electrodes, nonuniform wall thickness, or a variety of other reasons. This response may be accounted for by noting identifying marks, such as a serial number, and always orienting these marks the same way in the radiation beam.

Response independent of fraction of stem irradiated "Stem effect" is related to the percentage of the stem that is unguarded. This phenomenon is well known because of the widespread use of the Victoreen R meter, which clearly exhibits this effect. The standard discussions of the subject address how ionization created in an unguarded stem may increase the reading of the ion chamber itself. The implicit assumption is that stem ionization, if present, always adds to the true reading. However, at least one chamber widely used for mapping isodose distributions exhibits what I call,

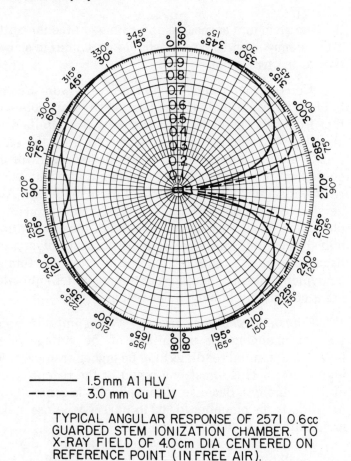

———— 1.5 mm Al HLV
------ 3.0 mm Cu HLV

TYPICAL ANGULAR RESPONSE OF 2571 0.6cc
GUARDED STEM IONIZATION CHAMBER. TO
X-RAY FIELD OF 4.0 cm DIA CENTERED ON
REFERENCE POINT (IN FREE AIR).

Figure 2–2 Angular response of a Nuclear Enterprises Farmer Chamber Model 2571. Used with permission of Nuclear Enterprises Limited.

for lack of a better term, "inverse stem effect." I have measured 2.5% more ionization with the PTW 0.1 cc micro chamber model # 30–332 oriented with the thimble on the central axis and its axis parallel to the 10 cm side of a 10 cm x 40 cm field, than with its axis perpendicular to the 10 cm side. Additional stem ionization subtracted from the signal rather than added to it in this case. Therefore, one should always check for stem ionization and never assume that if it exists it will be additive rather than subtractive.

The measured ionization may also be affected by radiation scattered from the stem. Rather than referring to this as "stem effect" it might be called "stem scatter." This phenomenon may be quantified by attaching a dummy stem to the thimble opposite the true stem and assessing any change in the ionization produced. This dummy stem, of course, should be similar in size and construction to the true stem.

Homogeneous construction of walls and electrode   Use of the Bragg-Gray principal (see Section III) to calculate dose to phantom from ion chamber measurements is simplified when the ion chamber and phantom are constructed from the same materials. I have already mentioned that the development of air and tissue equivalent plastics has lead to design of ion chambers constructed with walls and central electrode of these materials. Also, ion chambers have been constructed of polystyrene for use in polystyrene phantoms.[3,4] As stated, this simplifies the calculation of dose to polystyrene, but one must convert dose in polystyrene to dose in tissue. The ideal situation would be a water phantom with a "water equivalent" plastic chamber containing water equivalent gas creating a completely homogenous system.

Transient electrical effects   When initially applying a bias voltage, changing the magnitude of the voltage or switching its polarity, the initial readings may be higher or lower than the following readings. This effect is a result of the recent electrical history of the insulators. Because of this effect it is generally good practice to irradiate the chamber to 500 to 1000 cGy before making measurements after any change in the bias.

An additional electrical effect is leakage that occurs across any insulator. However, the leakage current on a ion chamber should be less than 10^{-14} amps 5 to 10 minutes after application of the bias voltage but prior to irradiation.

Collection efficiency   The collection efficiency is the ratio of the measured ionization to the amount of ionization collected at saturation. The value of the collection efficiency for any given irradiation condition is related to the electrode geometry and may be conveniently measured using the two voltage techniques of Boag described in Chapter 10. The collection efficiency for an ion chamber should be 99.5% or better in a megavoltage X-ray beam with a dose rate of 200 cGy/min.

Indestructibility   This characteristic has been included somewhat facetiously but it must be remembered that an ion chamber used for calibration purposes must be of robust construction. Any change in the active volume of the chamber will result in a change in the calibration factor. Also, if the chamber is to be used for daily constancy checks it may well be handled by personnel other than physicists who may not have a full appreciation of this fact. Therefore, a chamber used for primary calibrations should not be used for daily checks.

Acceptance tests

Ion chamber acceptance tests should verify that the chamber's specifications have been met. These tests should include checks for stem effect, energy dependence, polarity effect, orientation effects, electrical effects, atmospheric communication, and collection efficiency. Perpendicular radiographs should be made also. Reasonable specifications for ion chambers used for orthovoltage and megavoltage photon beams are given in Table 2–1.

Perpendicular radiographs are useful in examining for bent electrodes, irregular cavities, and non-uniform electrode spacing. These radiographs may be made with a technique of 60 kVp, 100 mA, small focus, 18 ms, 40 inch source-chamber distance and a "detail" film-screen combination.[5] Alternately I have found xeroradiographs from a mammographic unit useful because of the edge enhancement characteristics of this technique. A xeroradiograph of a Capintec Farmer type chamber is shown in Figure 2–3.

One should not assume atmospheric communication between the ion chamber's active volume and ambient air. This may be checked by altering the temperature in the room or making measurements on different days when the pressure has changed by more than 1%.

Selection of ion chambers

The selection of an ion chamber must be carefully matched to its intended use. For calibration of orthovoltage and megavoltage photon beams a chamber meeting the specifications given in Table 2–1 is appropriate. A chamber used for this purpose should have a volume of 0.5 cc to 1 cc with an internal radius of 4 mm or less. Such a chamber is also appropriate for calibrations of electron beams above 5 MeV incident electron energy. A chamber used as an in-house transfer standard to derive cobalt-60 calibration factors for other chambers may be somewhat larger. A reasonably large chamber is desirable for this purpose to attain a sizeable signal.

For measurements in the buildup region of megavoltage photon

TABLE 2-1. Typical Specifications for an Ion Chamber Suitable for Applications in Radiation Therapy Physics

---

Leakage

Leakage current prior to irradiation shall be 10^{-14} amps or less within 5 minutes of application of voltage. After irradiation leakage shall return to 5 x 10^{-13} amps or less within 1 minutes and 10^{-13} amps or less within 5 minutes.

Replicate readings

Following an irradiation of 500 cGy, repeated readings in a cobalt-60 unit shall be within 0.5% of each other.

Stem effect

The readings for an irradiation in a 10 cm x 35 cm field with the axis of the chamber oriented parallel to long axis of the field shall be within 0.5% of the reading with the field rotated 90°.

Energy dependence

The ion chamber's response to orthovoltage X-rays (HVL = 2 mm Al to HVL = 4 mm Cu) shall be within 5% of its response to cobalt-60 gamma rays. A buildup cap may be used for cobalt-60 measurements.

Angular dependence

The change in response of a cylindrical chamber should be less than 0.5% when the chamber is rotated about its major axis. A spherical chamber should show similar characteristics when rotated about an axis collinear with its supporting stem.

Polarity effect

The response of an ion chamber should vary less than 0.5% when the polarity is reversed. These measurements to be made in photon beams in accordance with the replicate reading specification above.

Collection efficiency

The collection efficiency shall be 99.5% or better when measured in an X-ray beam from a medical linear accelerator operating at 400 cGy/min. Measurement technique to be used is two-voltage method of Boag.

Atmospheric communication

The active volume of the ion chamber shall communicate with the atmosphere and it shall reach thermal equilibrium with the surrounding medium within 1 hour.

---

and electron beams a parallel plate chamber is necessary. This may be a chamber with either variable or fixed electrode spacing. A chamber with a variable electrode spacing may be used to make measurements with different spacings. These readings may be extrapolated to zero volume. Alternatively a chamber with fixed elec-

Figure 2–3   Xeroradiograph of a Capintec Farmer-type chamber.

trode spacing may be used and corrected to zero volume by the
method of Velkley, et al.[6] The polarity effect has been shown to
be significant and variable with depth in the buildup region;[7] therefore, care must be used for these measurements.

Beam profile measurements and central axis percent depth
dose should be performed with an ion chamber with a volume of
0.1 cc or less. Use of a small ion chamber minimizes the uncertainty
of the effective point of measurement that is crucial in the penumbral region where the dose gradient changes rapidly. Alternately,
for central axis measurements, a parallel plate chamber with a
narrow plate spacing may be used.

Measurements of low energy X-rays (below 150 kV) and electrons (below 5 MeV) require a parallel plate ion chamber with a
thin entrance window and a narrow electrode spacing. The thin
window is necessary to overcome absorption of the low energy

TABLE 2.2. Ion Chambers Listed by Type, Manufacturer, and Application

Type	Chamber	Model Number	Supplier
Shelf Standard	Farmer*	2505/3A or 2571 or 2581	Nuclear Enterprises
	Shonka–Wyckoff	A3	Exradin
	Farmer Type*	PR-06C or PR-06G	Capintec
		30–351	Victoreen
	Spherical 1 cc	IC17	Far West Technology
Orthovoltage and Megavoltage Photon Calibration	Farmer*	2505/3A or 2505/3B or 2571 or 2581	Nuclear Enterprises
	Farmer Type*	PR-06C or PR-06G	Capintec
		30–351	Victoreen
	Spokas*	A1 or T2	Exradin
	Memorial Hospital†	30–404	Victoreen
Low Energy X-ray Calibration	Soft Radiation	30–330 or 30–334	Victoreen
	Thin Window	PS-033	Capintec
Electron (5 MeV to 35 MeV) Calibration	Farmer*	2505/3A or 2505/3B or 2571 or 2581	Nuclear Enterprises
	Farmer Type*	PR-06C or PR-06G	Capintec
		30–351	Victoreen
	Electron	30–329	Victoreen
	Memorial Hospital†	30–404	Victoreen

Application	Type	Model	Manufacturer
Low Energy Electron Calibration	Soft Radiation	30-330 or 30-334	Victoreen
	Electron	30-329	Victoreen
	Thin Window	PS-033	Capintec
Orthovoltage and Megavoltage Photon and Electron (5 MeV to 35 MeV) Central Axis Depth Dose and Beam Profile Measurements	Micro Chamber*	30-332 or 30-350	Victoreen
	Miniature Shonka*	T1	Exradin
	Mini-Chamber*	PR-05P	Capintec
	0.2 cc Chamber*	2577	Nuclear Enterprises
	Farmer*	2505/3A or 2505/3B or 2571 or 2581	Nuclear Enterprises
	Farmer Type*	PR-06C or PR-06G	Capintec
		30-351	Victoreen
	Cylindrical .1 cc*	IC-18	Far West Technology
	Memorial Hospital† (central axis only)	30-404	Victoreen
Buildup Region or Other Transition Zone	Extrapolation Chamber	EIC-1	Far West Technology
	Electron	30-328 or 30-326	Victoreen
	Soft Radiation	30-329	Victoreen
	Thin Window	30-330 or 30-334	Victoreen
		PS-033	Capintec

* Requires buildup cap for "in air" measurements for cobalt-60
† Designed for use in phantom only

X-rays or scattering of low energy electrons. The narrow electrode spacing is important to minimize the uncertainty in the effective point of measurement. Examples of chambers that I have found useful for each of these applications are given in Table 2–2. The list is by no means complete (but is based on personal experience) and only includes chambers that are widely used and commercially available. Neutron dosimetry requires ion chambers of special design. They will be addressed in Chapter 12.

2.2.2 Electrometers

Currently the most popular electrometer for ionometric dosimetry is the negative-feedback operational amplifier design. Negative-feedback means that some or all of the output of the operational amplifier is fed back to its inverting input. A circuit element in this path is a feedback element. The function of the operational amplifier is to maintain a zero potential between its positive and negative inputs.

Negative-feedback operational amplifier electrometers are used in three modes: total capacitive feedback, total resistive feedback, and feedback with gain. The gain of a negative-feedback operational amplifier is approximately the reciprocal of the fraction of the output that is fed back to the input. Total feedback results in unity gain. For total capacitive feedback, a capacitor is the feedback element. Because of the unity gain of the total capacitive feedback system the charge stored on the capacitor is the charge collected from the ion chamber. The charge on the capacitor may be measured by determining the voltage across it. Similarly, a resistor is the feedback element in a total resistive feedback circuit. The current through the resistor is equal to the current from the ion chamber. Again this current may be determined by measuring the voltage across the resistor. By adjusting the fraction of the output which is fed back, the gain of an electrometer may be changed. This technique is frequently employed in the design of electrometers to yield direct reading in Roentgen for a given chamber at a given energy.

Characteristics desired for an electrometer

As we listed desirable characteristics of an ion chamber, we can also list characteristics important for an electrometer. These include: fast warm-up time, small pre- and post irradiation background current, linearity of scale, sensitivity independent of ambient conditions, accommodation of changes in chamber bias in

TABLE 2–3. Typical Specifications for an Electrometer Suitable for
Radiation Therapy Physics Applications

Warm-up time
Zero drift shall be less than 1 millivolt per 24 hours after warm-
up of 10 minutes.

Background current
Background current to be 5×10^{-15} amps or less prior to
irradiation and within 30 seconds after irradiation.

Scale linearity
Scale to be linear to 0.01% or better.

Sensitivity to ambient conditions
Zero drift shall be less than 150 microvolts per °C.

Leakage of feedback capacitor
Electrometer will hold a reading to 0.05% per minute or better.

magnitude and polarity, and negligible leakage of the feedback
capacitor. Specifications of these quantities should be included in
a purchase order and acceptance tests in accordance with these
specifications should be performed after receipt of the electrometer.
Electrometer specifications that one can reasonably expect are
given in Table 2–3.

How easily an electrometer can accommodate chamber bias
changes probably cannot be specified adequately in a purchase
order. Each model of electrometer considered should be examined
in this regard before a decision is made. If the electrometer cannot
accommodate changes to the user's satisfaction, then it should not
be purchased.

Selection of an electrometer

The electrometer, in addition to meeting the above specifications,
should be selected for its versatility. This is different from ion
chambers where the specific application is integral to the selection.
A number of electrometers suitable for dosimetry is listed in Table
2–4.

2.2.3 Readout Devices

The readout device with sufficient precision for dosimetric purposes
is a digital voltmeter (DVM). Some electrometers widely used for
dosimetry, for example the Keithley 616, has a $3\frac{1}{2}$ digit DVM. How-

TABLE 2–4. Electrometers Appropriate for Radiation Therapy Physics

Electrometer	Manufacturer
602,* 610C,* 616	Keithley Instruments
Farmer Dosemeter 2570	Nuclear Enterprises
192	Capintec
500	Victoreen

* Analog output only.

ever, many people prefer a $4\frac{1}{2}$ digit DVM because the commonly used Farmer Chamber has a chamber correction factor of approximately 4.8 R/nC. An exposure of 100 R means approximately 21nC will be stored on the feedback capacitor. On a 10^{-8}C scale a $3\frac{1}{2}$ digit DVM will read this as 2.10 volts. Obviously, the precision of the reading is 0.5% in this instance. For dosimetric purposes the precision of reading should be 0.1% or better with an accuracy as good as this precision. Some DVMs adequate for dosimetry are given in Table 2–5.

2.2.4 Connecting Cable

The choice of the ion chamber will determine the requirements of the interconnecting cable. Most ion chambers require triaxial cable although those manufactured by Far West Technology listed in Table 2–2 require coaxial cable. Desirable characteristics of cable are low radiation-induced signal, low microphonic noise, low leakage current, low capacitance, pliability, and rapid equilibration after a change in bias voltage. Spokas and Meeker[8] have listed values of these characteristics for several types of triaxial cables. The reader is referred to their paper for details.

TABLE 2–5. Digital Multimeters that May Be Used for Radiation Dosimetry

Multimeter	Manufacturer
245, 248, 255	Data Precision
135A	Keithley
8060A	Fluke

2.2.5 Calibration

Each radiation therapy department should have at least one iono-metric dosimetry system that serves as a shelf or transfer standard. This sytem should be calibrated every two years by the National Bureau of Standards (NBS) or an Accredited Dosimetry Calibration Laboratory (ADCL). It is preferable to have two such systems with one calibrated in odd-numbered years and the other calibrated in even-numbered years. This shelf standard should be used only for deriving calibration factors for other dosimetry systems and for comparison to other dosimetry systems to check their constancy. They should never be used for routine daily constancy checks.

The next level of ionometric dosimetry systems is that which is used for calibration purposes. These must have calibration fac-tors established by the NBS or an ADCL to conform to recent cali-bration protocols (see Chapters 10 and 11).

The final level of ionometric dosimetry systems includes those systems used for routine daily constancy checks. These systems may have a derived calibration factor or none at all. If the system has a derived factor then the daily constancy checks of the linear accelerator can be in terms of centigray per monitor unit (cGy/mu), which may be compared to the value of this check determined during the last calibration. Alternatively, for systems with no cali-bration factor the daily reading corrected for temperature and pres-sure may be compared to some value established at the time of the last calibration.

2.3 PHANTOMS

Once a ionometric dosimetry system has been selected, one must decide on a water phantom. Let's examine some requirements of a water phantom. It is recommended that a water phantom extend 5 cm beyond the radiation field on all sides and 10 cm beyond the deepest point of measurement. These requirements help one decide on the size of the water phantom.

Most accelerators are calibrated for a 10 cm x 10 cm field with output factors for other field sizes relative to this standard. Central axis percent depth doses are usually measured to a depth of at least 30 cm for input to a treatment planning computer. Since most accelerators have field sizes up to 40 cm x 40 cm, a water phantom of 50 cm x 50 cm x 40 cm or perhaps 50 cm x 50 cm x

50 cm would seem to be required. However, to fill this phantom with water would require 15 to 20 minutes and the weight of the water alone would be approximately 300 lbs.

For routine weekly calibrations, a phantom this size is tremendously inconvenient. If one considers that field sizes of 20 cm x 20 cm and depths of 30 cm will cover approximately 70 to 80% of all cases treated, then the size and weight of the phantom can be much smaller.

This analysis suggests that two water phantoms are required, a smaller one for routine calibrations and a larger one for the times when a more extensive data set is needed. Additionally by choosing the smaller water phantom to cover field sizes of up to 20 cm x 20 cm and depths to 30 cm, data taken with the two phantoms can be compared over a wide range of conditions to assure oneself of consistency in the measurements.

2.3.1 Water Phantoms for Calibration

A suitable size for a water phantom used for routine calibration would be 30 cm x 30 cm x 40 cm deep. This phantom should have a thin entrance window that does not deform when filled with water. This may be accomplished in numerous ways. A large entrance window might be constructed of $\frac{1}{8}$ in. lexan. Alternatively the entrance face of the phantom might be constructed of $\frac{1}{4}$ in. lucite with a small window grooved into the geometrical center of the face. This window could be closed with 0.01 in. mylar and the ionization chamber positioned behind it.

The phantom should allow the possibility of making measurements with the gantry positioned at any of the four principal angles of $0°$, $90°$, $180°$, and $270°$. There should be some facility for accurately and reproducibly positioning the ion chamber. This positioning device should hold the ion chamber rigidly and have a method of determining the depth to an accuracy of 0.5 mm. Finally, one should be able to position the center of a Farmer Chamber with its cobalt-60 buildup cap within 1 cm of the surface for both horizontal and vertical orientations of the radiation beam. A phantom of this design is ideal for routine calibration of megavoltage photon beams and electrons above 5 MeV. It may also be used to measure central axis percent depth dose to depths of 30 cm and output factors for field sizes up to 20 cm x 20 cm. Suppliers of water phantoms useful for calibration purpose are listed in Table 2–6.

TABLE 2–6. Suppliers of Phantoms for Radiation Therapy Physics Applications

Calibration	Scanners	Plastic
Capintec	Protea	Capintec
Victoreen	Radiation Associates	Victoreen
Nuclear Enterprises	Therados	Far West Technology
Radiation Products Design	Computerized Medical System	Radiation Products Design
	ATC Medical Group	
	Multidata Systems	
	PTW/Nuclear Associates	
	Wellhofer/Medical Physical Instrumentation	

2.3.2 Water Phantoms for Scanning of Radiation Distributions

In addition to a phantom for routine calibrations, a larger water phantom is required for acceptance tests and machine commissioning measurements. This phantom should allow an ion chamber, diode, or other detector to be scanned in a radiation beam at a speed slow in relation to the response time of the system. This phantom should be at least 50 cm x 50 cm x 50 cm. It should be able to make scans in at least two but preferably three dimensions. The minimum range of the scan should be 40 cm in all dimensions. One should be able to make measurements at three and preferably at all four principal angles. This phantom should allow the detector to be positioned with an accuracy of 1 mm and a precision of 0.5 mm. It must have a thin entrance window that does not deform when the tank is filled with water. One should be able to start taking measurements within one hour and preferably 30 minutes of beginning to set up this phantom. The phantom should have a device that allows the physicist outside the treatment room to position the ion chamber accurately in the beam. The physicist should be able to transfer the data to an $x-y$ recorder, computer, or both. The physicist should also be able to use the phantom in a continuous radiation beam from a cobalt-60 machine, a pulsed radiation beam from a linac or betatron, and also in a scanned beam from a linac or microtron. The phantom should have the capability of making isodose measurements at preprogrammed levels or scans perpendicular to the central axis of the beam at preselected depths. The phantom should also be able to make scans parallel to the beam's central axis. Suppliers of scanning devices are listed in Table 2–6. The physicist should study the specifications carefully and talk to users of the equipment before making a final decision.

2.3.3 Plastic Phantoms

For constancy checks and transition zone measurements, such as the buildup region, a polystyrene phantom is beneficial, if not essential. The phantom should be able to accommodate a variety of ion chambers for different applications, including the ability to measure a buildup curve with the initial measurements made with no material other than the entrance window of a pancake chamber in the beam. There should be a large selection of different thicknesses of polystyrene. A useful phantom would have two thicknesses of 0.5 mm and two of 1 mm, one thickness each of 2 mm, 4 mm, 8 mm, 2 cm, 4 cm, and 10 thicknesses of 5 cm. For ease of handling, the phantom should have a cross sectional area of 25 cm x 25 cm, but it should be designed so this can be easily increased to 50 cm x 50 cm by using ancillary plastic blocks. This might be accomplished by using four blocks 12.5 cm x 37.5 cm, which could be placed around the periphery or a 50 cm x 50 cm block with the central 25 cm x 25 cm removed. There should be at least 10 thicknesses of 5 cm each of these ancillary blocks. Suppliers of polystyrene phantoms are also listed in Table 2–6. After the phantom has been acquired, the density of the polystyrene should be measured. Polystyrene phantoms are also necessary to fully exploit the potential of film dosimetry, but these may be easily fabricated in-house as discussed in the following section.

2.4 FILM DOSIMETRY

Many different dosimetric applications have been found for film, including electron isodose curves, photon isodose curves, field flatness and symmetry measurements, radiation and light field congruence tests, electron energy determination, and entrance and exit dose measurements. To achieve satisfactory results for many of these tests requires either hand processing or a very strict quality assurance program for an automatic film processor. Frequently, an automatic processor may be shared with a diagnostic radiology or nuclear medicine department with the processor not being under control of the therapy department. In these instances, an adequately policed quality assurance program may not be possible on a continuing basis. However, it may be possible to establish and maintain the processor at standards necessary for therapy over a limited time frame, a weekend, for instance. This makes possible a series of measurements, like electron isodose curves, which require careful attention to details of processing but that are not repeated on a routine basis. I will limit my discussion to those situations that offer the maximum possible benefit from film dosimetry with the minimum time expenditure. In institutions where the processor is under the control of the therapy department and a rigid quality assurance program is in place, I would refer the reader to appropriate publications on other applications of film dosimetry.[9,10,11,12]

2.4.1 Applications

In all the applications discussed below, the relative dose is determined by relating it to the blackening of the film, which is expressed in terms of density or optical density. The optical density is defined to be the common logarithm of the quotient of I_0 divided by I_1 where I_0 is the intensity of light incident on a region of the film and I_1 is the intensity transmitted through that region. The curve or function relating the optical density of the film to the dose received by the film is the characteristic curve or the H and D curve. The terminology H and D curve refers to Hurter and Driffield who originated the concept of characteristic curves for photographic film. The characteristic curve may be linear or nonlinear with dose depending upon the film emulsion. Different emulsions also have different speeds or sensitivities to radiation. An emulsion with a low sensitivity may be referred to as a "slow" film while "fast" film has a high sensitivity.

I have found film useful for establishing and maintaining light-radiation field congruence, routine checking of field flatness and symmetry for electrons and photons, and measuring electron isodose curves. I have not attempted to use film for X-ray isodose curves because the atomic number of the emulsion is significantly higher than that of tissue. Film will "overrespond" to scattered X-rays because of the difference in photoelectric attenuation coefficients between the emulsion and tissue.

A quality control program for the rapid processor that yields acceptable diagnostic radiographs is adequate for the first two applications. I have used Kodak XV or XTL film for these measurements. Exacting dosimetry is obviously not required for checks of light-radiation field congruence. Routine checks (daily or weekly) of flatness and symmetry do not require precise dosimetry either if done in a judicious manner. For X-ray beams, these checks may be compared to benchmark films done the last time that an ion chamber was used to establish absolute values. The overresponse of the film to scattered radiation becomes unimportant because only a relative comparison is made. A similar procedure can be established for electron beams. If significant deviations are observed between the benchmark films and the check films, the measurements should be repeated. If these deviations are replicated, then precise ion chamber dosimetry is required to resolve any problem. Even when no significant deviations are seen, wisdom dictates that ion chamber measurements still be made on a quarterly or semiannual basis for additional verification.

The measurement of electron isodose curves demands much more precise dosimetry. Careful attention must be paid to the quality control of the film processor and a characteristic curve for the film must be established for each set of data.

2.4.2 Film

Numerous film emulsions manufactured by Kodak, DuPont, and Agfa Gevaert have found applications in radiation therapy dosimetry. Four commonly used emulsions produced by Kodak are XTL, XV, Translite, and M. Each of these have their special characteristics, which are listed in Table 2–7. A characteristic curve for XV film is given in Figure 2–4. Regardless of the quality control program in force for an automatic processor, one cannot expect the same precision from film as from repeated measurements with ionometric techniques. The precision that can be anticipated is 10% between different boxes of film, 5% between films from the same box but processed at different times, 3% between films of the same box

TABLE 2–7. Characteristics of Film That Have Found Applications in Radiation Therapy

Film	Processing	Characteristic curve optical density vs. dose	Approximate dose to yield optical density of 2
XTL	Rapid	Relatively Linear	10 cGy
XV	Rapid	Nonlinear	100 cGy
Translite	Hand	Linear	200 cGy
M	Hand	Relatively Linear	15 cGy

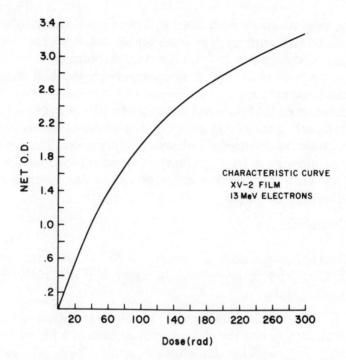

Figure 2–4 Typical characteristic curve of Kodak XV-2 film to 13 MeV electrons.

processed at the same time, and 2% across a single film. From these values one can see that exacting dosimetry requires that all the films used for a group of measurements be from the same box, that exposures be made to determine a characteristic curve with the film from that box, and that all these films be processed at the same time.

2.4.3 Instrumentation

Three pieces of equipment are necessary for film dosimetry: a phantom suitable for holding film, a manual densitometer, and a densitometer capable of automatically scanning the film. The manual densitometer is used to determine the absolute optical density of film while the scanning densitometer need only make relative measurements. Quality control of both of these units can be accomplished by using a calibrated film step tablet.

Polystyrene phantom

Polystyrene film phantoms are available commerically; however, it is quite easy and inexpensive to make one in-house. Sheets of opaque polystyrene 8 ft x 12 ft are available in $\frac{1}{8}$ in thicknesses at most plastic supply houses. These sheets may be cut into appropriate size squares, for instance 40 cm x 40 cm, which can then be glued together to form 5 cm thick blocks.

A means of uniformly compressing the film phantom is of utmost importance. No commercially available phantom should be considered that does not have this facility. For phantoms fabricated in-house, gluing clamps available at most hardware stores may be used to achieve a uniform compression. The kind I use fit on $\frac{3}{4}$ in pipe. Four sets of clamps placed on four lengths of $\frac{3}{4}$ in pipe give very uniform compression when the clamps are tightened about the phantom.

Densitometers

Densitometers are instruments that measure the optical density of film. The instrument may express the density in absolute or relative units.

Manual densitometers   The determination of the absolute optical density and the characteristic curve of a film requires a manual densitometer. This densitometer should have an aperture of 1 mm or less. It should have range from 0 to 4 optical density units with a $3\frac{1}{2}$ digit readout.

Scanning densitometers   A scanning densitometer is necessary to measure beam profiles and isodose curves efficiently. The measurement of absolute optical density is not required of this densitometer but it should be linear over a range of optical densities of 0 to 3. Its aperture should be no larger than 1 mm. It should be able to scan in two dimensions and the accuracy and precision of its movement should be the same as the scanning water phantom discussed above. This densitometer should also have outputs to an x–y recorder, a computer or both. It should be easy to set up so that the physicist can take data within 10 minutes and preferably 5 minutes of beginning. There should be some provision to allow for easy conversion from density to dose for films that may be nonlinear. Manufacturers of densitometers are given in Table 2–8.

2.4.4 Techniques

Measurement of light-radiation field congruence and of field flatness are accomplished simply by placing the film perpendicular to the beam's central axis at some depth in the plastic phantom.

TABLE 2–8. Manufacturers of Densitometers

Manual	Automatic
Macbeth	Therados
Victoreen	Victoreen
	ATC Medical Group
	Computerized Medical Systems
	Multidata Systems
	PTW/Nuclear Associates
	Wellhofer/Medical Physical Instrumentation

Light-radiation field checks should be made with enough plastic on top of the film to provide full buildup. Electron flatness checks should be measured at d_{max} generally. Photon flatness can be checked at d_{max} or some other convenient depth such as 5 cm or 10 cm.

Measurement of electron isodose curves with film requires a little more care. One places the film in the phantom parallel to the beam, being careful to align the edge of the film with the top edge of the phantom. If ready pack film is used, a small slit should be made in the corners of the paper to prevent air from being trapped next to the film. The top of the ready pack envelope extending outside the phantom should be folded down and taped in position against the top of the phantom. If bare film is used, the two sheets of polystyrene adjacent to the film must be taped so that no light exposes the film.

A typical central axis percent depth dose for 6 MeV electrons measured with film is compared to ion chamber measurements in Figure 2–5. Kodak XV was used for this data. Corrections from optical density to absorbed dose were made with a characteristic curve measured with film from the same box, which was exposed and processed at the same time as the film used for the data.

Isodose curves for a 20 cm x 20 cm 13 MeV electron beam are displayed in Figure 2–6. Kodak XV film, corrected in the same manner as the central axis depth dose curve, was used for this measurement. These curves were analyzed with a Therados scanning densitometer. This system allows for any set of density levels to be traced. I simply established the correlation between density and dose. For example, 94% density might correspond to 90% dose, 87% density to 80% dose, etc. Then the density lines were plotted and labeled with the appropriate dose, that is, the 94% density line was labeled 90% dose, etc.

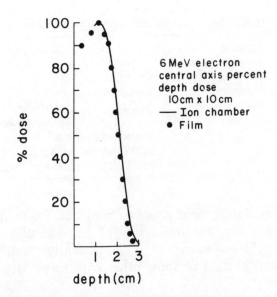

Figure 2–5 Comparison between a 6 MeV electron central axis depth dose curve measured with Kodak XV-2 film and with an ion chamber.

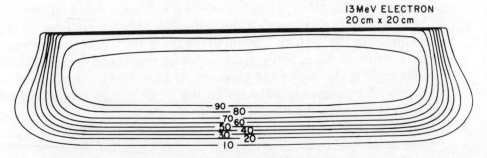

Figure 2–6 Isodose curves of a 13 MeV electron field, 20 cm × 20 cm, measured with Kodak XV-2 film.

2.5 OTHER DOSIMETRY SYSTEMS

2.5.1 Thermoluminescent Dosimetry

Thermoluminescent dosimetry (TLD) has found widespread application for *in-vivo* dosimetry. The most common TLD system in the hospital setting is lithium fluoride, although lithium borate, calcium sulfate, calcium fluoride, and magnesium borate have been used for health physics and environmental monitoring. LiF has an effective atom number and energy response similar to muscle. Its useful dose range extends from milligray to kilogray and with

TABLE 2–9. Manufacturers of Thermoluminescent Dosimetry Equipment and Supplies

Harshaw
Teledyne
Victoreen
Therados

proper handling and calibration a precision of 3 to 5% may be achieved. The reader is referred to the extensive references that exist on practical uses of TLD. Suppliers of TLD equipment are listed in Table 2–9.

2.5.2 Silicon Diodes

Silicon diodes have been used in commercial scanning water phantoms for relative measurements in photon and electron beams. Because of their small size they can be successfully employed as point detectors in regions of high dose gradients. However, they exhibit a loss of sensitivity with exposure to radiation and should not be used for absolute measurements.

2.5.3 Chemical Dosimetry

Ferrous sulfate is the most common chemical dosimeter although other materials, such as ceric sulfate, have also been used. Fricke and Morse[13] developed ferrous sulfate dosimetry in 1927 and it has subsequently been referred to as Fricke dosimetry. Although it has a absolute accuracy of approximately 2%, its use has been limited in radiation therapy because of its low sensitivity; a few thousand centigray are required to obtain a minimal reading. Additional problems with Fricke dosimetry are that precise chemical technique is required in the preparation and storage of the ferrous sulfate solution. Careful cleaning and choice of irradiation cells are also necessary.

2.6 SUMMARY

I have discussed the dosimetric systems most commonly employed in radiation therapy. Manufacturers of many of these systems have been listed in several tables. Several of these manufacturers also have representatives in each locality. It would be impossible to

TABLE 2–10. Addresses of Suppliers of Radiation Dosimetry Equipment

ATC Medical Group
One Factory Row
Geneva, Ohio 44041

Capintec
6 Arrow Road
Ramsey, New Jersey 07446

Computerized Medical Systems (CMS)
2294 Weldon Parkway
St. Louis, Missouri 63146

Data Precision Corporation
Audubon Road
Wakefield, MA 01800

E. I. DuPont deNemours and Co.
Photo Products Department
Concord Plaza-Wilson Building
Wilmington, Delaware 19898

Eastman Kodak Company
343 State Street
Rochester, New York 14650

Exradin
Box Q
Warrenville, ILL 60555

Far West Technology
330 D. South Kellogg
Goleta, California 93017

Harshaw Chemical Company
6801 Cochran Road
Solon, Ohio 44139

John Fluke Manufacturing Co., Inc.
P.O. Box C9090
Everett, WA 98206

Keithley Instruments, Inc.
28775 Aurora Road
Cleveland, Ohio 44139

Macbeth
Little Britain Road
P.O. Box 950
Newburgh, New York 12550

Medical Physics Instrumentation
P.O. Box 51
Roseland, N.J. 07068

Multidata Systems
10088 Manchester Road
St. Louis, Missouri 63122

Nuclear Enterprises America
23 Madison Road
Fairfield, N.J. 07006

Protea
3860 Industrial Way
Benicia, California 94510

PTW/Nuclear Associates
100 Voice Road
Carle Place, New York 11514

Radiation Associates
1906 Marlberry
Houston, Texas 77084

Radiation Products Design, Inc.
RR-3, Box 132-F
Buffalo, Minn. 55313

Teledyne
50 Van Buren Avenue
Westwood, New Jersey 07675

Therados
One Greentree Center
Suite 201
Marlton, N.J. 08053

Victoreen
10101 Woodland Avenue
Cleveland, Ohio 44104

list all of these manufacturer representatives here. I refer the reader to the manufacturer, whose address I give in Table 2–10, for that information.

Notes

1. Francis R. Shonka, John E. Rose, and G. Failla, "Conducting Plastic Equivalent to Tissue, Air, and Polystyrene," *Second United Nations Conference on Peaceful Uses of Atomic Energy* 21 (New York, New York: United Nations, 1958) pp. 184–87.

2. Jasper E. Richardson, "Effect of Chamber Voltage on Electron Buildup Measurements," *Radiol*. 62(1954), pp. 584–88.

3. David J. Keys, James A. Purdy, Martin H. Israel, and Donald E. Velkley, "Thin-Walled Parallel Plate Ionization Chamber for Use with Photon and Electron Beam Dosimetry," *Med. Phys*. 7(1980), pp. 163–64.

4. J. Garrett Holt, Alfonso Buffa, David J. Perry, I-Chang Ma, and Joseph C. McDonald, "Absorbed Dose Measurements Using Parallel Plate Polystyrene Ionization Chambers in Polystyrene Phantoms," *Int. J. Radiation Oncology Biol. Phys*., 5(1979), pp. 2031–38.

5. Leroy J. Humphries, "Dosimetric Instrumentation," presented at AAPM Continuing Education Workshop *Electron Linear Accelerators in Radiation Therapy*, February 1981.

6. D. E. Velkley, D. J. Manson, J. A. Purdy, and G. D. Oliver, Jr., "Buildup Region of Megavoltage Photon Radiation Sources," *Med. Phys*., 2(1975), pp. 14–19.

7. Daniel Bassano, "Relative Doses to Skin and Superficial Nodes from 10 MV Photons as a Function of Field Size and Distance From Shadow Tray," *Radiol*., 115(1975), pp. 707–10.

8. John J. Spokas and Ralph D. Meeker, "Investigation of Cables for Ionization Chambers," *Med. Phys*. 7(1980), pp. 135–40.

9. A. G. Haus, K. Strubler, and J. E. Marks, "A Film Technique for Determining the Absorbed Dose at Exit from the Patient During Radiation Exposure," *Radiol*., 104(1972), pp. 197–200.

10. Philip D. LaRiviere, "Surface Dose From 6 MV Photon Interactions in Air," *Phys. Med. Biol*., 28(1983), pp. 285–87.

11. Leonard Stanton, "Determination of Isodose Curves for Supervoltage and Cobalt-60 Teletherapy Machines with X-ray Film," *Radiol*., 78(1962) pp. 445–60.

12. Arnold Feldman, Carlos E. deAlmeida, and Peter R. Almond, "Measurements of Electron-Beam Energy With Rapid-Processed Film," *Med. Phys*., 1(1974), pp. 74–76.

13. Hugo Fricke and Sterne Morse, "The Chemical Action of Roentgen Rays on Dilute Ferrosulphate Solutions as a Measure of Dose," *Am. J. Roentgenol Radium Therapy Nucl. Med.*, 18(1927) pp. 430–32.

Additional Reading

JAMES A. PURDY, "Instrumentation for Dosimetric Measurements," presented at AAPM Special Workshop for Radiological Physics, *Electron Linear Accelerators in Radiation Therapy*, March 1978.

R. LOEVINGER, "Precision Measurement with the Total-Feedback Electrometer," *Phys. Med. Biol.*, 11(1966), 267–79.

Electrometer Measurements (Cleveland, Ohio: Keithley Instruments, 1972).

The Fundamental of Radiography (Rochester, N.Y.: Eastman Kodak, 1980).

ANDRÉE DUTREIX, "Film Dosimetry," presented at AAPM Summer School *Radiation Dosimetry*, July 1976.

Photographic Quality Assurance in Diagnostic Radiology, Nuclear Medicine, and Radiation Therapy: The Basic Principles of Daily Photographic Quality Assurance. HEW Publication 76–8043, (Washington, D. C.: Food and Drug Administration, 1976).

HUGO FRICKE AND EDWIN J. HART, "Chemical Dosimetry," in *Radiation Dosimetry Vol. II*, ed. Frank H. Attix and William C. Roesch, (New York, N.Y.: Academic Press, 1966), pp. 167–239.

J. R. CAMERON, N. SUNTHARALINGAM, AND G. N. KENNEY, *Thermoluminescent Dosimetry*, (Madison, Wis.: University of Wisconsin Press, 1968).

THREE

SELECTION OF A COMPUTERIZED TREATMENT PLANNING SYSTEM

3.1 INTRODUCTION

The acquisition of a computerized treatment planning system, like a treatment machine, involves a major expenditure and must be considered carefully. Each department has its different immediate needs and future goals and the treatment planning system should be configured to attain these aims. Does the department include a programming staff? What is the interest in computerized billing? Is the department oriented toward research or clinical service? Are there personnel in the department who, although not full-time programmers, are interested and enthusiastic about programming? If so, in what languages do they program; assembler, BASIC, FOR-TRAN, PASCAL? Does the department have electron capabilities or access to a CT scanner? How much money is budgeted for this purchase? These questions are just a few of the many which must be asked and answered before deciding on a treatment planning system.

If programmers are employed in the department it may be desirable to use the funds to purchase the most sophisticated hardware available and develop the software in-house, or perhaps one should consider buying hardware that is common in other departments and joining a users group to share software.

If there are personnel who are interested in programming but who are not full-time programmers, it would be prudent to follow an intermediate course. In this case the decision might be to acquire a complete system of hardware and software from a vendor that encouraged outside development of the system and supported it with an active user's group.

If a department is oriented primarily toward clinical service with little or no interest in research or programming, the logical choice is to purchase a system of hardware and software that fulfills the needs of the department. The decision in this instance might be based on which company supports the system with trained personnel who can answer questions about the software and who are as close as a phone call.

The money invested in phone calls to users to get their comments is well spent. Also, a purchaser should insist that he or she be given "hands-on" experience with his or her own sample cases to determine the convenience of the system.

In the following discussion I will consider the three minimum requirements for any treatment planning system; an external beam program, an irregular field routine and a brachytherapy package. If a system does not have these three components fully developed, it should not be considered further. I have seen too many companies with one or two of these components who promise to deliver the remainder but subsequently drop all developments in the area.

I will discuss different algorithms used in external beam, irregular field, and brachytherapy programs and briefly consider the merits and problems of each. This discussion should enable a purchaser to ask pertinent questions of the vendor. If the vendor's representative cannot answer these questions, either personally or with a quick phone call one should consider another system. This discussion should also help the purchaser evaluate the strengths and weaknesses of each system and balance them against his or her own needs.

3.2 EXTERNAL BEAM ROUTINES

All photon external beam treatment planning programs are based on the manipulation of isodose charts measured in a standard geometry of a beam normally incident on semi-infinite water phantom. Corrections are made to this standard geometry for oblique beam incidence and non-unit density heterogeneities. Accordingly, I will begin this discussion of treatment planning computers with a review of the different techniques for storing the basic data that will be followed by an explanation of the corrections for sloping skin surfaces and inhomogeneities.

There are four categories of computerized beam models that may be referred to as

1. Matrix Model
2. Decrement Lines
3. Generating Functions
4. Separation of the Beam into Primary and Scatter Components

I will now address each in turn.

3.2.1 Matrix Model

This model divides measured isodose curves or beam profiles into a matrix of dose points, $D(x,y)$, and stores these points. A typical example of this technique is the algorithm of Milan and Bentley.[1] In this formulation the matrix points are the intersections of 47 equally-spaced divergent fan lines with five equally-spaced depths. The 47 fan lines are the central axis and 23 each to the right and left of the central axis. The central axis is further divided into 17 equally spaced depths. The necessary input for each field is a) the central axis percent depth dose at the 17 depths from d_{max} to the greatest depth of interest and b) beam profiles in the plane containing the central axis (principal plane) at five equally-spaced depths from d_{max} to the greatest depth measured for the central axis percent depth dose. As an example, for an 18 MV X-ray beam with d_{max} of 3 cm the greatest depth of interest might be 43 cm, therefore beam profiles would be required at 3, 13, 23, 33, and 43 cm and percent depth dose values from 3 to 43 cm in steps of 2.5 cm.

Data in this format would be required over the range of square field sizes of interest. For a square field that has not been measured, the algorithm interpolates linearly between measured field sizes. Consequently the greater the number of field sizes measured the less the interpolation error. For rectangular fields, the beam profiles for the square field that has the same dimension as the side of the rectangular field are used but the percent depth dose values correspond to that of an equivalent square field calculated as four times the area over the perimeter ($4A/P$). This approximation is generally adequate except for highly elongated fields, in which case it is advisable to measure and store these fields as special beams.

The Milan-Bentley algorithm expresses the dose at any point in a principle plane as the product of the central axis percent depth dose and an off-axis factor, $f(d,x)$.

$$D(d,x) = \%dd(d)f(d,x) \tag{3-1}$$

where d = depth

x = off-axis distance

$\%dd(d)$ = central axis percent depth dose at depth d

For the dose in a plane parallel to a principal plane (paraxial plane) the dose is multiplied by the off-axis factor in the perpendicular plane, $g(d,y)$.

$$D(d,x,y) = \%dd(d)f(d,x)g(d,y) \tag{3-2}$$

where y = distance between principal plane and paraxial plane.

However, for highly elongated fields on linear accelerators this may be an inappropriate technique[2] because some linacs may display off-axis factors up to 1.15 to 1.20 at d_{max} for large field sizes. In these instances one should measure and store the isodose curves as special cases.

3.2.2 Decrement Lines

An alternative method of storing isodose curves is the decrement line technique originally described by Orchard.[3] With this approach beam profiles are stored not as a grid of points but rather as "decrement lines," curves that yield the distance between the central axis and a given off-center ratio. This concept may be clarified

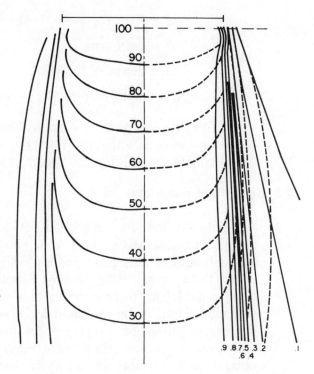

Figure 3-1 Isodose curves with decrement lines superimposed on right hand side. Used with permission of International Commission on Radiation Units and Measurements from *Determination of Absorbed Dose in a Patient Irradiated by Beams of X or Gamma Rays in Radiotherapy Procedures* ICRU Report 24.

with reference to Figure 3–1, which has decrement lines superimposed on the right side of an isodose curve. Decrement lines of high energy photon beams can usually be expressed by a second order polynomial such as $a + bx + cx^2$ where x is the off-axis distance. Furthermore a, b, and c can be written as a function of field size. Clearly a family of decrement lines may be stored in a computer with relatively few constants. These constants could then be used to account for the off-axis dependence for any field size.

In addition to off-axis values the central axis percent depth dose is required. Several techniques to calculate the central axis percent depth dose have been presented. One of these models was formulated by Glover[4] and describes percent depth dose values with three equations and eight constants. These equations are

$$\%dd = 100\left\{1 - [1 - e^{-\alpha(d - d_{max})}]^\beta\right\} \qquad \textbf{(3–3)}$$

$$\alpha = C_1 e^{-C_2 A} + C_3 e^{-C_4 A} \qquad \textbf{(3–4)}$$

$$\beta = C_5 + C_6 (1 - e^{-C_7 A}) e^{-C_8 A} \qquad\qquad (3\text{–}5)$$

A = field area

d = depth of interest

$C_1 \ldots C_8$ = eight empirically determined constants.

With this approach any isodose curve may be calculated with a small set of constants describing the decrement lines and another set of constants yielding the central axis behavior.

3.2.3 Generating Functions

A number of models have been developed that yield the dose at any point in the beam using some simple mathematical functions. These functions may have some physical basis or they may result solely from curve fitting. In 1964 Sterling, Perry and Katz[5] formulated a model to fit the profiles of a cobalt-60 machine; however, this model had to be modified for linear accelerators because of the increase in the off-axis factor for linacs. Several other investigators have proposed other beam models. This technique has the advantage that wedge fields may be calculated simply by modifying the generating function to account for the wedge.

Appropriate parameters for the generating functions may be found in an iterative process of comparing measured to calculated isodose curves until satisfactory agreement is achieved or by fitting measured beam profiles.

3.2.4 Separation of a Radiation Beam into Primary and Scattered Components

In 1941 Clarkson[6] proposed a method separating the radiation beam into primary and scattered components. This technique has been elaborated by Cunningham.[7] The primary component may be written as

$$D_{\text{prim}} = D_a(d) f(x,y) TAR(d,0) \qquad\qquad (3\text{–}6)$$

$D_a(d)$ = dose in air for a given field size at d

$TAR(d,0)$ = TAR for zero area field size at depth d

$f(x,y)$ = a function dependent on penumbra, collimator transmission, source size, and type of filter

The scatter dose is determined by adding the scatter-air-ratios at each point and multiplying the sum by $D_a(d)$. Scatter-air-ratios are defined as

$$SAR(d,r) = TAR(d,r) - TAR(d,0) \qquad \text{(3–7)}$$

$SAR(d,r) =$ scatter-air-ratio at depth d and distance r from edge of beam

$TAR(d,r) =$ tissue-air-ratio at depth d for field size of radius r.

$TAR(d,0)$ as defined in equation 3–6.

With this model $f(x,y)$ is found by comparing the measured and calculated isodose curves or in-air beam profiles in an iterative process similar to the approach used with the generating function technique. Further details of this technique are given in Section 3–6.

3.2.5 Comparison of Beam Models

Let's recap and summarize the overview of external photon beam treatment planning algorithms. Of the four basic techniques, the Matrix Model is the fastest in terms of computer time. The big disadvantage of the Matrix Model is for beams in a nonstandard geometry, such as a tangential irradiation. The algorithm has no means to correct for lack of scattering material and will overestimate the delivered dose. The Clarkson–Cunningham technique can generate tangential irradiations more accurately because it separates the beam into primary and scattered components; however, the algorithm requires the most computer time. In terms of computer time the decrement line method and the generating function approach are intermediate between the Matrix Model and the Clarkson–Cunningham technique.

One must also consider what basic machine specific data is required by the program. Some algorithms demand data in a very specific format, such as beam profiles at certain depths or isodose curves for certain field sizes. Other algorithms are more general allowing the physicist more latitude on data input. A large amount of measured data is required with the Matrix Model to reduce interpolation error but only a few beam profiles are required with the TAR/SAR model of Clarkson–Cunningham. However, with a modern beam scanner beam profile measurements are simple and quick.

An attractive hybrid would be a system that not only used a Matrix Model for external beam computations, but also had the option of generating an external beam for special cases, such as tangential irradiations with the Clarkson–Cunningham technique. This special beam could then be stored on a floppy disc or other storage device for use in the Matrix Model external beam planning system.

3.3 CORRECTIONS FOR OBLIQUE BEAM INCIDENCE

Because a patient does not present a flat surface normal to a radiation beam, corrections must be made for oblique beam incidence. The problem is illustrated in Figure 3–2. A radiation beam is incident on a sloping surface with the SSD at the central axis indicated by S. The points of interest are A, B, and C. Point C is on the central axis at a depth d, points A and B are off the central axis at the same distance from the source as point C; however, point A is at a depth in tissue of $d - h$ and point B is at a depth of $d + k$, where d, h, and k are measured along a ray line.

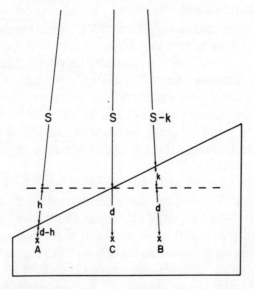

Figure 3–2 Illustration of geometry of sloping skin surface. Distance from source to skin at the central axis is S, surplus tissue above B is represented by k, and tissue deficit above A is h.

3.3.1 Effective Attenuation Coefficient

Probably the simplest method employed to account for sloping patient contours is the effective attenuation coefficient method. If one uses the terminology in Figure 3–2, the correction factor at a point A, CF_A, calculated with this method is

$$CF_A = e^{\mu' h} \qquad (3\text{–}8)$$

and at point B

$$CF_B = e^{-\mu' k} \qquad (3\text{–}9)$$

where μ' is some empirically determined "effective attenuation coefficient." The value of μ' for cobalt-60 is generally taken as 5% per cm. These correction factors are multiplied by the uncorrected dose at points A and B to yield the corrected values. If we take $h = 5$ cm, $k = 3$ cm, $d = 7$ cm

$$CF_A = e^{0.25} = 1.28$$
$$CF_B = e^{-0.15} = 0.86$$

The shortcomings of this correction are μ' is an empirically determined constant whose value is not established for all energies, the size of the beam is not taken into account, and the scatter is handled only indirectly.

3.3.2 Effective SSD Method

A second technique is the effective SSD method. With this model the depth d and field size are taken into account. The correction factors become

$$CF_A = \frac{\%dd(d-h,W,S)}{\%dd(d,W,S)} \left(\frac{S + d_{\max}}{S + d_{\max} + h} \right)^2 \qquad (3\text{–}10)$$

and

$$CF_B = \frac{\%dd(d+k,W,S)}{\%dd(d,W,S)} \left(\frac{S + d_{\max}}{S + d_{\max} - k} \right)^2 \qquad (3\text{–}11)$$

where $\%dd(d,W,S)$ is the central axis depth dose (see Chapter 14) at a depth d and SSD of S for a field width W defined at S. The percent depth doses at the actual depths are, $\%dd(d-h,W,S)$ and $\%dd(d+k,W,S)$, but at an SSD of S rather than an SSD of $S+h$ at point A and $S-k$ at point B.

$$\text{The factors} \left(\frac{S+d_{\max}}{S+d_{\max}+h}\right)^2 \quad \text{and} \quad \left(\frac{S+d_{\max}}{S+d_{\max}-k}\right)^2$$

correct to the appropriate SSD at points A and B.

If we use the same values of d, h, and k as above and take the field width W to be 10 cm x 10 cm the correction factors are

$$CF_A = \frac{\%dd(2,10,80)}{\%dd(7,10,80)} \times \left(\frac{80+0.5}{80+0.5+5}\right)^2$$

$$CF_A = \frac{93.7}{69.3} \times \left(\frac{80.5}{85.5}\right)^2$$

$$CF_A = 1.20$$

$$CF_B = \frac{\%dd(10,10,80)}{\%dd(7,10,80)} \times \left(\frac{80+0.5}{80+0.5-3}\right)^2$$

$$CF_B = \frac{56.4}{69.3} \times \left(\frac{80.5}{77.5}\right)^2$$

$$CF_B = .88$$

where the values of $\%dd(2,10,80)$, $\%dd(10,10,80)$, and $\%dd(7,10,80)$ are from British Journal of Radiology Supplement 17.[8] This publication will be used for all subsequent cobalt-60 examples in this chapter. Note this method assumes no change in percent depth dose with a change in SSD.

3.3.3 Tissue-Air Ratio Method

The tissue-air-ratio method is similar to the effective SSD method but it uses TARs (see Chapter 14) rather than percent depth dose values and the field size is specified at the depth of interest. The correction factors are

$$CF_A = \frac{T(d-h,W_d)}{T(d,W_d)} \qquad (3\text{--}12)$$

$$CF_B = \frac{T(d+k,W_d)}{T(d,W_d)} \qquad (3\text{--}13)$$

where $T(d,W_d)$ is the TAR at a depth of d for field width W_d defined at d. If we use the same values of d, k, h, and W as above and $W_d = W \times \left(\frac{87}{80}\right)$ the correction factors are

$$CF_A = \frac{T(2,10.9)}{T(7,10.9)}$$

$$CF_A = \frac{1.009}{.838}$$

$$CF_A = 1.20$$

$$CF_B = \frac{T(10,10.9)}{T(7,10.9)}$$

$$CF_B = \frac{.727}{.838}$$

$$CF_B = 0.87$$

3.3.4 Isodose Shift Method

The isodose shift method is convenient when making corrections to isodose curves by hand. With this method the isodose curves are shifted some distance along a ray line toward the skin surface keeping the central ray aligned. This shift distance is some fraction of the depth of the missing or surplus tissue. If this fraction were f the isodose curves would be displaced a distance fh along a ray line at A and fk along a ray line at B. In both cases this shift distance is taken to be $\frac{2}{3}$ for cobalt-60. If we continue to use the same values as the above, the shift at A and B would be

$$\frac{2}{3} \times 5 = 3\tfrac{1}{3} \text{ cm at } A$$

$$\frac{2}{3} \times 3 = 2 \text{ cm at } B$$

To compare this method to the previous technique the percent depth dose at 7 cm for a 10 cm $\times$ 10 cm field at 80 cm SSD is 69.3. If we apply the $\frac{2}{3}$ shift at A the depth of interest is $7 - 3\frac{1}{3} = 3\frac{2}{3}$ cm and at B, $7 + 2 = 9$ cm. The corresponding depth dose values at A and B are 85.4 and 60.5. These values yield the following correction factors

$$CF_A = \frac{85.4}{69.3}$$

$$CF_A = 1.23$$

$$CF_B = \frac{60.5}{69.3}$$

$$CF_B = 0.87$$

3.3.5 Comparison of Corrections for Oblique Beam Incidence

Of the four corrections just discussed, the effective attenuation is the simplest and the least accurate. The TAR method is the most accurate and is easy to apply for hand calculations at points of interest. The effective SSD and isodose shift methods yield answers close to the TAR method for many cases and are convenient for making corrections along a ray line as all corrections along the ray line are the same. For these reasons the effective SSD method is used in a large number of computer programs.

One must be careful though, because none of the methods are accurate for tangential beam irradiations. To improve the accuracy of treatment planning in these instances one must either make measurements in a tangential beam geometry or generate a beam with the Clarkson–Cunningham technique and use this representation in the external beam program.

3.4. CORRECTIONS FOR INHOMOGENEITIES

A patient is neither flat, as discussed earlier, nor homogeneous. The initial techniques for inhomogeneity corrections were based on equivalent radiological path length and were fairly simple to apply. The lack of interest in developing more accurate methods resulted because detailed information about each individual patient's cross sectional anatomy was not known. However, with widespread availability of CT scanners, a serious effort has been applied to improving the algorithms for heterogeneity corrections. I will begin the discussion of these corrections with the simpler models and progress to the more complex.

3.4.1 Effective Attenuation Coefficient

This heterogeneity correction is a varient of the same technique used for sloping skin surfaces. The correction factor is

$$CF = e^{\mu'(d - d_{eff})} \tag{3-14}$$

where d_{eff} = equivalent radiological path length
          d = actual thickness
          μ' = effective attenuation coefficient

As an example consider Figure 3–3.

The point of interest, P, lies in a unit density material 3 cm beyond a 10 cm slab of density 0.3g/cc which is covered by 5

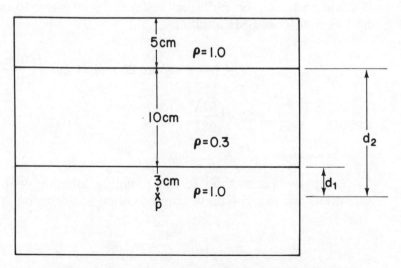

Figure 3–3 Example of an inhomogeneous phantom with the point of interest in unit density material.

cm of unit density material. The equivalent radiological path length is

$$d_{eff} = 5 \times 1 + 10 \times .3 + 3 \times 1 = 11 \text{ cm}$$

As mentioned above, the μ' is taken as 0.05 cm^{-1} for cobalt-60. The correction factor becomes

$$CF = e^{0.05(18-11)}$$

$$= e^{0.35}$$

$$= 1.42$$

3.4.2 Effective SSD Method

The effective SSD method as applied to inhomogeneities assumes the corrected percent depth dose equals the percent depth dose for d_{eff} multiplied by an inverse square correction term.

$$\%dd_{\text{corrected}} = \%dd(W_s, S, d_{eff}) \left(\frac{SSD + d_{eff}}{SSD + d} \right)^2 \qquad (3\text{–}15)$$

where $\%dd_{\text{corrected}}$ is the percent depth dose corrected for the inhomogeneity and $\%dd(W_s, S, d_{eff})$ is the percent depth dose at a depth d_{eff} for a field width W_s at an SSD of S. If we consider Figure 3–3 again and take the radiation beam to be 10 cm x 10 cm cobalt-60 beam with an SSD of 80 cm

$$\%dd_{\text{corrected}} = \%dd \ (10 \text{ x } 10 \text{ cm, } 80 \text{ cm, } 11 \text{ cm}) \left(\frac{80 + 11}{80 + 18} \right)^2$$

$$= 52.5 \left(\frac{91}{98} \right)^2$$

$$\%dd_{\text{corrected}} = 45.3$$

To compare this method to the effective attenuation coefficient technique we can calculate the correction factor to be

$$CF = \frac{45.3}{31.7} = 1.43$$

where 31.7 is the percent depth dose for a 10 cm x 10 cm cobalt-60 field at 18 cm.

3.4.3 Isodose Shift Method

Another method that has been used for both sloping skin surface and heterogeneity corrections is the isodose shift. The isodose lines are shifted by some constant times the thickness of the inhomogeneity for points within and beyond the heterogeneity. Frequently quoted values of these constants for cobalt-60 are

air cavities	-0.6
lung	-0.4
hard bone	$+0.6$
spongy bone	$+0.25$

The minus indicates a shift away from the surface and a plus is for a shift toward the surface. We may not compare this technique to the previous two because the heterogeneity in Figure 3–3 is defined as a material of density 0.3 and not as any of the above anatomical structures.

3.4.4 Tissue-Air Ratio Model

The correction factor calculated with the tissue-air ratio model is the ratio of the TAR at d_{eff} to the TAR at d for the field size at the depth of calculation. If we consider Figure 3–3 once more, a 10 cm x 10 cm field at 80 cm becomes 12.25 cm x 12.25 cm at 98 cm and the correction factor is

$$CF = \frac{T(d_{eff}, W_d)}{T(d, W_d)}$$

$$CF = \frac{T(11, 12.25 \times 12.25)}{T(18, 12.25 \times 12.25)} \tag{3--16}$$

$$CF = \frac{0.704}{0.487}$$

$$= 1.45$$

3.4.5 Power Law Tissue-Air Ratio Model

An extension of the TAR method was proposed by Batho[9] and generalized by Young and Gaylord.[10] With this method the correction factor is

$$CF = \left(\frac{T(d_2,W_d)}{T(d_1,W_d)}\right)^{\rho e^{-1}} \qquad \text{(3--17)}$$

where ρ_e is electron density relative to water, d_1 is the distance of the point of calculation beyond the exit surface of the heterogeneity and d_2 is the distance of the point of calculation beyond the entrance surface of the heterogeneity. In Figure 3–3, d_1 is 3 cm and d_2 is 13 cm. For point P in Figure 3–3 the correction factor is

$$CF = \left(\frac{T(13,12.25)}{T(3,12.25)}\right)^{.3-1}$$

$$= \left(\frac{.637}{.985}\right)^{-.7}$$

$$= 1.36$$

This expression is valid for points lying downstream from the heterogeneity but not within it.

3.4.6 Generalized Batho Correction

Sontag and Cunningham[11] have generalized the Batho method to include the points within the inhomogeneity. Consider the situation in Figure 3–4 where $\rho_1 \neq \rho_2 = 1$. The correction factor in this instance

$$CF = \frac{[T(d_1,W_d)]^{\rho_1-\rho_2}}{[T(d_2,W_d)]^{1-\rho_2}} \cdot \frac{\left(\frac{\mu_{en}}{\rho}\right)_{\rho_1}}{\left(\frac{\mu_{en}}{\rho}\right)_{\rho_2}} \qquad \text{(3--18)}$$

$\left(\frac{\mu_{en}}{\rho}\right)_{\rho_1}$ is the mass energy absorption coefficient for the heterogeneity with electron density ρ_1

$\left(\frac{\mu_{en}}{\rho}\right)_{\rho_2}$ is the mass energy absorption coefficient for the heterogeneity with electron density ρ_2

As an example consider point P in Figure 3–3 again. In this case $W_d = 12.25$, $\rho_1 = 1, d_1 = 3$, $\rho_2 = .3$, $d_2 = 13$. If we substitute these values into Equation 3–18

$$CF = \frac{[T(3,12.25)]^{.7}}{[T(13,12.25)]^{.7}}$$

$$= \left(\frac{.985}{.637}\right)^{.7}$$

$$= 1.36$$

However, this technique also permits the calculation of dose within the heterogeneity. If we take point P in Figure 3–4 which is at a depth of 5 cm in the heterogeneity

$$\rho_1 = .3; \ d_1 = 5; \ \rho_2 = 1; \ d_2 = 10 \text{ and}$$

$$CF = \frac{[T(5,12.25)]^{-0.7}}{[T(10,12.25)]^{0}} \frac{\left(\dfrac{\mu_{en}}{\rho}\right)_{\rho_1}}{\left(\dfrac{\mu_{en}}{\rho}\right)_{\rho_2}}$$

$$= \frac{(0.920)^{-0.7}}{1} \frac{\left(\dfrac{\mu_{en}}{\rho}\right)_{\rho_1}}{\left(\dfrac{\mu_{en}}{\rho}\right)_{\rho_2}}$$

$$= 1.06 \frac{\left(\dfrac{\mu_{en}}{\rho}\right)_{\rho_1}}{\left(\dfrac{\mu_{en}}{\rho}\right)_{\rho_2}}$$

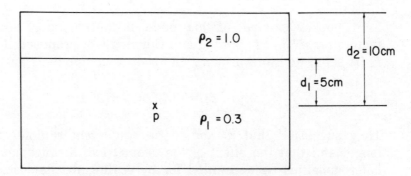

Figure 3–4 Example of an inhomogeneous phantom with the point of interest in the heterogeneity.

Note if we are to complete this calculation, a knowledge of the mass energy absorption coefficients is required; however, this example illustrates the technique.

This method has been extended to n layers of inhomogeneities by Webb and Fox.[12] The interested reader is referred to the original article for additional information.

One should note that the generalized Batho correction is the first method I have discussed that permits calculation within the heterogeneity. One should also recognize from Figures 3–3 and 3–4 that a tacit assumption has been made that the lateral extent of the inhomogeneity is greater than the size of the beam. Now I will discuss methods that are applicable to heterogeneities smaller than the cross sectional area of the radiation beam.

3.4.7 Equivalent TAR Method

The equivalent TAR method was proposed by Sontag and Cunningham.[13] In this model the field size as well as the depth is scaled for heterogeneities. The scaling of field sizes for a beam irradiating a non-unit density phantom was first suggested by O'Connor[14] in 1957. The correction factor becomes

$$CF = \frac{T(d',\tilde{r})}{T(d,r)} \tag{3–19}$$

where $d =$ depth of calculation point
          $r =$ radius of equivalent circular field (circular field with
               same central axis percent depth dose behavior as
               the field of interest)
          $d' =$ scaled depth
          $\tilde{r} =$ scaled radius

The key element of this model is the choice of the scaling factors for d' and $\tilde{r}$. Sontag and Cunningham proposed that $T(d', \tilde{r})$ be separated into primary and scatter components such that

$$T(d', \tilde{r}) = T(d', 0) + S(d',\tilde{r}) \tag{3–20}$$

They suggested that d' should be equivalent radiological path length and that the effect of the geometrical arrangement of the heterogeneities be accounted for by scaling the field size in the scatter component. Sontag and Cunningham formulated this model for use with a sequence of CT scans. Several scans are "coalesced" into one slice, which is a distance Z_{eff} from the plane of calculation. With this technique, it is possible to account for inhomogeneities which are smaller than the size of the beam. Sontag and Cunningham state the average accuracy expected with this technique is approximately 2.5%. The reader is referred to the original articles for further discussion.

3.4.8 Delta-Volume Method

Cunningham[15] has shown that scatter-air ratios in differential form can be used to calculate the scatter radiation from each volume element at the point of interest. Beaudoin[16] applied this approach to calculate the total scatter at a point by summing over all volume elements in the irradiated volume. This summation can then be added to the primary to yield the total dose at a point. To calculate the effect of an inhomogeneity, a weighting factor is assigned to volume elements occupied by the heterogeneity. The use of this technique requires volume integration over a large number of CT slices. This procedure also can correct for heterogeneities smaller than the radiation beam, but its implementation is not yet practical because of the large amount of computational power required. Again the reader is referred to the original articles for more complete discussion.

3.4.9 Monte Carlo Method

Monte Carlo techniques have been used in many situations for which the basic physics is understood but that are not amenable to an exact analytical solution. The interaction of photon radiation and matter is one of these situations. In this instance, a large number of photon paths through a material are generated. The distance a photon travels between interactions, the angle through which it is scattered, and its energy after the interaction are modeled by random numbers that are weighted by appropriate cross sections.

The Monte Carlo method should give the most complete description of dose distributions in homogeneous or inhomogeneous materials.

It is also the only technique that can properly account for interface effects in the region between different materials. However Webb and Parker[17] have shown a 20 cm x 20 cm 6MV X-ray field requires an analysis of 1.8×10^7 photons to achieve a 2% uncertainty.

This immense calculational effort is not possible for routine clinical applications with present computer facilities.

3.4.10 Comparison of Heterogeneity Corretions

The methods of inhomogeneity corrections have been presented in order of increasing complexity and length of computer time. Several reports have appeared assessing the validity of each algorithm and it can be stated generally that the accuracy increases with the increasing complexity. It is currently unrealistic to expect a commercially available system to have the delta-volume method or Monte Carlo techniques. However, one should demand a system with either the generalized Batho or equivalent tissue-air ratio algorithm as well as one of the simpler techniques such as the effective SSD approach. One should also demand a system with both bulk corrections for user outlined inhomogeneities and CT pixel-by-pixel corrections. This allows one to do preliminary calculations with the simpler corrections and to use the more complex approach for the final plans.

3.5 EXTERNAL ELECTRON BEAM TREATMENT PLANNING

Electron beam treatment planning algorithms have enjoyed a greater evolutionary development over the years than have photon treatment planning models. Initial electron beam codes were empirical fits to measured data. The effects of irregular skin surfaces were corrected using an effective SSD technique. Other empirical techniques were introduced to correct for heterogeneities. These algorithms included the Absorption Equivalent Thickness,[18] Absorption Coefficient Model,[19] Coefficient of Equivalent Thickness,[20] and Modified Absorption Coefficient.[21] In general, these methods provided adequate approximations if the inhomogeneities were uniform slabs of material with a lateral extent greater than the area of the beam. However, as pointed out by Pohlit,[22] significant edge effects occur for heterogeneities smaller than the beam. Pohlit introduced another empirical method to estimate these edge effects to within 10–15%.

Several investigators realized that electron beam treatment planning was becoming a hierachy of empirical techniques. Lillicrap[23] and others demonstrated that broad, parallel beams of electrons could be built up from a number of narrow "pencil" beams. This idea models an accelerator or a betatron produced electron beam, which is a narrow beam transformed to a broad beam either with a scattering foil or scanning magnets. Others appreciated that the behavior of narrow beams of electrons was controlled by Coulomb multiple scattering and that this mechanism was described by Fermi's transfer equation which had been solved by Eyges. The Fermi–Eyges theory was adapted for electron beam treatment planning resulting in algorithms with solid foundations in basic physics.[24,25,26,27] In addition to the Fermi–Eyges method, an alternative pencil beam model based on the age-diffusion equation[28] has been developed.

The electron beam algorithm available on a commercial treatment planning system depends upon the vendor. A wide spectrum is offered from the early empirical models to the latest developments with pencil beam techniques. However, if a department offers electron treatments or even if there is a possibility of adding electrons in the future, one should select a treatment planning system with pencil beam capabilities. One should study the algorithm carefully and investigate the publications relating to its validity. The reader is referred to the articles listed in the bibliography of this chapter for further details.

3.6 IRREGULAR FIELD ALGORITHMS

All irregular field calculations are performed with some variant of the Clarkson[6]–Cunningham[7] technique of dividing the radiation field into primary and scattered components. Cundiff, et al.[29] proposed the basic equation for calculating the dose to a point in an irregular field treated with an SSD technique should be

$$D_p = D_{ac} \, T_T \, FO \left(\frac{X_{ac}}{SSD + g + d} \right)^2 (TAR_d + S_d) \qquad \text{(3–21)}$$

where D_p = dose to point of interest, P

D_{ac} = dose to small mass of tissue sufficient to provide electronic equilibrium (miniphantom) at calibration distance for calibration field size

X_{ac} = calibration distance

T_T = blocking tray transmission factor

$F =$ field size dependence for the unblocked field determined by the collimator opening used for the treatment, measured in air, relative to the calibration field size

$O =$ off-axis factor at off-axis distance of P. This factor should be measured in air

$SSD =$ source-skin-distance at central axis for irregular field treatments

$g =$ distance between SSD and skin surface at point P

$d =$ depth below skin surface of point P

$TAR_d =$ tissue-air ratio for primary beam at depth d

$S_d =$ average scatter-air ratio at point P at depth d for the treatment field

Hallberg, et al.[30] have modified this equation to allow for the inclusion of several beam defining devices at various distances. The four different beam defining devices allowed are

1. collimator jaws
2. field-shaping blocks
3. lack of tissue
4. secondary blocks

They have also modified the multiplicative off-axis factor O. In their formulation, this multiplicative factor is a function of the depth as well as the distance off-axis. This change was introduced to account for off-axis changes in beam quality on linear accelerators. This multiplicative factor is then multiplied only by the primary component and not the scattered component as was the dose in Equation 3–21. The approach of multiplying only the primary component by the off-axis factor is in accordance with Cunningham's original formulation.

Hanson et al,[31,32] have suggested an alternative modification to Equation 3–21 to account for the off-axis change in beam quality on a linear accelerator. In this model, the TAR of the primary beam is a function of radial distance off-axis as well as depth. The expression for TAR_0 becomes

$$TAR_0\,(d,r) = \exp\left[-\frac{0.693(d - d_{\max})}{HVL(r)} \right] \qquad (3\text{–}22)$$

where HVL(r) is the HVL in water at radial distance r and TAR_0 (d,r) is the zero-area TAR at depth, d, and radial distance, r. Of course, this requires a knowledge of the HVL in water as a function of off-axis position. Techniques for the measurement of this quantity are discussed in Chapter 6. This model follows the suggestion of Cundiff, et al.[29] and multiplies the off-axis factor by the sum of the primary and scattered components.

Unfortunately, it is impossible to state which of these approaches yields the most accurate result, because a complete, detailed comparison of each of these algorithms to measured data has not been performed. Preliminary analyses[30,32,33] indicate that any of them can predict the dose to within 5% for most points, but each technique has weaknesses that manifest themselves in special situations. The penumbral region and the dose under shielding blocks are examples. Also, other differences exist between systems that cloud the interpretation of various comparisons. For example, some systems store the SAR values in tabular form, while other systems use a polynomial function fit to measured data. Large errors in the SAR calculation may occur with both these techniques, either from interpolation errors or a poor polynomial fit. Other uncertainties exist in the determination of the zero area TARs. Were these values found by measuring the attenuation coefficient of water in good geometry or were they found by extrapolating to zero area from the large field TARs?

One should carefully examine the basic algorithm used as well as its implementation in each treatment planning system. Convenience of patient data input is another factor requiring serious consideration. For instance, is the digitizer tablet large enough that irregular fields may be entered directly from films or must they first be reduced? Does the program sum the anterior and posterior dose contributions or must this be done off-line? Is it possible to generate and store a set of isodose curves for use in the external beam program? Can the program accept CT data and construct coronal and sagittal planes? These and a multitude of other questions must be examined prior to deciding on a treatment planning system.

3.7 BRACHYTHERAPY COMPUTATIONS

All computerized brachytherapy line-source calculations are performed with one of two methods, the Sievert integral[34] or the interval method.[35] The Sievert integral has been the more widely applied technique in commercial treatment planning systems. This integral was evaluated by Rolf Sievert in 1921. With this method the dose rate from a line source to a point is

$$\dot{D} = \frac{\Gamma A f k}{\lambda y} \int_{\theta_1}^{\theta_2} e^{-\mu d \sec \theta} \, d\theta \qquad (3\text{--}23)$$

where $\quad A$ = activity
Γ = specific gamma-ray constant
f = Roentgen-to-rad conversion factor
λ = active length
d = effective wall thickness
k = a factor that accounts for the scatter and attenuation of tissue
μ = effective attenuation coefficient
θ_1, θ_2, and y are defined in Figure 3–5.

Several investigators have calculated dose tables at points around linear sources using the equation and most commercial treatment planning systems perform brachytherapy calculations with a table lookup using one of these techniques. At various times, the factor k has been modeled with one of three equations.[36,37,38] These equations are

$$k = e^{-\mu R} \qquad (3\text{--}24)$$

$$k = 1 - \alpha R^\beta \qquad (3\text{--}25)$$

or $\quad k = A + BR + CR^2 + DR^3 \qquad (3\text{--}26)$

where $\quad R$ is the distance from the source to the point of calculation and μ, α, β, A, B, C, D are empirically determined constants for a given isotope.

The interval method considers a line source to consist of several point sources. In this case, the dose at a given point is equal to the sum of the contributions from each point source. This method has the advantage that the dose from each point source may be calculated with the inverse square law by including factors for source absorption and the effective wall thickness of the encapsulating material. If a line source is divided into sufficiently many point sources, the accuracy possible is greater with the interval method than with the Sievert integral method, particularly near the ends of the line source. Tissue scattering and absorption is

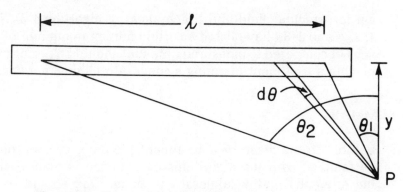

Figure 3–5 Geometry used for Sievert integral for a source of active length *l*.

calculated with one of the models discussed earlier for Sievert intervals.

All commercial treatment planning systems assume that seeds are point sources and calculate the dose rate from seeds using inverse square law. The effect of attenuation and scattering in tissue is calculated as previously discussed.

Source locations of a brachytherapy implant may be determined either with orthogonal or stereo shift radiographs. The stereo shift technique may be done in one of two ways. The most common of these is to shift either the X-ray tube or the patient a fixed distance. This shift may be along the patient's axis or transverse to this axis. An alternative technique is to radiograph the patient on an isocentric X-ray unit, such as a simulator, and move the tube through a known number of degrees between exposures. A brachytherapy treatment planning system should allow the user a choice of the orthogonal and at least one, but preferably both, of the stereo shift techniques. Other features to consider are ease of data input and speed of calculation.

3.8 COMMISSIONING TESTS

After the treatment planning system has arrived and one's own machine specific data has been entered a series of commissioning tests should be performed before placing the computer into clinical service. McCullough and Krueger[39] have a protocol for verification of an external beam system and other investigators have reported comparisons of measured to calculated values for their protocols for photon,[40,41,42,43] electron,[44] and neutron[43,45] external beam treatments. Less information is available outlining a verification protocol for irregular field and brachytherapy algorithms. In Tables 3–1, 3–2, and 3–3 I have listed a certain minimum number of comparisons of computed to measured data that should be performed before placing a treatment planning system into clinical service.

3.9 SUMMARY

Before the purchase of a treatment planning system, one should be familiar with the algorithms used in the various systems and the strengths and weaknesses of each. One should extensively question the vendor about the algorithms used in their system and expect detailed information. After one becomes satisfied with the physics, one should look at the relative convenience of the systems and their capabilities. For instance, what is the size of the input digitizer, does the system read CT tapes, can it do CT corrections for inhomogeneities, what are the output devices? One should also

TABLE 3–1. Suggested Protocol for a Comparison of Values Computed with an External Beam Treatment Planning Program to Values Measured in a Water Phantom

	Square field
Field Size	15 cm x 15 cm
Beam Incidence	45° and 90°
Depth of Measurement	5 cm, 10 cm, 15 cm, 20 cm
Position of Measurement	On central axis and 5 cm both sides of central axis

	Rectangular field
Field Size	6 cm x 40 cm
Beam Incidence	90°
Depth of Measurement	5 cm, 10 cm, 15 cm, 20 cm
Position of Measurement	2 cm from central axis along 6 cm side of field and 19 cm from central axis along 40 cm side of field

	Tangential beam
Field Size	12 cm x 12 cm
Beam Incidence	90°
Depth of Measurement	10 cm
Position of Measurement	On central axis with the following distances between central axis and edge of phantom 1 cm, 2 cm, 3 cm, 4 cm, 5 cm, 6 cm, 7 cm, 8 cm, 9 cm, 10 cm, 11 cm

TABLE 3–2. Suggested Protocol for a Comparison of Values Computed with an Irregular Field Program to Values Measured in a Water Phantom

Square field

Field Size	35 cm x 35 cm
Beam Incidence	90°
Depth of Measurement	d_{max}, 5 cm, 10 cm, 15 cm, 20 cm
Position of Measurement	On central axis and off-axis at 1 cm intervals to edge of field

Rectangular field

Field Size	6 cm x 40 cm
Beam Incidence	90°
Depth of Measurement	d_{max}, 5 cm, 10 cm, 15 cm, 20 cm
Position of Measurement	In a plane parallel to the 40 cm side but 2 cm off the central axis along the 6 cm side at 1 cm intervals from the center of the plane to the edge of the field in this plane

Tangential beam

Field Size	20 cm x 20 cm
Beam Incidence	90°
Depth of Measurement	10 cm
Position of Measurement	On the central axis with the following distances between the central axis and the edge of the phantom: 1 cm, 2 cm, 3 cm, 4 cm, 5 cm, 6 cm, 7 cm, 8 cm, 9 cm, 10 cm, 11 cm, 12 cm, 13 cm, 14 cm, 15 cm

TABLE 3–3. Suggested Protocol for a Comparison of Values Computed with a Brachytherapy Program to Values from Standard Tables

Radium needle

Compare computer values to Tables of Shalek and Stovall for a 2 cm and a 3 cm active length needle

Cesium needle

Compare computer values to Tables of Krishnaswamy for a 1.5 cm and a 3 cm active length needle

Seed

Compare dose rate from a 1 mCi ^{192}Ir seed to the dose rate from 20 seeds of .05 mCi with all 20 seeds occupying the same position

TABLE 3–4. Addresses of Suppliers of Computerized Treatment Planning Systems

ADAC Laboratories
4747 Hellyer Avenue
San Jose, CA 95138

ATC Medical Group
One Factory Row
Geneva, OH 44041

Atomic Energy of Canada Limited
413 March Road
P.O. Box 13140
Kanata, Canada K2K 1X8

Capintec
6 Arrow Road
Ramsey, NJ 07446

Computerized Medical Systems
  (CMS)
2294 Weldon Parkway
St. Louis, MO 63146

General Electric Company
Medical Systems Division
P.O. Box 414
Milwaukee, WI 53201

MARx Plan
499 Seaport Court
Suite 301
Port of Redwood City, CA 94063

Medicalibration
2816 Niabell Place
Modesto, CA 95355

Oncology Systems
1400 112th Avenue, SE
Suite 100
Bellevue, WA 98004

Philips Medical Systems, Inc.
710 Bridgeport Avenue
Shelton, CT 06484

Picker International
595 Miner Road
Highland Heights, OH 44143

Siemens Medical Systems, Inc.
186 Wood Avenue South
Iselin, NJ 08830

look carefully at the vendor's track record in therapy planning systems, the vendor's future committment to software development, and the financial viability of the company. Finally, one should consider additional capabilities of the system. Does the machine have a FORTRAN, BASIC, or PASCAL compiler? Does the vendor encourage outside software development? After the decision is made and the machine is delivered, a series of commissioning tests should be performed to illuminate for the user the strengths and weaknesses of a particular system. When all these things have been done, one will have a system that may not make one blissful, but at least it will provide comfort and solace. Finally, in Table 3–4, I have listed vendors of treatment planning systems along with their addresses.

Notes

1. J. Milan and R. E. Bentley, "The Storage and Manipulation of Radiation Dose Data in a Small Digital Computer," *Brit. J. Radiol.*, 47(1974), pp. 115–21.

2. Wing-Chee Lam and Kam-Shing Lam, "Errors in Off-Axis Treatment Planning for a 4 MeV Machine," *Med. Phys.*, 10(1983), pp. 480–82.

3. P. G. Orchard, "Decrement Lines: A New Presentation of Data in Cobalt-60 Beam Dosimetry," *Brit. J. Radiol.*, 37(1964), pp. 756–63.

4. J. R. Glover, "A System of Three Equations Allowing Calculations of Central Axis Percent Depth Dose and Related Quantities," *Phys. Med. Biol.*, 12(1967), pp. 119–20.

5. Theodor D. Sterling, Harold Perry, and Leo Katz, "Automation of Radiation Treatment Planning. IV. Derivation of a Mathematical Expression for the Per Cent Depth Dose Surface of Cobalt-60 Beams and Visualisation of Multiple Field Dose Distributions," *Brit. J. Radiol.*, 37(1964), pp. 544–50.

6. J. R. Clarkson, "A Note on Depth Doses in Fields of Irregular Shape," *Brit. J. Radiol.*, 14(1941), pp. 265–68.

7. J. R. Cunningham, P. N. Shrivastava, and J. M. Wilkinson, "Program IRREG—Calculations of Dose from Irregularly-Shaped Radiation Beams," *Computer Programs in Biomedicine*, 2(1972), pp. 192–99.

8. *Central Axis Depth Dose Data for Use in Radiotherapy*, British Journal of Radiology Supplement 17, (London: British Institute of Radiology, 1983).

9. H. F. Batho, "Lung Corrections in Cobalt-60 Beam Therapy," *Journal of the Canadian Association of Radiologists XV* (1964), pp. 79–83.

10. M. E. J. Young and Judith D. Gaylord, "Experimental Tests of Corrections for Tissue Inhomogeneities in Radiotherapy," *Brit. J. Radiol.*, 43(1970), pp. 349–55.

11. Marc R. Sontag and J. R. Cunningham, "Corrections to Absorbed Dose Calculations for Tissue Inhomogeneities," *Med. Phys.*, 4(1977), pp. 431–36.

12. S. Webb and R. A. Fox, "Verification by Monte Carlo Methods of a Power Law Tissue-Air Ratio Algorithm for Inhomogeneity Corrections in Photon Beam Dose Calculations," *Phys. Med. Biol.*, 25(1980), pp. 225–40.

13. Marc R. Sontag and John R. Cunningham, "The Equivalent Tissue-Air Ratio Method for Making Absorbed Dose Calculations in a Heterogeneous Medium," *Radiol.*, 129(1978), pp. 787–94.

14. J. E. O'Connor, "The Variation of Scattered X-Rays with Density in an Irradiated Body," *Phys. Med. Biol.*, 1(1957), pp. 352–69.

15. J. R. Cunningham, "Scatter-Air-Ratios," *Phys. Med. Biol.*, 17(1972), pp. 42–51.

16. L. Beaudoin, *Analytical Approach to the Solution of the Dosimetry in Heterogeneous Media*, M. Sc. Thesis, University of Toronto, 1968.

17. S. Webb and R. P. Parker, "A Monte Carlo Study of the Interaction of External Beam X-radiation with Inhomogeneous Media," *Phys. Med. Biol.*, 23(1978), pp. 1043–59.

18. John S. Laughlin, "High Energy Electron Treatment Planning for Inhomogeneities," *Brit. J. Radiol.*, 38(1965), pp. 143–47.

19. Arne Dahler, Alan S. Baker, and John S. Laughlin, "Comprehensive Electron-Beam Treatment Planning," *Ann. N. Y. Acad. Sci.*, 161(1969), pp. 198–213.

20. P. R. Almond, A. E. Wright, and M. L. M. Boone, "High Energy Electron Dose Perturbations in Regions of Tissue Heterogeneity, Part II: Physical Models of Tissue Heterogeneities," *Radiol.*, 88(1967), pp. 1146–53.

21. Farideh Bagne, "Electron Beam Treatment-Planning System," *Med. Phys.*, 3(1976), pp. 31–38.

22. W. Pohlit, "Calculated and Measured Dose Distributions in Inhomogeneous Materials and in Patients," *Ann. N.Y. Acad. Sci.*, 161(1969), pp. 189–97.

23. S. C. Lillicrap, Patricia Wilson, and J. W. Boag, "Dose Distributions in High Energy Electron Beams: Production of Broad Beam Distributions from Narrow Beam Data," *Phys. Med. Biol.*, 20(1975), pp. 30–38.

24. David J. Perry and J. Garrett Holt, "A Model for Calculating the Effects of Small Inhomogeneities on Electron Beam Dose Distributions," *Med. Phys.*, 7(1980), pp. 207–15.

25. Kenneth R. Hogstrom, Michael D. Mills, and Peter R. Almond, "Electron Beam Dose Calculations," *Phys. Med. Biol.*, 26(1981), pp. 445–59.

26. Barry L. Werner, Faiz M. Kahn, and Firmin C. Deibel, "A Model for Calculating Electron Beam Scattering in Treatment Planning," *Med. Phys.*, 9(1982), pp. 180–87.

27. David Jette, Antonio Pagnamenta, Lawrence H. Lanzl, and Martin Rozenfeld, "The Application of Multiple Scattering Theory to Therapeutic Electron Dosimetry," *Med. Phys.*, 10(1983), pp. 141–46.

28. N. Suntharalingam, "Three Dimensional Electron Dosimetry Model," *Proceedings of the Symposium on Electron Dosimetry and Arc Therapy*, ed. Bhudatt Paliwal (New York, N. Y.: American Association of Physicists in Medicine, 1982).

29. J. H. Cundiff, and others, "A Method for the Calculation of Dose in the Radiation Treatment of Hodgkin's Disease," *Am. J. Roentgen, Rad. Ther. Nucl. Med.*, 117(1973), pp. 30–44.

30. Jerome R. Hallberg, and others, "Computational Analysis and Dosimetric Evaluation of a Commercial Irregular-Fields Computer Program," *Med. Phys.*, 4(1977), pp. 528–34.

31. W. F. Hanson, L. W. Berkley, and M. Peterson, "Off-Axis Beam Quality Change in Linear Accelerator X-Ray Beams," *Med. Phys.*, 7(1980), pp. 145–46.

32. W. F. Hanson, L. W. Berkley, and M. Peterson, "Calculative Technique to Correct for the Change in Linear Accelerator Beam Energy at Off-Axis Points," *Med. Phys.*, 7(1980), pp. 147–50.

33. M. E. Masterson, and others, "Effects of Off-Axis Beam Quality Changes on Irregular Field Dose Calculations for Clinac 4's," *Med. Phys.*, 10(1983), pp. 529–30.

34. R. M. Sievert, "Die Intensitätsverteilung der Primären Gamma-Strahlung in der Nähe Medizinischer Radiumpräparate," *Acta Radiol.*, 1(1921), pp. 89–128.

35. Robert J. Shalek and Marilyn Stovall, "The M. D. Anderson Method for the Computation of Isodose Curves Around Interstitial and Intercavitary Radiation Sources, I. Dose from Linear Sources," *Am. J. Roent. Rad. Ther. Nucl. Med.*, CII(1968), pp. 662–72.

36. K. I. Ponnunni Kartha, Gordon N. Kenney, and John R. Cameron, "An Experimental Determination of the Absorption and Buildup Factor in Water for Radium, Cobalt 60 and Cesium 137 Gamma Rays," *Amer. J. Roent. Rad. Ther. Nucl. Med.*, 96(1966), pp. 66–69.

37. H. F. Batho and M. E. J. Young, "Tissue Absorption Corrections for Linear Radium Sources," *Brit. J. Radiol.*, 37(1964), pp. 689–92.

38. Leo L. Meisberger, Ronald J. Keller, and Robert J. Shalek, "The Effective Attenuation in Water of the Gamma Rays of Gold 198, Iridium 192, Cesium 137, Radium 226, and Cobalt 60, *Radiol.*, 90(1968), pp. 953–57.

39. Edwin C. McCullough and Ana Maria Krueger, "Performance Evaluation of Computerized Treatment Planning Systems for Radiotherapy: External Photon Beams," *Int. J. Radiation Oncology Biol. Phys.*, 6(1980), pp. 1599–1605.

40. U. Rosenow, "An Intercomparison of Commerical Treatment Planning Systems Based on Standardized Field Data and Prescribed Treatment Plans," in *Proceedings of the Sixth International Conference on the Use of Computers in Radiation Therapy*, ed. U. Rosenow, (Göttingen: 1978), pp. 777–93.

41. U. Rosenow and U. Burmester, "The Quality of Dose Computation: A Systematic Approach to Program Intercomparison," in *Proceedings of the Sixth International Conference on the Use of Computers in Radiation Therapy.*, ed. U. Rosenow, (Göttingen: 1978), pp. 475–87.

42. C. F. Westermann, B. J. Mijnheer, and H. J. van Kleffens, "Determination of the Accuracy of Different Computer Planning Systems for Treatment with External Photon Beams," *Radiotherapy and Oncology*, 1(1984), pp. 339–47.

43. J. L. Horton, W. K. Roberts, J. W. Blue, and R. A. Gahbuaer, "Verification of a Commercially Available Treatment Planning System Used for Neutron Treatment Planning," in *Proceedings of the Fifth Symposium on Neutron Dosimetry*, ed. H. Schraube, G. Burger, and J. Booz (Munich: 1985), pp. 1155–63.

44. Kenneth R. Hogstrom, and others, "Dosimetric Evaluation of a Pencil-Beam Algorithm for Electrons Employing a Two-Dimensional Heterogeneity Correction," *Int. J. Radiation Oncology Biol. Phys.*, 10(1984), pp. 561–69.

45. B. J. Mijnheer, S. Vynckier, and G. Burger, "An Intercomparison of the Treatment Planning Systems Used for Neutron Beams in Europe," in *Proceedings of the Fifth Symposium on Neutron Dosimetry*, ed. H. Schraube, G. Burger, and J. Booz (Munich: 1985), pp. 1131–42.

Additional Reading

SATISH C. PRASAD, GLENN P. GLASGOW, AND JAMES A. PURDY, "Dosimetric Evaluation of a Computed Tomography Treatment System," *Radiol.*, 130(1979), pp. 777–81.

MORRIS TATCHER AND SHULA PALTI, "Evaluation of Density Correction Algorithms for Photon-Beam Dose Calculations," *Radiol.*, 141(1981), pp. 201–5.

JOHN W. WONG AND R. MARK HENKELMAN, "Reconsideration of the Power-Law (Batho) Equation for Inhomogeneity Corrections," *Med. Phys.*, 9(1982), pp. 521–30.

STANLEY C. MCDONALD, BOWEN E. KELLER, AND PHILIP RUBIN, "Method for Calculating Dose When Lung Tissue Lies in the Treatment Field," *Med. Phys.*, 3(1976), pp. 210–16.

V. KRISHNASWAMY, "Dose Distributions About ^{137}Cs Sources in Tissue," *Radiol.*, 105(1972), pp. 181–84.

FOUR

REQUIREMENTS OF ACCURACY IN RADIATION THERAPY

4.1 INTRODUCTION

The objective in radiation therapy is to treat a tumor with a dose of radiation large enough either to eradicate the malignancy or to palliate the pain, but small enough that no untoward effects are produced in healthy tissue. Generally, this goal must be compromised. The art of the radiation therapist is balancing the achievable percentage of cure against an acceptable level of complications.

The dose-response functions of cure and complications are idealized in Figure 4–1. They are sigmoid curves rising very steeply with dose. The curve for complications is at higher dose levels than for cure for diseases that are treated with radiation therapy. If the curve for complications is at lower dose levels than the one for cure, then the disease would be treated with some other modality. Let us assume that 6500 centigray (cGy) is the "optimal" dose in this example. This yields a probability of cure of 80% and a

IDEALIZED DOSE-RESPONSE CURVES

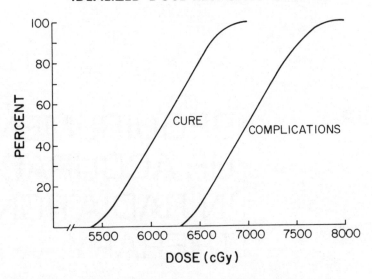

Figure 4–1 Idealized representation of the relationships of cure and complications to dose levels.

complication rate of 10%. A reduction in dose of 5% would be 6175 cGy. This would give no complications but the cure rate would be only 50%. By increasing the dose 5% to 6825 cGy, one would achieve a 98% cure rate, however, the complications would be 35%.

In practice the optimal dose and the dose-response curves for cure and complications are not known; however, clinical studies indicate behavior similar to the idealized dose response curves above. Herring and Compton[1] have analyzed data from various sources using nominal standard dose (NSD).[2] They concluded the probability of tumor control is a steep function of dose, at least for some tumors. In one instance, a 10% increase in the NSD increased the probability of control from 10% to 70%.[3] Stewart and Jackson[4] published similar conclusions for laryngeal carcinoma. They demonstrated a decrease in recurrences for T_3 tumors from 68% to 30% when the dose was increased by 10%. Further, necrosis increased from 0% to 8% over the same dose range for patients with T_1, T_2, or T_3 tumors.

A study of complications was presented by Svensson, et al.[5] They analyzed radiation-induced neurological lesions of the brachial plexus following post-operative radiation therapy for mammary carcinoma. The Cumulative Radiation Effect (CRE)[6] was used rather than dose levels to group patients. They found a very rapid increase in frequency of lesions above a certain CRE value. An increase in the CRE value of 7% increased the complications from 15% to 50%. Based on the above clinical information, ICRU Report 24[7] recommends that the accuracy in delivery of dose to the target volume should be 5% for photon therapy. Johansson[8] has analyzed more recent data and arrived at the same conclusion for electron as well as photon therapy.

4.2 SOURCES OF INACCURACY

The sources of inaccuracy in dose delivery may be broken down into three main areas:

1. Physical dosimetry—the commissioning and calibration of the treatment machine
2. Clinical dosimetry—the delineation of the target volume and acquisition of patient specific factors
3. Daily patient treatment—the set-up of the patient and the recording of the treatment.

These three areas have been listed in the chronological order in which they are performed. Also, this order is indicative of the impact that a physicist may have in eliminating these errors. A physicist has sole responsibility for machine commissioning and calibration, works in concert with other members of the radiation therapy team on step 2, and has the least effect in step 3 although he or she may still make significant contributions.

4.3 ACCURACY OF PHYSICAL DOSIMETRY

Loevinger and Loftus[9] have focused on each step in the process of calibration of a ^{60}Co beam in an attempt to estimate the uncertainties involved. They have formulated two models, one a "lowest acceptable" and the other an "optimal" model. Six steps have been identified in the physical dosimetry process. These steps are:

0. Physical constants employed in the conversion of ionization measurements to dose determination such as W/e, the energy required to create an ion pain, and S/ρ, stopping power ratios

1. Standardization of the beam at the National Laboratory
2. Calibration of secondary instrument at the Regional Calibration Laboratory
3. Calibration of field instrument
4. Calibration of treatment beam
5. Delivery of dose to tissue phantom

Uncertainties are estimated for each step with the overall uncertainty taken to be the sum of the individual numbers added in quadrature. In the optimal model this sum is 2.5% and in the lowest acceptable it is 4.9%. If the total uncertainty, including the clinical dosimetry and daily treatment, is to be kept below 5%, it is clear the lowest acceptable is really unacceptable and the optimal model should be attained.

Fortunately, the physicist exercises greatest control in this area and the optimal model is readily attainable. To achieve this level of accuracy though, does require dedication and diligence on the part of the physicist. Examples of the difference between the two models are:

1. Field size diameter uncertain to 5 mm versus 1.5 mm
2. SSD uncertain to 4 mm versus 2 mm
3. Shutter error 750 ms versus properly corrected shutter error
4. Use of published versus measured depth dose values
5. Field instrument not suitable for phantom work versus instrument corrected for phantom use

These are all points that a physicist can address.

The American Association of Physicists in Medicine Radiological Physics Center (RPC)[10] analyzed review visits to 188 institutions. Such factors as percent depth dose, tray factors, chamber factors, wedge factors, beam symmetry, shutter corrections and light-radiation field congruence were examined. From this review the RPC developed standards that they deemed acceptable and readily achievable. These standards are:

1. Basic calibration—photons and electrons within 3%
2. Relative measurements such as output factors, percent depth dose values, wedge factors, tray factors—within 2%

3. Coincidence of light and radiation field—each side to agree to within 3 mm

4. Beam symmetry—should be within 3% for any two points equidistant from the central axis

5. Monitor end effect—no criterion established, should be measured and considered in calibration and treatment

The National Bureau of Standards and the Bureau of Radiological Health[11] conducted a mailable TLD survey of ^{60}Co teletherapy units. Response was received from 684 facilities with 737 ^{60}Co units. Of these units the agreement between the stated dose and the TLD measured dose was within 5% for 599 units, between 5% and 10% for 102 units, and greater than 10% for 20 units. Sixteen units were excluded for various reasons. The mean deviation of the stated dose and measured dose of the 701 units within the 10% agreement was 0.6%.

These two surveys indicate that 2 to 3% accuracy of calibration is not an unreasonable level to attain. However, careful work is required by the physicist.

4.4 ACCURACY OF CLINICAL DOSIMETRY

A general assessment of clinical dosimetry is impossible because it is dependent upon the individual patient. Items to be considered for each patient are:

1. Measurement of patient's contour on the central plane

2. Change in contour off the central plane

3. Determination of depth of dose calculation

4. Effects of inhomogeneities

5. Difference between data measured in a large water phantom and data needed if small patient volume is irradiated

6. Accuracy of calculation of machine beam-on time

The first three problems may be handled with a CT scanner. A CT slice is needed through the position of the central plane. Other slices may be necessary off-axis where the patient contour changes drastically. From the CT data, a treatment plan may be generated. Many treatment planning units will accept CT data di-

rectly from magnetic tape. Other units may require the physicist
to make a hard copy of the CT data and then trace the hard copy
into the computer. The dose may be prescribed to some isodose
level or to some point, the midline, for instance. If dose is prescribed
to a point, the depth of that point may be easily measured from
the CT scan.

The usefulness of CT data depends in great measure on the
patient being scanned in treatment position. With isocentric machines it is generally possible to treat all fields with the patient
in one position. However, if an isocentric unit is not available,
the patient may be required to change from a supine to prone position to treat an AP–PA parallel opposed pair. Tsujii, et al.[12] have
investigated the effect of this change on internal anatomy using
CT scans. They found most organs were displaced caudally when
the patient was in the prone position as compared to the supine
position. This was attributed to differences in respiration. The body
contour also changed with the different position. To maintain accurate clinical dosimetry in this case, it may be necessary to compute
isodose distributions separately for the two positions. The same
anatomical point should be identified in the two positions and the
total dose found by adding the contributions from the two fields.

The effects of inhomogeneities can be handled with most treatment-planning computers. The accuracy of this correction depends
on the specific algorithm used. Several articles have compared the
effective SSD method, the Batho, the generalized Batho, and the
equivalent TAR. These are discussed in Chapter 3.

The applicability of data taken in a large water phantom to
the anatomical regions that are treated is not always straightforward. The effect of irregular skin surfaces can be calculated with
a high degree of accuracy; however, if a small volume such as a
hand is treated, isodose curves generated in a 40 cm x 40 cm x
40 cm cubic water tank may require some correction. Alternatively,
additional scattering material may be placed around the hand to
simulate the conditions under which the data were taken.

Calculation of machine beam-on time is a lengthy error-prone
process. Kartha, et al.[13] found 10% of the cases had at least a 5%
error in calculation of beam-on time. The impact of these errors
is negated if they are detected before the patient begins treatment.
Thus, a well-policed system of calculation checks before treatment
is necessary. At the Cleveland Clinc, the calculation is done by
a technologist, checked by a dosimetrist, and reviewed by a physi-

cist prior to treatment. All of these individuals initial the calculations.

In the area of clinical dosimetry the physicist plays an important part. He or she must assure that CT scans or contour measurements are correctly performed and determine the appropriate depth for calculation of beam-on time. His or her expertise should be used to evaluate any inhomogeneity corrections and assure that the measured data is appropriate for the clinical situation. Finally, the physicist should be intimately involved in the checks of any calculation before treatment is initiated.

4.5 DAILY PATIENT TREATMENT

Changes that occur during a course of treatment which lead to errors include:

1. Change in patient contour due to weight loss or gain
2. Movement of internal organs relative to skin marks due to respiration
3. Change in position of internal organs due to physiological changes during treatment

Other errors are introduced because of mistakes in patient setup. These include:

1. Incorrect use of a wedge (wrong way, leaving it out, wrong wedge, etc.)
2. Incorrect blocking (shielding area to be treated, missing area to be shielded)
3. Inaccurate skin marks
4. Incorrect setting of machine parameters (wrong time, wrong field size, wrong gantry angle, etc.)
5. Incorrectly charting treatment

Although the contribution of the physicist in this area is less than the two previous areas, there are still a number of things that may be done to minimize the effect of these errors on the outcome of treatment. The patient's cross sectional diameter can be measured weekly. This is easily done after the patient is in treatment position. A simple requirement of having the technologist measure each patient on a certain day, for example Tuesday, can be instituted. The technologist can record this data in the chart and if a significant change is noted, appropriate action can be taken.

The problem of organ movement because of respiration can be tackled only in simulation. This is an excellent reason for having fluoroscopic capabilities on the simulator. The physician can observe the effects of respiration during fluoro and can decide on the appropriate treatment volume. It must be understood that the target may not be an immobile structure and margins must be generous enough to include any effects of respiration.

The physician must use his or her clinical expertise for the problem of change in organ position due to physiological change. This will be accomplished by closely following the patient during treatment and resimulating if it is felt appropriate.

Errors resulting from mistakes are unavoidable and sometimes undetectable. If a technologist inadvertently sets a wrong treatment time, he or she may never realize it or report it. Similar errors, such as using the incorrect wedge, may be made and never realized. This is a reason for having a technologist supervisor on the floor who moves from treatment unit to treatment unit observing and assisting with the patient setups. This person may see mistakes that others are making and institute procedures to correct them. Of course, this supervisor does not eliminate the need for clear, concise, well-written instructions in the chart.

Port films and verification films are also important in detecting field placement and blocking errors. Port films are defined as films taken with the patient in treatment position with all blocks in place but with a brief exposure. Verification films are in place during the actual treatment. Marks, et al.[14] report on localization errors during treatment of Hodgkin's disease and malignant lymphoma with extended mantle fields. Localization errors are defined to occur when improperly placed blocks lead to reduced dose to areas of disease or an overdose to healthy tissue. Marks, et al[14] found that the number of localization errors decreased with increased use of verification films. In a two-year period, the localization error rate declined from 55%, when an average of 3 verification films per patient were used, to 29% when the average number of verification films was 18 per patient.

Inaccurate skin marks occur because the original marks applied in simulation may fade or disappear entirely during treatment. These marks must be reinforced periodically and during this process they might be redrawn inaccurately. Some of these problems may be eliminated by using bony landmarks or by tattooing. The possibility of inaccurate skin marks is further reason to take frequent port or verification films.

Kartha, et al.[15] addressed the problem of incorrect machine settings. They define two types of errors "systematic" and "accidental." Systematic errors are errors associated with the degree of accuracy a parameter can be repetitively set on a treatment machine. They included, as systematic errors deviations up to 3 mm for field size, 3° for gantry and collimator angles and 3 seconds for timer. Ninety-five percent of the treatments met these criteria. Accidental errors were defined as setting of a parameter with a much larger deviation than systematic errors, for example, deviations of 1 cm or more for field size, 15° or more for gantry angle, 10° or more for collimator angle, and 30 seconds or more for time. These errors occurred with a frequency of about 2 to 3% for each operation. Of all the parameters analyzed, the one having the most significance on the tumor dose was the setting of the timer. In light of this data a record and verification system for a treatment machine should strongly be considered with the purchase of new equipment.

The most common cause of charting errors is simple addition mistakes. Occasionally during the addition of cumulative tumor dose, a mistake of one fraction too few or too many occurs. Considering a standard course of treatment to be 30 fractions, a cumulative tumor dose incorrect by one fraction would be a 3% error. Fortunately, this type of error can be found with weekly chart checks by the physicist or dosimetrist. When weekly chart checks are performed, all other aspects of treatment should be checked in addition to cumulative tumor dose. One should check that:

1. Dose delivered complies with prescription
2. Field size is correct
3. Depth of calculation is correct and whether it has changed due to patient weight loss or gain
4. Cumulative given dose is correct
5. Calculated beam-on time corresponds to beam-on time being delivered

When errors of this type are detected, it is frequently possible to make corrections before the end of treatment so that their effect is negligible.

4.6 SUMMARY

It is generally held that the accuracy required in radiation therapy is ±5% in the delivery of tumor dose. Errors arise in three general areas: a) physical dosimetry, b) clinical dosimetry, and c) daily patient treatment. Because of the physicist's involvement in all three areas, he or she can have significant impact on achieving this goal through a carefully policed and rigorously enforced quality control program of cross checks and verifications.

Notes

1. D. F. Herring and D. M. J. Compton, "The Degree of Precision Required in the Radiation Dose Delivered in Cancer Radiotherapy," in *Computers in Radiotherapy*, *Proceedings of the Third International Conference on Computers in Radiotherapy*, ed. Arvin S. Glicksman, (London: British Institute of Radiology 1971), pp. 51–58.

2. Frank Ellis, "Dose, Time, and Fractionation: A Clinical Hypothesis," *Clin. Radiol.* 20(1969), pp. 1–7.

3. Leonard J. Shukovsky, "Dose, Time, Volume Relationships in Squamous Cell Carcinoma of the Supraglottic Larynx," *Am. J. Roent.* 108(1970) 27–29.

4. J. G. Stewart and A. W. Jackson, "The Steepness of the Dose Response Curve Both for Tumor Cure and Normal Tissue Injury," *The Laryngoscope* LXXXV, 1975, 1107–11.

5. H. Svensson, P. Westling, and L. -G. Larsson, "Radiation-Induced Lesions of the Brachial Plexus Correlated to the Dose-Time-Fraction Schedule," *Acta Radiol.* (*Ther. Phys. Biol.*) 14(1975) pp. 228–38.

6. J. Kirk, W. M. Gray and E. R. Watson, "Cumulative Radiation Effect Part I: Fractionated Treatment Regimes," *Clin. Radiol.*, 22(1971) pp. 145–55.

7. *Determination of Absorbed Dose in a Patient Irradiated by Beams of X or Gamma Rays in Radiotherapy Procedures*, *ICRU Report 24*, (Washington, D. C.: International Commission on Radiation Units and Measurements, 1976).

8. K.- A. Johansson, "Studies of Different Methods of Absorbed Dose Determination and a Dosimetric Intercomparison at the Nordic Radiotherapy Centers," Thesis, University of Gothenburg, Sweden, 1982.

9. R. Loevinger and T. P. Loftus, "Uncertainty in the Delivery of Absorbed Dose," in *Ionizing Radiation Metrology*, ed. E. Casnati (Bologna, Italy: Editrice Compositori, 1977), pp. 459–73.

10. William F. Gagnon, Lawrence W. Berkley, Paula Kennedy, William F. Hanson, and Robert J. Shalek, "An Analysis of Discrepancies Encountered by the AAPM Radiological Physics Center," *Med. Phys.*, 5(1978) pp. 556–60.

11. D. L. Thompson, F. E. Kearly, H. O. Wyckoff, J. N. Gitlin, E. B. Reffit, and E. J. Shangold, *Nationwide Survey of Cobalt-60 Teletherapy*, *Final Report*, Department of Health and Human Services HHS Publication (FDA) 80–8130, 1980.

12. Hirohiko Tsujii, Malcolm A. Bagshaw, Alfred R. Smith, Carl F. von Essen, Fredrick A. Mettler, and Morton M. Kligerman, "Localization of Structures for Pion Radiotherapy by Computerized Tomography and Orthodiagraphic Projection," *Int. J. Radiation Oncology Biol. Phys.*, 6(1980), pp. 319–25.

13. Ponnunni K. I. Kartha, Anthony Chung-Bin, and Frank R. Hendrickson, "Accuracy in Clinical Dosimetry," *Brit. J. Radiol.* 46(1973) pp. 1083–84.

14. J. E. Marks, A. G. Haus, H. G. Sutton, and M. L. Griem, "Localization Error in the Radiotherapy of Hodgkin's Disease and Malignant Lymphoma with Extended Mantle Fields," *Cancer* 34(1974) pp. 83–90.

15. Ponnunni K. I. Kartha, Anthony Chung-Bin, Thomas Wachtor, and Frank R. Hendrickson, "Accuracy in Patient Setup and its Consequence in Dosimetry," *Med. Phys.*, 2(1975) pp. 331–32.

Additional Reading

LESTER J. PETERS AND GILBERT H. FLETCHER, "Causes of Failure of Radiotherapy in Head and Neck Cancer," *Radiotherapy and Oncology* 1(1983), pp. 53–63.

PONNUNNI K. I. KARTHA, ANTHONY CHUNG-BIN, THOMAS WACHTOR, AND FRANK R. HENDRICKSON, "Accuracy in Radiotherapy Treatment," *Int. J. Radiation Oncology Biol. Phys.*, 2(1977) pp. 797–99.

FRANK R. HENDRICKSON, "The Four P's of Human Error in Treatment Delivery," *Int. J. Radiation Oncology Biol. Phys.*, 4(1978) pp. 913–14.

W. F. HANSON, W. GRANT, III, P. KENNEDY, J. H. CUNDIFF, W. F. GAGNON, L. W. BERKLEY, AND R. J. SHALEK, "A Review of the Reliability of Chamber Factors Used Clinically in the United States (1968–1976), *Med. Phys.* 5(1978) pp. 552–55.

FIVE | ACCEPTANCE TESTS

5.1 INTRODUCTION

The scenario for the purchase of a therapy machine too frequently may be written as follows: the Therapy Department gathers statistics on the number of patients currently treated, the growth in the number of patient treatments over the last five years, and the projected increase in the next five years to demonstrate to the hospital administration the necessity of new equipment. The administration carefully analyzes its current and projected income, its commitments to other departments and to the community at large, the expected benefit of adding a new therapy unit, and then budgets a certain amount of money for the purchase of this unit and the new construction necessary to house the unit. The Therapy Department, working within these constraints, gathers data on all appropriate machines from the manufacturers, makes site visits to other facilities that have machines similar to the one in which they are interested, holds departmental meetings which include physicians, physicists, architects, and technologists, to determine the most appropriate unit, and then decides which one to purchase. After all this careful work and detailed analysis a purchase order is executed something like this:

1 Linac 27 $1,250,000.00
Payment Schedule: 10% with order
                    70% on delivery
                    20% on acceptance
Delivery schedule 90 days

Occasionally a statement may appear in the purchase order that reads as:

per Manufacturer's Specifications LX 2701/4.

However, the purchasers may not be satisfied with the manufacturer's specifications and they may draft their own specifications to meet their particular needs. If the manufacturer bids on the contract with these specifications they should be included with the purchase order. One key ingredient is still missing though. That ingredient is how it will be determined that the specifications are met.

Every purchase order should include a list of acceptance tests. This list should address each specification and detail the equipment and methods to make these tests. The tests should be designed to yield unambiguous results. Additionally, it is essential that they be accomplished in a timely fashion. This is important because after the unit is accepted it must still undergo commissioning measurements before it can be placed in clinical service for the benefit of the patient. These tests must be executed in some logical sequence so that the results of one test do not force a change in the equipment that would mean that a completed test must be performed again.

If the list of acceptance tests is not included, then the manufacturer generally has a protocol of acceptance tests by which the purchaser must abide. These tests minimize the manufacturer's time in gaining the purchaser's final approval, so that the manufacturer can get the final 20 to 30% of the purchase price. These tests will demonstrate that certain key specifications are met. The protocol is designed as a document to protect the manufacturer in court if a disagreement arises. However, they are almost certainly inadequate for the purchaser's needs.

In the following sections, I have listed a number of tests to verify certain aspects of the machine's performance. These might be referred to as "generic" tests because all of them will not be applicable in every situation and they will be incomplete in other situations. However, they cover 80 to 90% of the cases. Some tests may be eliminated and others added as warranted. These tests are divided into three broad categories: mechanical tests, radiation protection surveys, and radiation therapy performance tests.

5.2 MECHANICAL TESTS

These tests are listed in a logical sequence, so that any changes necessitated by one test will not invalidate the results of any earlier test. Although the radiation protection tests are listed after the mechanical tests, it would be prudent to do a quick survey of any occupied area with a Geiger counter when the radiation beam is first used during the mechanical tests. These checks verify that no egregious mistakes have been made in the shielding calculations or in the construction techniques. In the following discussion the term "film" will be used many times. It should be understood as a shorthand for ready-pack film in all instances in this chapter. Also it must be stated that most of the tolerance values given in the mechanical test section are in accordance with the National Council on Radiation Protection (NCRP) Report #69.[1] Following the discussion on therapy machines, there will be a short review of treatment simulators.

5.2.1 Collimator Axis of Rotation

A mechanical pointer can be attached to the collimator such that its point is at the SAD near the collimator's presumed axis of rotation. The front pointer supplied by the manufacturer is generally sufficient for this purpose. As the collimator is rotated through 360°, a small circle will be traced out. The center of this circle is on the collimator's axis of rotation. The image of the cross hairs should be within 2 mm of this point. Also, the image of the cross hairs should trace out a circle no greater than 1 mm in radius as the collimator is rotated.

If the image of the cross hairs describes a larger circle, then the cross hairs, light, or both are off-center and should be corrected. In some machines the light rotates with the collimator, while in others the light is fixed as the collimator rotates. For those machines with a fixed light, collimator rotation will reveal whether the cross hairs describe a circle about the axis, describe a circle about a point off-axis, or remain at a fixed point off-axis. If the cross hairs trace a circle about the axis, then the cross hairs are off. If they trace a circle centered off-axis, both light and cross hairs are off. Finally, if they remain fixed off-axis, the light is off.

For machines with a light that rotates with the collimator, an indicator must be secured independently of the collimator to determine if it is the cross hairs or the light that is off-axis. The point of a pencil held in a ring stand placed on the treatment table is an adequate indicator. If the light is off the image of the pointer will define a circle as the collimator is rotated. If this occurs, the light must be corrected. When the light is centered the pointer may be removed. If the cross hairs then trace a circle off-axis as the collimator is rotated, then they are off and must be corrected.

5.2.2 Collimator Symmetry

The edges of the light field should be located symmetrically about the cross hairs to within 2 mm at the SAD. This may be measured easily with a ruler. Alternatively, one may mark the edges of the light field on a piece of millimeter graph paper secured to the treatment table at the SAD. The edges may be remarked on the graph paper after rotating the collimator 180°. Then one can measure the difference.

5.2.3 Congruence of Light and Radiation Field

The congruence of the light and radiation field may be determined by placing a film on the treatment table perpendicular to the beam axis. The light field can be delineated by pin pricks, radioopaque markers, or pressure marks made with a ball point pen. A very useful device for checking the light-radiation field congruence is a sheet of plastic with metal shot, which define a 10 cm x 10 cm field, embedded in it. Additional plastic should be used, if needed, to provide electron equilibrium. The film is irradiated to a dose that will yield an optical density of approximately 2 when it is developed. The congruence between the 50% dose level and the edge of the light field should be within 2 mm for a 10 cm x 10 cm field. If not, either the light field or the radiation field is not coaxial with the collimator. After performing the above tests to define the collimator axis, the light field should be correct. However, further verification is possible using a technique describe by Feldman.[2]

Two exposures are necessary for Feldman's test. One film is taken as described above, followed by another film exposed with the collimator rotated 180°. If the light field is off, then the difference between the light and radiation field will be in opposite directions for the two collimator orientations. For instance, with the collimator at 0° the light field may be to the right of the radiation field and with the collimator at 180° the light field would be to the left. However, if the radiation field is off-axis, then the shift will be in the same direction for both exposures. In this case, the light field might be to the right for both the 0° and 180° exposure.

After the light and radiation field are both aligned on axis, a final verification is possible by exposing a film with a "star" pattern. In this test the collimator is adjusted to a long, narrow field, perhaps .5 cm x 40 cm. A film is placed on the treatment table, a pinprick made at the position of the cross hair's image, and a series of exposures made rotating the collimator between exposures but leaving the film in place. One might choose to make four exposures each of which expose the film to an optical density of 0.5. The collimator angles could be 0°, 110°, 225°, and 330°. This radiation pattern will form a double cross with somewhat unusual angles between the arms. If the radiation source and light source are both on the axis of the collimator, the center of this double cross should be at the position of the pinprick indicating the position of the image of the cross hairs.

5.2.4 Accuracy of Gantry Angle Indicators

The accuracy of the mechanical and digital indicators for the gantry angle should be verified. A spirit level is the only equipment necessary to accomplish this task at the four principal angles of 0°, 90°, 180°, and 270°. With the gantry at 0°, a spirit level placed against the collimator housing should indicate level. Similar tests may be performed at 90°, 180°, and 270°. If the indicators are not accurate to 0.5° or better, they should be corrected. If it is desired to verify the indicators at other angles, a gravity-oriented universal protractor with a magnetic base may be attached to the collimator housing. The readings from the protractor can be compared to the indicators.

5.2.5 Accuracy of Collimator Angle Indicators

With the gantry at 90° and a collimator angle of 0° or 180° the collimator jaws should be horizontal. This may be checked by placing a small spirit level on the jaws. Similarly, collimator angles of 90° and 270° can be checked with a spirit level as these angles orient the jaws vertically. Other angles can be checked with a gravity-oriented protractor as was done for the gantry angle. If the indicators are off by more than 0.5° they should be corrected.

5.2.6 Location of Mechanical Isocenter

If the light field and cross hairs are both centered on the collimator's axis of rotation, the mechanical isocenter may be determined. A pointer must be mounted independently of the gantry. The point of a pencil secured in a ring stand on the treatment table will suffice. Another useful device is the isocentric beam checker manufactured by Mick-Radionuclear,[3] seen in Figure 5–1. This device consists of a white lucite sheet (paddle) 5 mm thick with lead shot delineating 10 cm x 10 cm and 5 cm x 5 cm squares. Another lead shot is located at the center of these squares. This paddle is held by a base that has a bullseye level and leveling screws. The base also allows the paddle to be rotated through 360° about an axis that is contained in the front surface of the paddle.

In the following sections, I will describe the use of this device to locate the mechanical isocenter. A similar approach could be employed with any other pointer mounted independently of the gantry.

Place the isocentric beam checker on the treatment table with paddle extending over the end of the table, as in Figure 5–1, so that the paddle may be rotated through 360°. Level the base using the bullseye level and leveling screws. With the gantry at 0° and the paddle perpendicular to the central axis of the beam, move the treatment table to place the image of the cross hairs on the lead shot in the center of the paddle. Rotate gantry to 90° and rotate paddle 90° so that it is again perpendicular to the beam axis. Because the axis of rotation passes through the front surface of the paddle, the central shot remains at a fixed point in space

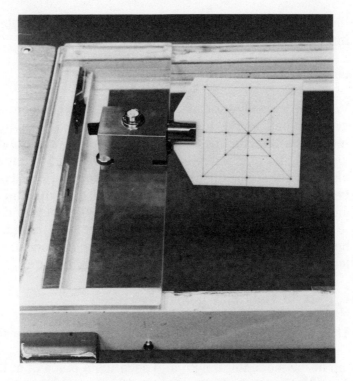

Figure 5-1 Mick Radionuclear Isocentric Beamchecker.

as the paddle is rotated. Adjust the table height to again place the image of the cross hairs on the central lead shot. Rotate gantry back to 0° and the paddle back to its initial position to verify that the cross hair's image is still on the central shot. Rotate gantry to 270° and rotate the paddle to again be perpendicular to the central axis. The image of the cross hairs should be within 2 mm of the central shot on the paddle. Rotate gantry to 180° and rotate paddle to be perpendicular to beam. Again, the image of the cross hairs should be within 2 mm of the central shot. If the image of the cross hairs is not within 4 mm of the central shot, a problem with the gantry's bearing is indicated and should be corrected.

The height of the table and its lateral and longitudinal positions should be adjusted to minimize the distance between the central shot on the paddle and the image of the cross hair at all four principal angles. For instance, the image of the cross hair may be 0.5 mm high with a gantry angle of 90° and 0.5 mm low with a gantry angle of 270°. Similarly, the image may be 0.5 mm right of the central shot at a gantry angle of 0° and to the left 0.5 mm at 180°. When this has been accomplished the central shot is on the mechanical isocenter and the accuracy of the optical distance indicator (ODI) may be checked.

5.2.7 Accuracy of Optical Distance Indicator

With the central shot of the paddle on the mechanical isocenter as described in the test above, and the paddle perpendicular to the beam, the reading of the ODI should correspond to the SAD distance. If a mechanical front pointer has been supplied, it should also indicate this distance. The accuracy of the ODI should be verified at the four principal angles. Also with the gantry at 0° and 180°, the table should be moved 20 cm up and 20 cm down to verify that the ODI is accurate over this range. Similarly at both 90° and 270° the table should be moved 20 cm right and left. The ODI should be accurate to within 2 mm.

5.2.8 Accuracy of Field Size Indicators

The accuracy of both the mechanical and digital field size indicators should be verified. This is easily accomplished by placing the table top at the isocenter height and securing a piece of millimeter graph paper to it. With the gantry at 0° various field sizes can be set and compared to measurements on the graph paper. This should be done over the range of field sizes.

5.2.9 Location of Radiation Isocenter

The location of the radiation isocenter should now be established. This may be done by closing the collimators to as small a field size as possible. A film is placed in the plane defined by the central axis of the beam as the gantry is rotated. This film will be perpendicular to the gantry's axis of rotation. To support the film it may be placed between two blocks of plastic. A pinprick should be made in the film at the point of the mechanical isocenter. A series of exposures can be made with the gantry being rotated 70° to 80° between exposures but without moving the film. Each exposure should result in an optical density of approximately 0.3. A star pattern will be produced with the center of the star indicating the radiation isocenter. This should be within 2 mm of the mechanical isocenter.

However, this test does not completely define the radiation isocenter because it may be off in the direction parallel to the gantry's axis of rotation. This may be checked by placing a film on the table top at isocenter height. With the gantry at 0° the film should be perpendicular to the central axis of the beam. A pinprick should be made in the film at the position of the mechanical isocenter. The collimator should form a long narrow field. An exposure should be made with the gantry at 0° and the collimator at 10°. The gantry should be rotated to 180° and another exposure made. The image of an X will appear on the film, with the center of the X being the radiation isocenter in this plane. This should be within 2 mm of the mechanical isocenter.

5.2.10 Treatment Table Rotation

If the treatment table is mounted on a turntable, this turntable should rotate about an axis that passes through isocenter. This may be checked by placing a film flat on the table top at isocenter height. A pinprick should be made at the location of the isocenter. A long narrow field should be set with the collimator. A series of exposures can be made rotating the turntable through 40° or 50° between exposures. The center of the resulting star pattern indicates the turntable's axis of rotation which may be compared to the location of isocenter.

5.2.11 Treatment Table Motion

The treatment table should move in a true vertical and horizontal plane. The vertical motion may be checked by securing a piece of white paper to the table top and raising the table to its highest position. With the gantry at 0°, mark the position of the cross hair image on the paper. Move the table to its lowest position. The image of the cross hair should be within 2 mm of its original position. The horizontal motion can be checked similarly with the gantry at 90° and moving the table through its full horizontal range.

5.2.12 Scales on the Treatment Table

Any scales on the treatment table to indicate table movement should be checked for accuracy.

5.2.13 Alignment of Side Lights

All side lights should be aligned in true vertical and horizontal planes and should pass through isocenter.

5.3 RADIATION PROTECTION TESTS

Wisdom dictates that a thorough radiation protection survey should be done before any extensive radiation measurements are performed. Therefore many of the tests listed below are not true acceptance tests in that the therapy machine manufacturer cannot be held accountable for things such as ozone concentrations and hot spots at junction boxes. Nevertheless, for the safety of all concerned, including the manufacturer's representative who will be present, this survey should precede the radiation therapy performance acceptance tests.

5.3.1 Interlocks and Warning Devices

All electrical and mechanical interlocks should be verified. One should check not only door interlocks and emergency off buttons, but also any interlocks for accessories, such as wedges or electron cones. All warning devices, both visual and aural, should be tested.

5.3.2 Survey of Operator's Area

To assure that one's safety survey is meaningful the output of the machine must be known. A preliminary output measurement can be done "in-air" using a calibrated ion chamber with an appropriate buildup cap. When it is determined the machine is operating as expected, one can proceed with the survey.

The first place to survey is the area where the operator will be. When one surveys walls irradiated by primary beam, no phantom should be in the beam. A phantom should be placed in the beam for surveys performed on walls that are exposed to scattered radiation. Measurements should be made for several frequently-used gantry and collimator angles. These measurements should be done with a suitable ionization chamber survey meter. Assuming these measurements are satisfactory, one can proceed with the following survey.

5.3.3 Location of Hot Spots in Head Shielding

For this test, the primary beam should be blocked by closing the collimators as far as possible, then using lead blocks to shield any remaining collimator opening. Films should be taped to cover the entire accelerator head. These films should be coded in a way to permit one to determine, after development, which area of the head the film covered. These films should be exposed long enough that the expected optical density will be one. Referring to Table 2–7 in Chapter 2, one could expect approximately 5 rad to yield an optical density of 1 on XTL film. The shielding on the head should limit the leakage radiation to 0.1% of the useful beam at 1 m, therefore one can assume 0.5% at the shielding. One would calculate that 5 rad/.005 or 1000 rad at isocenter should be an appropriate dose. Any hot spots detected on the film can be subjected to closer scrutiny in the following test.

5.3.4 Quantifying Head Leakage

Using an ion chamber survey meter with and without a buildup cap of 1/32″ lead the effective energy of the leakage radiation may be determined.[4] The in-air dose from the leakage radiation may then be measured. In NCRP Report #33,[5] the location of 26 points where head leakage should be checked one meter from the source is given. Although this section of this NCRP report was drafted for cobalt-60, these points may also be used for accelerators to quantify lead leakage. Particular attention should be given to the hot spots determined above with film. The dose rate at these 26 points should be 0.1% or less of the dose rate at isocenter. However, NCRP Report 33 allows small areas to exceed this value if the dose averaged over 100 cm² at one meter is below the limit.

Because the high radiation levels exclude the possibility of being in the room during this survey, the survey meter should be secured in position with a ring stand or similar device. If the survey meter does not have a remote reading, a television camera might be used to monitor the dose levels attained.

Following measurements at these 26 points and at any hot spots revealed by the film, the collimator transmission should be measured in-air with the ionization chamber survey meter. This transmission should be less than 2%.

5.3.5 Area Survey

A radiation survey of all occupied space outside the treatment room should be performed under conditions expected to be the worst case. This means primary barriers should be checked without a phantom in the beam, but secondary barriers should be examined with a phantom in the beam. This phantom should have a cross-sectional area at least 10 cm larger than the beam. The largest field size possible should be used. A quick survey, to determine hot spots, should be done with a rapid response instrument such as a Geiger counter. During the survey, particular attention should be focused on doors, windows, ventilation ducts, and areas inset for junction boxes, conduits, and pipes. This initial survey should be followed by a more thorough survey with an ionization chamber survey meter to determine absolute dose levels. Again, close scrutiny should be given to any hot spots detected in the initial survey. This survey should be done for a number of commonly used gantry angles. After this survey is completed expected dose levels for a week may be calculated using methods discussed in Chapter 13.

5.3.6 Neutron Survey

Above 6 to 8 MeV photon energy the photoneutron channel opens up in many nuclei because of electric dipole absorption of the incident photon. The cross section for neutron production increases with energy up to approximately 20 to 25 MeV photon energy and then decreases for light elements. For heavy elements the peak cross section occurs between 10 and 15 MeV. This cross section generally increases with the atomic number of the material. Because high Z materials are used in the target, flattening filter, and collimators of linear accelerators, neutron production may constitute a hazard for medium and high energy accelerators. There are several devices that may be used for neutron survey. These devices include neutron rem counters, activation foils, and Bonner spheres. This survey should be performed in a manner similar to the photon area survey.

5.3.7 Induced Radioactivity

Because of photoneutron production, artificial radioisotopes are created in the shielding, target, collimators, cross hairs, flattening filters, and accessories. These areas should be surveyed after an exposure of several kilorad to determine if there is a problem. Radioactivity also may be induced in the air; however, this is generally less of a problem than ozone production.

5.3.8 Ozone Production

If one anticipates a number of treatments that require a very extended SSD such as total body irradiation with photons or electrons, then the ozone concentration should be determined for these conditions.

5.4 RADIATION THERAPY PERFORMANCE TESTS

The difference between acceptance tests and commissioning measurements is ill-defined. Commissioning the unit after it has been accepted requires a much more extensive set of measurements, but many of the acceptance tests investigate the same details. For instance, beam profiles for a large number of field sizes at several depths may be required for input to a treatment planning computer; these must be considered commissioning measurements. However, verification of flatness and symmetry of the beam will require a somewhat smaller set of profile measurements; these are acceptance tests. In general, acceptance tests must be designed to verify the specifications whether these be the manufacturer's or the hospital's. In the following sections, I will address the minimum amount of information required for radiation therapy performance tests. Other areas will be covered in the next chapter on commissioning measurements.

5.4.1 Determination of Depth of Maximum Dose

For X-rays above 4 MV and electrons above 5 MeV, the depth of maximum dose (d_{max}) is great enough that it may be measured in a water phantom with most cylindrical ion chambers. For medium and high energy photons, d_{max} may shift toward the surface as the field size increases. The reason for this has been postulated to be scattered photons[6] or electrons.[7] The position of d_{max} will move toward the surface also for electron beams if the field size is less than twice the range of the electrons.

5.4.2 Energy Specification

The energy of an accelerator is typically specified by the potential through which the electrons are accelerated. The penetration of an X-ray beam is usually quoted as the value of the central axis percent depth dose of a 10 cm x 10 cm field at a depth of 10 cm in water for a 100 cm SSD. Frequently a correlation is made between this depth and a nominal voltage. Generally electron beam energies are determined with the Markus equation.

$$E_p\,(MeV) = 1.95\ R_p\,(cm) + .48 \tag{5-1}$$

with R_p = the practical range (see Chapter 11)

and E_p = the most probable energy at the surface of the phantom

Alternative energy specifications have been enunciated in the latest protocol of Task Group 21 of the AAPM.[8] In this document, X-ray beams are specified in terms of a nominal accelerating potential, which is determined by measuring the ratio of the ionization at a depth of 20 cm in water to the ionization at a depth of 10 cm in water for a source-chamber-distance equal to the normal SAD. Electron beam energies are determined by measuring the central axis percent depth ionization curve. The average energy in MeV is then specified to be 2.33 times the depth in cm of water where the ion chamber reading is reduced to 50% of its maximum reading. Further details for X-ray and electron measurements may be found in Chapters 10 and 11.

5.4.3 Flatness and Symmetry

The flatness and symmetry of a therapy beam is specified at some depth in a water phanton positioned at the normal SSD. Electron beams are usually specified at d_{max} and photon beams at either 5 cm or 10 cm depth. The depth of specification for the photon beam is dependent upon the design of the flattening filter. If the specification is for 5 cm one should generally expect smaller "horns" at d_{max} but more rounded isodose curves at 15 cm than for a machine with flatness and symmetry specified at 10 cm. The flatness and symmetry should be verified along both principal axes at the four principal angles of 0°, 90°, 180°, 270°. Specifications are typically ±3% on flatness and ±1% on symmetry over the central 80% of the beam for photons. For electrons typical values for flatness are ±3% to ±5% and ±1% to ±2% for symmetry. These specifications may be for the largest field size or for a range of field sizes.

If one is using a scanning water phantom with data output to an $X-Y$ recorder, the flatness and symmetry may be determined easily. After removing the graph paper with the beam profile on it from the recorder, the paper should be folded to align the beam edges. This paper can then be placed on a light box and the symmetry and flatness evaluated.

5.4.4 Dose Rate

The dose rate should be accurately determined for a single field size at all four principle angles. This may be done using an ion chamber in a water phantom. Calibration details are given in Chapter 10 for megavoltage photons and Chapter 11 for electrons. The dose rate should be the same at these four angles to within 1% or better.

5.4.5 Monitor Linearity and End Effects

The monitor linearity and end effects should be determined. The monitor should be linear to within 1% or better over its entire range. A method for checking monitor linearity and end effects is discussed in Chapter 10.

5.4.6 Arc Therapy

The dose rate specification during arc therapy should be verified. This may be done using an ion chamber in a cylindrical water phantom or in a plastic phantom rigidly attached to and rotating with the gantry. If the phantom is rotating with the gantry, one must be careful to assure that the ion chamber will not move during this motion.

5.5 RADIATION THERAPY SIMULATORS

The treatment simulator has become an essential tool in the radiation therapy armamentarium. For this reason it must be subjected to acceptance tests as rigorously as the therapy machines themselves. Many of the acceptance tests conducted on the treatment machines are also applicable to the simulator. All the mechanical tests are relevant. However, additional tests may be added to the list. Since a simulator has a variable target-axis-distance (TAD), the congruence of light and radiation field, the accuracy of the gantry angle indicators, and the accuracy of the field size indicators should be verified over the entire range of TADs. Also, the accuracy of the TAD indicator must be determined over the range of motion. One should determine if the mechanical isocenter remains in the same place over the range of TADs as well as over the range of movement for the image intensifier (II).

The radiation therapy performance tests are not applicable, of course, to the simulator. But other tests suggest themselves, which will be discussed in the coming sections.

5.5.1 Shift of X-ray Image with Change of Focal Spot

The diagnostic X-ray tube has two focal spots. One is used for fluoroscopy and the other for films. The shift in the X-ray image when the focal spot is changed should be less than 1 mm. This may be checked by aligning a device like the Mick Radionuclear isocentric beam checker with the fluoro image of the cross hairs and then taking a spot film.

5.5.2 Position of Cross Hairs' Image

The X-ray image of the cross hairs should remain on isocenter as the machine rotates. A radioopaque pointer at isocenter mounted independently of the gantry is necessary. In the fluoro mode, the X-ray image of the cross hairs should remain on the pointer as the gantry is rotated. Following this initial fluoro check, spot films should be taken at the four principal angles. A similar test should be performed with the light field. These tests also demonstrate the congruence of the X-ray and optical image of the cross hairs. These tests should be performed over the range of TADs and target-image intensifier distances (TID). The movement in the cross hair's image should be less than 1 mm as the gantry is rotated through 360°.

5.5.3 Size of Image of Field Size Delineators

The image of the wires that delineate the field size should be 3 mm or less for both the X-ray and optical image at 100 cm TAD.

5.5.4 Diagnostic Image Quality

The diagnostic image quality is an essential element of any treatment simulator; however, its evaluation is beyond the scope of this book. One would be well advised to consult with one's own diagnostic radiology department or refer to a standard reference.[9,10,11,12]

Notes

1. *Dosimetry of X-Ray and Gamma-Ray Beams for Radiation Therapy in the Energy Range 10 KeV to 50 MeV, NCRP Report No. 69.*, (Washington, D. C.: National Council on Radiation Protection and Measurements, 1981).

2. Arnold Feldman, "A Method of Aligning a Light Field with a Radiation Field," *AAPM Q. Bull.*, 5(1971), p. 174.

3. Mick Radionuclear Instruments, Inc., 1470 Outlook Avenue, Bronx, N.Y. 10465.

4. Richard G. Lane, "Effective Energy Determination in Leakage Radiation Measurements," *Health Physics*, 33(1977), pp. 626–28.

5. *Medical X-Ray and Gamma-Ray Protection for Energies Up to 10 MeV: Equipment Design and Use*, NCRP Report No. 33., (Washington, D. C.: National Council on Radiation Protection and Measurements, 1968).

6. James R. Marbach and Peter R. Almond, "Scattered Photons as the Cause for the Observed d_{max} Shift with Field Size in High Energy Photon Beams," *Med. Phys.*, 4(1977), pp. 310–14.

7. Peter J. Biggs and C. Clifton Ling, "Electrons as the Cause of the Observed d_{max} Shift With Field Size in High Energy Photon Beams," *Med. Phys.*, 6(1979), pp. 291–95.

8. "A Protocol For the Determination of Absorbed Dose From High-Energy Photon and Electron Beams," Task Group #21, Radiation Therapy Committee, American Association of Physicists in Medicine, *Med. Phys.*, 10(1983), pp. 741–71.

9. William R. Hendee and Raymond P. Rossi, "Performance Specifications for Diagnostic X-Ray Equipment," *Radiol.*, 120(1976), pp. 409–12.

10. William R. Hendee, Edward L. Chaney, and Raymond P. Rossi, *Radiologic Physics Equipment and Quality Control*, (Chicago: Year Book Medical Publishers, Inc, 1977).

11. Edwin C. McCullough and John D. Earle, "The Selection, Acceptance Testing, and Quality Control of Radiotherapy Treatment Simulators," *Radiol.*, 131(1979), pp. 221–30.

12. Pei-Jan Paul Lin, and others, eds., *Acceptance Testing of Radiological Imaging Equipment AAPM Symposium No. 1*, (New York, N. Y.: American Association of Physicists in Medicine, 1982).

Additional Reading

"A Suggested Procedure for the Mechanical Alignment of Tele-Gamma and Megavoltage X-Ray Beam Units," H.P.A. Report Series No. 3, Hospital Physicists Association, London, England, 1970.

C. K. BOMFORD, and others, *Treatment Simulators*, British Journal of Radiology Supplement 16, (London: British Institute of Radiology, 1981).

Measurements of the Performance Characteristics of Diagnostic X-Ray Systems Used in Medicine. Part I: X-Ray Tubes and Generators, (London, England: Hospital Physicists Association, 1981).

Measurement of the Performance Characteristics of Diagnostic X-Ray Systems used in Medicine. Part II: X-Ray Intensifier Television Systems, (London, England: Hospital Physicists Association, 1981).

ROBERT G. WAGGENER AND CHARLES R. WILSON, eds., *Quality Assurance in Diagnostic Radiology AAPM Monograph No. 4*, (New York, N. Y., American Association of Physicists in Medicine, 1980).

SIX | COMMISSIONING
         | MEASUREMENTS

6.1 INTRODUCTION

Upon completion of the acceptance tests, the physicist must perform an extensive set of measurements on a therapy machine before it may be used for patient treatments. This process is referred to as "commissioning a unit."

A number of people, including the physicist, will be eager to begin treatments with the machine. The reasons are manifold. Foremost is that aspect of human nature that everyone wants "to play with a new toy." But more practical reasons exist as well. The hospital administrator has just spent a million dollars and he or she would like to see the machine become financially productive. The therapists see patients in dire need every day and they would like to see the new machine used for the patients' benefit. The technologists have been working until 8:00 every night because of the schedule on the existing machines and they would like to see the new machine assume part of this load so they can get off at 5:00. The dosimetrist is tired of doing treatment plans with cobalt-60 and would like to see the new machine in use so he or she can use his or her creative talents to plan imaginative new treatments. And finally, the physicist would like to see the new machine in clinical practice because he or she is sick of everyone asking, "When is it going to be ready?"

Although these are all valid reasons, it is still incumbent upon the physicist to do a thorough, rigorous, and complete job. The commissioning measurements must provide the data necessary to answer questions involving 90 to 95% of all treatments performed. However, the physicist should not view commissioning as a time to acquire data for his or her next publication or for highly specialized treatments. He or she cannot possibly anticipate future needs or developments that may require additional data. The physicist must remember these are the reasons we have nights and weekends.

To acquire the data necessary in a timely fashion requires a well-organized approach. The measurements should be done systematically with those that will yield data most needed for clinical treatments performed first. In the following discussion, commissioning measurements for megavoltage photon beams will be examined first and then the tests for electrons will be addressed.

6.2 MEGAVOLTAGE PHOTON MEASUREMENTS

The exact nature of the data taken will depend on a particular institution. If an institution uses isocentric technique exclusively, central axis percent depth dose measurements may not be necessary. Similarly, for an institution treating only SSD, tissue-maximum ratios (TMR) may be a waste of time. Furthermore, many treatment-planning computers require that data be taken in a particular format. For instance, it may be necessary to measure beam profiles at specified depths. The following, therefore, is an attempt to outline a series of measurements that may be altered to meet an institution's needs.

I have made an effort to list the tests in the order which I feel corresponds to the most immediate needs of a department. Since it is conceivable that a number of palliative cases could be treated with output factors and either central axis percent depth dose or TMRs, these measurements are listed first. This should not be interpreted as implying that this is all that is necessary before treatments begin. On the contrary, the complete set of measurements should be done prior to placing the machine in clinical service. There are two reasons for this practice. In the first place treatment planning, which is essential to the full utilization of the equipment, is impossible with only central axis percent depth dose. In the second place, it is very inefficient for a physicist to set up measuring apparatus after 5:00 P.M., take data for a few hours and then remove the equipment before the next day's treatment. Realistically, it takes at least one hour to set up equipment with the precision necessary to take useful data and at least half that time to remove it. If the equipment can be left in place, much more can be accomplished in a given period. In the long run, the machine may be used to its maximum capabilities sooner if all commissioning measurements are completed first. Also, it becomes more and more likely that the job may never be completed in view of the extremely frustrating situation that exists if the physicist is continually setting up and removing equipment.

6.2.1 Central Axis Percent Depth Dose

The central axis percent depth dose should be measured for 8 to 12 field sizes spanning the range of sizes possible on the machine. These measurements should be made with an ion chamber that is as small as practicable. Unless diodes have been shown to give identical results to ion chambers they should not be used. Several commercially available ion chambers with a volume of 0.1 cc are an appropriate choice. Measurements for field sizes smaller than 4 cm x 4 cm should be made with caution because the ion chamber will integrate the dose over its active volume. For example, one 0.1 cc chamber has a cylindrical volume of 1.425 cm in height x .35 cm in diameter. The height of this chamber occupies a significant portion of a 3 cm x 3 cm field.

6.2.2 Tissue–Maximum Ratios

I will use the term tissue–maximum ratio (TMR)[1] although it may be more appropriate to speak of tissue–air (TAR)[2] or tissue–phantom ratios (TPR).[3] These are similar concepts; each being applicable over a certain energy range. These values are generally used for isocentric and rotational treatments. A more complete discussion of these terms will be found in Chapter 14.

Regardless of whether TAR, TMR, or TPRs are measured, the technique is similar and quite time-consuming. For purposes of this discussion, I will outline TMR measurements. To determine these values, an ion chamber is placed at the isocenter in a phantom at the depth of d_{max}. For 6 MV X-rays d_{max} is 1.5 cm. This implies that the source-phantom-distance is 98.5 cm assuming a 100 cm SAD. The measurement made here is the reading or "dose" at d_{max} in the definition of TMRs. Subsequent readings are taken at a number of depths without changing the field size. For these readings, the ion chamber is maintained at isocenter by adjusting the surface of the phantom and depth of the chamber. For example, the 10 cm reading is made with a source-chamber-distance of 100 cm and a source-phantom distance of 90 cm. The TMR for 10 cm is equal to the ratio of reading with the chamber at 10 cm to the reading at d_{max}.

The measurement of TMRs is time consuming because the phantom must be adjusted for each measurement. Tissue-maximum ratios should be measured at depth intervals of at least 1 cm to a depth of 20 cm and then in intervals of 2 cm. This should be done for a minimum of eight field sizes spanning the range available.

6.2.3 Output Factors

The dose per monitor unit at d_{max} will change with field size. Output factors measure this change. Generally, the output (dose per monitor unit), for all field sizes is normalized to the output for a 10 cm x 10 cm field size. This procedure means the output factor for a 10 cm x 10 cm field equals one. To measure output factors the ion chamber is placed at d_{max} and readings are taken for a number of field sizes. For high energy beams, the position of the ion chamber must be adjusted as the depth of the maximum dose changes. Further discussion of the shift in d_{max} is given in Chapter 5. In a department that uses isocentric techniques, the output factors should be measured with the ion chamber at isocenter and the surface of the phantom at SAD $- d_{max}$. If SSD techniques are used, the ion chamber should be placed at the normal SSD $+ d_{max}$ and the surface of the phantom at the normal SSD. Output factors should be determined for rectangular as well as square fields. For rectangular fields, output factors should also be measured for both orientations of collimator jaws that form the rectangular field. For instance, the output factor for an 8 cm x 12 cm field with the upper jaw forming the 8 cm side may be different than the output factor when the lower jaw forms the 8 cm side.

For cobalt-60 these measurements are frequently performed "in-air." These factors should be referred to as the "field size dependence." This technique separates the output factor into two components, the field size dependence and the peak scatter factor (see Chapter 14). To get the dose at d_{max} in phantom when this is done, one must multiply the dose in-air for the calibration field by the peak scatter factor and the field size dependence. Most institutions use the peak scatter factors for cobalt-60 in *British Journal of Radiology Supplement 11*[4] or Supplement 17.[5]

6.2.4 Wedge Factors

The wedge factor is the ratio of the output on the central axis for certain specific conditions with a wedge in the beam to those same conditions with no wedge in the beam. This may be measured on the central axis of a 10 cm x 10 cm field at a depth of 5 cm, for example. The axis of the ion chamber should be aligned parallel to a constant thickness of the wedge. Because the dose may change rapidly off-axis with a wedge in the beam, two measurements should always be taken for each wedge. The collimator or wedge should be rotated 180° between these measurements, assuming the output has been shown to be independent of collimator rotation. If these two measurements differ by more than 5%, further investigation is required. Possibly the ion chamber is not on the central axis or the wedge is not positioned correctly. If there is less than 5% difference it is generally acceptable to average the two readings and divide the average by the reading with no wedge in the beam. This ratio is the wedge factor. This is clearly an incomplete description as these factors may vary with depth and field size. Because of the complexity of the problem, complete isodose curves should be available before wedges are employed clinically. However, for limited applications, wedge factors can prove useful.

6.2.5 Blocking Tray and Block Factors

The shielding of certain areas in the irradiated volume is frequently desirable. This is usually accomplished by placing lead or tungsten blocks on a tray located near the collimator opening. The attenuation of the tray must be known to deliver the proper dose to the tumor and the degree of shielding provided by the blocks should be known to determine if it is adequate for the intended purpose.

The attenuation of the tray may be measured in a manner similar to the wedge factors. An ion chamber is placed at a given depth in a phantom on the central axis of the beam for a certain field size; then measurements are made with and without the tray in the beam. The ratio of these two measurements is the tray factor.

The degree of shielding provided by the blocks depends on the size of the block, the size of the field, and the depth of measurement because of scatter into the shielded area from unshielded areas. The easiest way to quantify all these variables is to make beam profile measurements for various field sizes and various depths with and without a selection of blocks in the beam. An example is Figure 6–1 showing beam profiles at depths of d_{max}, 5 cm, 15 cm, and 25 cm for a 25 cm x 25 cm field of a 6 MV X-ray beam. The areas of reduced intensity are shielded by two different size blocks.

6.2.6 Beam Profiles

To provide isodose curves necessary for treatment planning, the value of the dose at any depth must be known off-axis as well as on-axis. The most straightforward approach is to measure beam profiles at several depths. The number of profiles, the specific depths, and the number of field sizes will depend on the treatment-planning computer in use. Many planning systems require the data in a particular format. It is necessary to measure profiles for both wedged and unwedged fields.

The measurement of beam profiles is readily accomplished with a three-dimensional scanning water phantom. The surface of the water should be at the SAD and the phantom positioned with the direction of the detector's travel parallel to the side of the field and passing through the central axis. This plane is referred to as a "principal plane." Care should be taken to assure that both the gantry and phantom are level. Transverse scans can be made at a number of depths in this principal plane. If information is desired in planes that do not pass through the central axis, the detector should be incremented to the appropriate position. The physicist may also wish to take data in the principal plane and off-axis planes orthogonal to the initial plane.

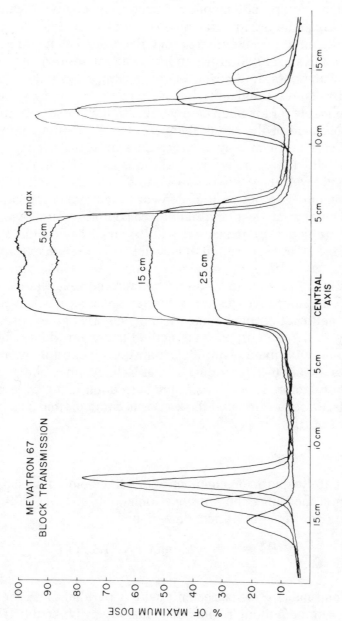

Figure 6–1 Beam profiles performed with two different size shielding blocks in the beam. Depths of measurement are d_{max}, 5 cm, 15 cm, and 25 cm.

6.2.7 Entrance Dose and the Buildup Region

The buildup region of megavoltage photon beams is the most widely studied area of transition zone dosimetry and one with which most people are familiar. In spite of this widespread knowledge, data in this region are frequently characterized by incomplete measurements, analysis, and interpretation. Let's first address the interpretation of the data. In a strict sense, the Bragg–Gray theory, which is used to convert ionization measurements to the dose values, is not applicable for air-filled cavity ionization chambers in transition zones because of the rapid change in the electron spectrum with depth. This problem may be overcome by using a homogeneous system with the chamber wall and gas having the same atomic composition.[6] Unless this is done, one should not speak of percent of maximum dose but only of percent of maximum ionization.

The entrance dose and buildup region of megavoltage photon beams are generally measured with a parallel plate ion chamber with a fixed plate separation. It is well known that an extrapolation chamber gives different results. Although the values taken with an extrapolation chamber should be more correct, the use of this type of chamber involves three to four times as much work. In a clinical setting, this much time is usually not available. Fortunately, Velkley et al.[7] have proposed a method to convert data taken with a chamber with fixed electrode separation to extrapolation chamber data. Figure 6–2, reproduced from Velkley, gives the necessary correction factor. The y–axis is the correction factor in % per mm of electrode separation and the x–axis is depth plotted as a fraction of depth of d_{max}.

Example

A parallel plate ion chamber with a fixed electrode separation of 1.5 mm measures the entrance ionization of 25 MV X-rays as 10%. The corrected entrance ionization (E.I.) is

$$E.I. = 10\% - 1\% \text{ mm}^{-1} \times (1.5 \text{ mm})$$
$$= 8.5\%$$

When making measurements with a parallel plate ionization chamber in the buildup region, one must always take data for both polarities. Significant differences in the readings may exist between positive and negative bias on the entrance window and these differ-

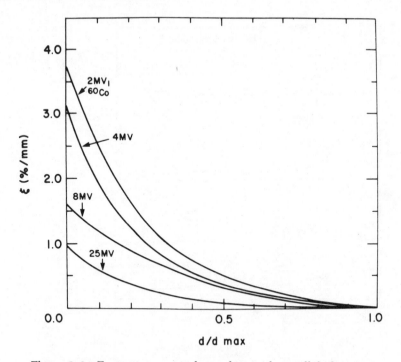

Figure 6–2 Factor to correct data taken with parallel plate ion chamber with fixed plate separation to correspond to data taken with extrapolation chamber. From Velkley, et al., *Medical Physics* 2, pp. 14–19, 1975. Used with permission.

ences may change with depth.[8] It is necessary to make a measurement with both polarities at each depth. The average reading of the two polarities is the true reading.[9]

Measurements should be taken off-axis and outside the primary beam as well as on the central axis in the buildup region. Purser[10] first showed that megavoltage photons may have a significant dose outside the field in the buildup region. Doses outside the primary beam for cobalt-60 gamma rays and 6 MV and 18 MV X-rays are shown in Figures 6–3, 6–4, 6–5.[11] Doses as high as 20% of the central axis d_{max} dose are observed 1 cm outside the primary beam for cobalt-60 at a depth of 1 mm. Even 10 cm from the edge of the beam, doses exceed 5% of the central axis d_{max} dose in the buildup region.

In light of the caveats just mentioned, let's turn to a discussion of measurement of the buildup region and the entrance dose. A polystyrene phantom is generally used. This phantom may either have a thin-window parallel plate ion chamber, which is integral

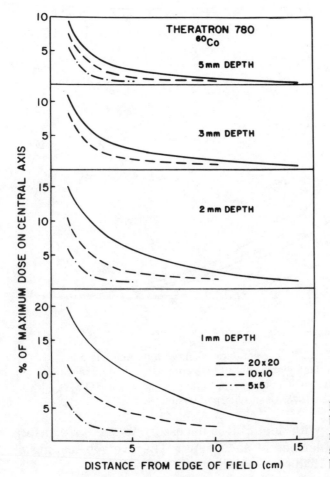

Figure 6–3 Dose in the buildup region outside the primary beam for several field sizes on a Theratron 780 cobalt-60 unit.

to a polystyrene plate, or a polystyrene block may be machined to accept such a chamber. In either case, it is important that the thin window be located at the surface of the block so the only material between the source and the air cavity is the thin window.

Readings can be taken at other depths by placing thin sheets of polystyrene on top of this configuration. For institutions that treat isocentrically this presents no problem because adding plastic to the top of the phantom changes the source-surface-distance (SSD) but not the source-detector-distance. At institutions that do not treat isocentrically, an easy method to maintain a constant SSD is to make the initial measurement with all the thin sheets of plastic at the bottom of the phantom. These thin sheets can

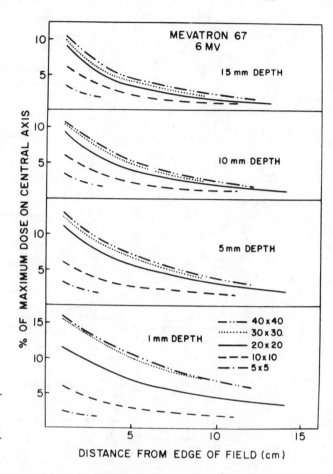

Figure 6–4 Dose in the buildup region outside the primary beam for several field sizes for a 6 MV X-ray beam from a Mevatron 67 linear accelerator.

then be moved from the bottom of the phantom to the top. This technique maintains a constant SSD as the ion chamber measures the ionization at greater depths in plastic. This method is easier and more accurate than attempting to lower the table as the plastic is added. All of the readings should be replicated with the opposite polarity on the entrance window. The average value of the two readings can be found and corrected as discussed earlier. These measurements should be repeated for a number of field sizes and also with any bolus materials that may be in use.

A final caution regards the use of computerized treatment planning in the buildup region. Commercially available systems have done a notoriously poor job. Very little attention has been focused on the development of accurate algorithms because of a mistaken belief that a therapist never considers this area. On the contrary,

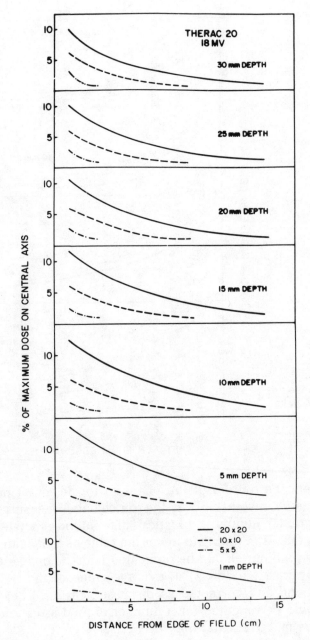

Figure 6–5 Dose in the buildup region outside the primary beam for several field sizes for a 18 MV X-ray beam on a Therac 20 linear accelerator.

it has been my experience that a therapist considers this component of the distribution in his or her decision for 5 to 10% of the cases. If he or she does not consider plans critically from a commercial system, he or she may well make the wrong decision. It is imperative that the physicist help the therapist make a proper evaluation in these instances by using the measured data to supplement the computer plan.

6.2.8 Beam Quality

In recent years commercial treatment planning systems have begun to address the problem of a change in the beam quality off-axis on a linear accelerator. A differential hardening of the beam results because of the conically-shaped flattening filter centered on the beam axis.[12] The beam has a higher effective energy on-axis than off-axis.

A method to measure this change in quality and to correct for it in computerized treatment plans has been described by Hanson, et al.[13][14] The measurement technique involves measuring the HVL in water on-axis and off-axis in good geometry. This measurement is made with the maximum collimator opening but with secondary blocking used to yield a beam of 2 cm x 2 cm or 3 cm x 3 cm at the point of measurement. The ion chamber with appropriate buildup cap should be placed on the central axis at least 2 meters from the source. A small cylindrical container of water should be positioned midway between the chamber and source. By varying the level of the water, the HVL can be obtained. All exposures should be done in-air with a buildup cap of appropriate thickness in place. Points off-axis may be measured simply by repositioning the chamber at the appropriate point, changing the secondary blocking to yield the opening at that point, and repeating the measurements. A typical curve for a 6 MV linac is shown in Figure 6–6.[15]

6.2.9 Applicability of Inverse Square Law

At times it may be necessary to treat patients at an extended distance. This typically happens for mantle, hemi-body, and whole body treatments. One must never assume that inverse square is applicable for these situations. Data should be acquired to either

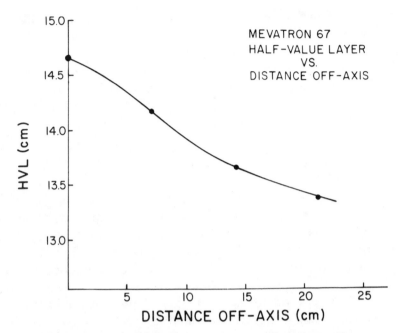

Figure 6–6 Change in HVL as a function of position off-axis. The off-axis position refers to distances measured at 100 cm from the target.

demonstrate the applicability or quantify what the output is if inverse square is not applicable.

These measurements should be made for a number of field sizes. The detector should be placed in a plastic phantom at d_{max} and the SSD varied over some range, say 60 to 300 cm. The data can be plotted on cartesian graph paper with the x–axis being source-chamber distance and the y–axis being the reciprocal of the square root of the ion chamber reading. If inverse square is applicable this plot will result in a straight line. For some machines the effective position of the source may be different than the position of the target even though inverse square may be applicable. If this is true, the straight line will not pass through the origin but will intersect the x–axis at some other value. For example, if a straight line results that crosses the x–axis at a value of 2, then inverse square may be applied if the effective position of the source is used rather than the nominal position of the target. In this example for a 100 cm SAD machine the effective source position would be $100 - 2 = 98$ cm. To determine the output at 2 meters for this example, one would calculate the inverse square factor as

$$ISF = \left(\frac{100-2}{200-2}\right)^2$$

$$= \left(\frac{98}{198}\right)^2$$

$$= 0.245$$

If the straight line intercepted the x–axis at a negative value, say -2, then the effective source position would be $100 + 2 = 102$ cm.

The effective source position may change with field size. If this is true it may be possible to fit the data for various field sizes with an analytical expression. In this case the effective source position might be calculated with a polynominal equation.

The data may be subjected to a linear regression analysis as an alternative to graphing it. This has the advantage of eliminating any bias in drawing a straight line. The correlation coefficient indicates the applicability of the inverse square law with a value of one resulting from a straight line. A sample set of data is given below:

$$d_{max} = 1.5 \text{ cm}$$

Source-surface distance (cm)	Source chamber distance (cm)	Reading $(10^{-8}C)$	$(\text{Reading})^{-1/2}$
58.5	60	11.75	0.292
100	101.5	4.12	0.493
150	151.5	1.873	0.731
200	201.5	1.064	0.969
250	251.5	0.687	1.21
300	301.5	0.479	1.44
350	351.5	0.353	1.68

correlation coefficient $= 0.9999$

x intercept $= -2.0$

The above results indicate inverse square is applicable if the effective source position is taken to be 2 cm further from the point of measurement than the nominal target position.

Example

From the above, the reading at SCD = 101.5 cm is 4.12 and the reading at SCD = 301.5 cm is 0.479. Using effective source position and inverse square calculate the expected reading at SCD = 301.5 cm.

$$\left(\frac{103.5}{303.5}\right)^2 \times 4.12 = 0.479$$

This is in agreement with the measured value.

6.3 ELECTRON MEASUREMENTS

6.3.1 Central Axis percent Depth Dose and X-ray Contamination

Electron central axis percent depth dose curves are not equivalent to depth ionization curves. Measurement of electron depth dose curves involves correcting the ionization values by various factors that are detailed in Chapter 11. Also, unlike photons, the percent depth dose values are generally independent of field size for field diameters greater than twice the electron range. One important factor that may be quantified from the depth dose curve is the percent of X-ray contamination. The X-rays in an electron beam are the result of bremsstrahlung interactions between the incident electrons and nuclei in the collimators, scattering foils, and patients. The value of this contamination may be seen in Figure 6–7. 6 MeV and 20 MeV electron beams are compared by plotting their central axis percent depth dose against fraction of practical range. It is observed there is some dose deposited even for depths greater than the practical range. This dose results from the X-ray contamination. It is noted also that the 20 MeV beam has a larger X-ray component than the 6 MeV one. This difference results from the increase of the cross section for bremsstrahlung production with increasing electron energy.

6.3.2 Output Factors

The dose per monitor unit for electron beams depends on field size. This dependence may be determined by placing the ion chamber at d_{max} and measuring the ionization as a function of field size. These readings are generally normalized to a 10 cm x 10 cm

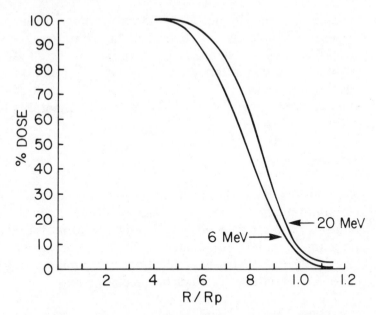

Figure 6–7 Comparison of central axis percent depth dose curves from a 6 MeV and a 20 MeV electron beam plotted as a function of fraction of practical range (R/R_p).

field. If the field diameter is smaller than twice the range, d_{max} may shift toward the surface. The ion chamber should be moved to the new position of d_{max} for these cases. The output factor may be affected by secondary blocking also. If blocks cover more than 25% of the area, a special calibration should be performed.

6.3.3 Beam Profiles

Film is useful medium for determining electron beam profiles or alternatively isodose curves. A polystyrene phantom of the type described in Chapter 2 is essential. Beam profiles may be conveniently measured by exposing the film perpendicular to the beam and isodose curves measured by exposing the film parallel to the beam. All the precautions given in Chapter 2 regarding uniform pressure on film, removal of all excess air from the film packet, and any corrections for optical density to dose should be observed.

6.3.4 Effect of Blocks

Unlike photons, areas may be effectively shielded from electrons with very small thicknesses of lead. However, the amount of shielding required to "attenuate" the beam to a given level is critically dependent upon the depth of interest because of the scattering of the electrons. There are reports in the literature for the amount of lead required to shield 7, 9, 11, 15, 18, 19, 22, 28 MeV electrons to the 95 and 98% attenuation level when the depth of interest is 5 mm,[16] the amount of cerrobend for 6, 9, 12, 16, 20 MeV electrons at d_{max},[17] and the amount of lead for 13 MeV electrons for a variety of depths.[18]

6.3.5 Entrance Dose

The entrance dose should be measured for electron fields as well as photon fields. Clinicians are generally more concerned with the value of the entrance dose with electrons than photons because of its higher value with electrons. All the cautions given in Section 6.2.7 apply here. However, the paper of Velkley, et al. does not address corrections for electron measurements.

6.3.6 Applicability of Inverse Square Law

The applicability of inverse square law should be investigated for each electron energy over the range of field sizes. The technique is the same as given in Section 6.2.9.

Notes

1. J. Garrett Holt, John S. Laughlin, and John P. Moroney, "The Extension of the Concept of Tissue-Air Ratios (TAR) to High-Energy X-Ray Beams," *Radiol.*, 96(1970), pp. 437–46.

2. H. E. Johns, G. F. Whitmore, T. A. Watson, and F. H. Umberg, "A System of Dosimetry for Rotation Therapy with Typical Rotation Distributions," *J. of Canadian Association of Radiologists*, IV(1953), pp. 1–14.

3. C. J. Karzmark, Angela Deubert, and R. Loevinger, "Tissue-Phantom Ratios—An Aid to Treatment Planning," *Brit. J. Radiol.*, 38(1965), pp. 158–59.

4. M. Cohen, D. E. A. Jones, and D. Greene, eds., *Central Axis Depth Dose Data for Use in Radiotherapy, British Journal of Radiology Supplement 11*, (London: British Institute of Radiology, 1972).

5. *Central Axis Depth Dose Data for Use In Radiotherapy, British Journal of Radiology Supplement 17*. (London: British Institute of Radiology, 1983).

6. U. Fano, "Note on the Bragg-Gray Cavity Principle for Measuring Energy Dissipation," *Radiat. Res.*, 1(1954), pp. 237–40.

7. D. E. Velkley, D. J. Manson, J. A. Purdy, and G. D. Oliver, Jr., "Buildup Region of Megavoltage Photon Radiation Sources," *Med. Phys.*, 2(1975), pp. 14–19.

8. Daniel Bassano, "Relative Doses to Skin and Superficial Nodes from 10 MV Photons as a Function of Field Size and Distance from Shadow Tray," *Radiol.*, 115(1975), pp. 707–10.

9. Jasper E. Richardson, "Effect of Chamber Voltage on Electron Buildup Measurements," *Radiol.*, 62(1954), pp. 584–88.

10. P. R. Purser, "Electrons Scattered from Supervoltage Photon Beams," *Phys. Med. Biol.*, 16(1971), pp. 700–701.

11. J. L. Horton, "Dose in the Buildup Region Outside the Primary Beam," *Med. Phys.*, 11(1984), pp. 331–34.

12. Douglas Jones, "Communication," *Med. Phys.*, 5(1978), pp. 452–53.

13. W. F. Hanson, L. W. Berkley, and M. Peterson, "Off-Axis Beam Quality Change in Linear Accelerator X-Ray Beams," *Med. Phys.*, 7(1980), pp. 145–46.

14. W. F. Hanson, L. W. Berkley, and M. Peterson, "Calculative Technique to Correct for the Change in Linear Accelerator Beam Energy at Off-Axis Points," *Med. Phys.*, 7(1980), pp. 147–50.

15. J. L. Horton, "Dosimetry of the Siemens Mevatron 67 Linear Accelerator," *Int. J. Radiation Oncology Biol. Phys.*, 9(1983), pp. 1217–23.

16. Joseph C. Giarratano, Robert J. Duerkes, and Peter R. Almond, "Lead Shielding Thickness for Dose Reduction of 7 to 28 MeV Electrons," *Med. Phys.*, 2(1975), pp. 336–37.

17. James A. Purdy, Myung C. Choi, and Arnold Feldman, "Lipowitz Metal Shielding Thickness for Dose Reduction of 6–20 MeV Electrons," *Med. Phys.*, 7(1980), pp. 251–53.

18. Faiz M. Khan, Barry L. Werner, and Firmin C. Deibel, Jr., "Lead Shielding for Electrons," *Med. Phys.*, 8(1981), pp. 712–13.

SEVEN | QUALITY ASSURANCE PROGRAM

7.1 INTRODUCTION

Once the acceptance tests, commissioning measurements, and calibration of a therapy machine or treatment simulator are completed, a quality assurance program must commence. A protocol for these quality assurance tests should specify the equipment to be used, the frequency of the assessment, the techniques to be followed and the required level of agreement between daily checks and benchmark values. The equipment and techniques should be as simple as possible so that the tests may be performed with an economy of effort in a minimum amount of time. The frequency of these measurements should reflect both the likelihood of a change and the impact on treatment if a change does occur. Finally, action and notification levels must be established.

7.2 DAILY TESTS

Each morning before treatment it is advisable to verify certain parameters of a treatment machine or simulator. The quantities that should be checked are certain gauges specified by the equipment manufacturer and the accuracy of the optical distance indicator (ODI) and sidelights. If the machine is a linear accelerator, it is also imperative that the radiation output be checked. The reading of gauges and verification of the ODI and sidelights should require no more than 10 to 15 minutes. For a linac, these tests can be performed during the warm-up period and then the radiation output can be checked in an additional 5 to 10 minutes.

The operator's manual of a therapy machine or simulator lists certain gauges that should be checked daily. These gauges monitor subsystems important to proper machine operation. If these gauges read outside the range specified by the manufacturer, incipient problems may be indicated. After these gauges are checked, a lamp test should be performed. Most therapy units have a switch that activates all indicator lights to ensure that all are operating.

A mechanical front pointer indicating the isocenter is convenient for checking the ODI and sidelights. The table can be raised to the isocenter height determined with this front pointer and the ODI read on the table. Often, sidelights are lasers forming a cross. If these sidelights are at isocenter height, the horizontal line of the cross should intercept the top edge of the table. The vertical line should pass through the central axis of the beam. This may be checked by holding a 3″ x 5″ index card in the light field at 45° to the central axis of the beam. The vertical line of the laser should coincide with the image of the crosshair. If a sagittal laser is used it may be checked in a similar manner. If the ODI or lasers are off by more than 5 mm, the physicist should be contacted before treatment. If the discrepancy is between 2 mm and 5 mm, the technologist can begin treatment but should contact the physicist as soon as practicable. The physicist does not have to be contacted for error less than 2 mm.

If these tests are for a linac, the warm-up time should be completed and the radiation output can be checked. The technologist should be able to verify the output using straightforward techniques and simple equipment. One method is to use a lucite cube 15 cm on each side. A hole is drilled 5 cm from one surface to accommodate a Victoreen R-Meter. The technologist places the face of the block at 100 cm in a 10 cm x 10 cm field. The Victoreen chamber is placed in the block and irradiated to yield a reading of approximately mid-scale. These readings are corrected for temperature and pressure and compared to a value established at the time of the last calibration. If the daily value varies by more than 2% from this benchmark, the technologist must contact the physicist before treatment can begin. These daily output checks are not necessary for cobalt-60, as monthly checks by the physicist are adequate.

If the facility does rotational treatments, then the radiation output during arc therapy should be checked. A test similar to the one for radiation output for fixed SSD treatment can be designed and compared to benchmark values. A technologist should be able to complete all of these tests within 25 minutes. Those tests that don't require radiation output can be performed during the warm-up period of a linac. The radiation output tests should demand no more than an additional 10 minutes.

Examples of checklists that might be used for daily tests are given in Figure 7–1 and 7–2. Daily safety checks are indicated on the form in the first figure. The technologist records the readings of several gauges, checks various interlocks, dates and initials the form. Additional space is provided for comments. The second form is used to verify the correct position of all lasers and the reading of the ODI. The accuracy of the ODI is checked at isocenter and at 15 cm above isocenter. The first of these ODI checks is performed by reading the ODI on the treatment table with the table at the height of the isocenter. The lucite block used for the radiation output check is then placed on the table and the reading of the ODI noted on top of the block. The technologist then lowers the table to bring the top of the block to 100 cm and performs the radiation output check. These output checks are recorded in a hardback data book with consecutively numbered sewn-in pages. All information is recorded in ink and initialed.

7.3 WEEKLY TESTS

In addition to the daily tests, the mechanical isocenter, collimator rotation, light-radiation field congruence, energy, flatness, and symmetry should be verified weekly. The technologist can check the position of the mechanical isocenter with the test described in Chapter 5. The accuracy of the collimator rotation can be deter-

Linac Daily Safety Check

Date	Int.	Freon pressure	Water purity	Motion stop	Lamp test	Water temperature (100°–104°)	Water pressure (62 to 65 lbs.)	Door switch	Gantry rotate limit switch	Back-up readout	Rotational interlock	Comments

Figure 7–1 List of daily safety checks performed on linac.

Linac Daily Quality Assurance Check
Gantry 0°

Lasers
  Horizontal   _____ (Intercepts end of mechanical
                                                           front pointer)

  Vertical   _____ (Aligned with image of cross hair)
  Sagittal   _____ (Aligned with image of cross hair)

Optical Distance Indicator   _____ At isocenter (0)
                                                   _____ On calibration block (15 cm)

Comments: _____

_____

_____

_____

                                               _____ Initial
                                               _____ Date

Figure 7–2 Form used daily to record the position of laser sidelights and accuracy of optical distance indicator on a linac.

mined by turning the collimator and observing the image of the cross hair. If the mechanical isocenter or collimator rotation are off by more than 2 mm the physicist should be notified and no treatment should be given if either of these values exceeds 5 mm. During the determination of the mechanical isocenter, the gantry angle indicators may be checked using a spirit level. Following procedures in Chapter 5, the technologist may check the collimator angle indicators at the four principal angles and the field size indicators for a 5 cm x 5 cm and 30 cm x 30 cm field. The technologist may check the light-radiation field coincidence with film. These additional tests should require no more than 25 minutes.

    The physicist can verify the energy by measuring the output in a polystyrene phantom at a number of depths. For photons, 5 cm, 10 cm, and 15 cm are convenient depths. For electrons, a mini-

Linac Weekly Quality Assurance Check

Isocentric rotation   _____
Collimator rotation   _____

	Gantry Angle Indicators		*ODI Accuracy*	*Collimator Angle Indicator*	
	Digital	Mechanical		Digital	Mechanical
0°	_____	_____	_____	_____	_____
90°	_____	_____	_____	_____	_____
180°	_____	_____	_____	_____	_____
270°	_____	_____	_____	_____	_____

	Digital	Mechanical
5 cm × 5 cm field size indicators	_____ × _____	_____ × _____
30 cm × 30 cm field size indicators	_____ × _____	_____ × _____

Attach Light-Radiation Field Coincidence Film

COMMENTS _____

_____

_____

Initial   _____
Date   _____

Figure 7–3   Linac weekly quality assurance checklist.

mum of three depths should be chosen in the region of linear decrease in dose. Flatness and symmetry can be verified with a film in a polystyrene phantom. The film should be perpendicular to the central axis of the beam of a 30 cm x 30 cm field. For electrons, this exposure should be at d_{max}; for photons d_{max} or 5 cm are satisfactory. The energy and flatness and symmetry measurements can be compared to standards from the last calibration. The form used by the technologist for the weekly quality check is shown in Figure 7–3. The data taken by the physicist are recorded in the log book used for daily radiation output checks.

7.4 MONTHLY TESTS

All interlocks and emergency off switches should be checked on a monthly basis. The physicist should also perform a calibration for one field size in accordance with the procedures outlined in Chapters 10 and 11. This calibration should include measurement of central axis percent depth dose at five or six depths, dose rate, and monitor linearity and end effects. Flatness and symmetry of photon fields should be verified with an ion chamber in water for a field size of at least 30 cm x 30 cm. Film may be used for electron field flatness and symmetry measurements. A physicist should be able to complete these tests in two hours.

7.5 QUARTERLY TESTS

A full calibration should be performed quarterly. This calibration should include a check of the dose rate or dose per monitor unit and the flatness and symmetry at all four principal angles. A plastic phantom is convenient for checking these parameters at the different angles. It is advisable, though, to verify flatness and symmetry for at least one gantry angle in a water phantom using an ion chamber. In addition to these tests, the applicability of the inverse square law, output factors, central axis percent depth dose for a number of fields, monitor linearity and end effects, and wedge and tray factors should be verified.

7.6 SUMMARY

Table 7–1 summarizes a suggested minimum schedule for quality assurance tests. It may be essential to increase the frequency of these tests. Any major modification or repair of the mechanical and electrical systems will necessitate a full calibration. A source change in a cobalt-60 unit or an alteration to a flattening filter in a linac are examples of such a change. Also, the flatness and symmetry of linac should be checked daily for at least a month following the installation of the machine. If any changes are observed it will be necessary to continue these tests on a daily basis.

TABLE 7-1. Synopsis of Daily, Weekly, Monthly, and Quarterly Quality Assurance Checks

Daily	Weekly	Monthly	Quarterly
A. Gauges	A. mechical isocenter	A. emergency off switches and interlocks	A. Calibration at one gantry angle
B. Interlocks	B. collimator rotation	B. calibration for one field size at one gantry angle	1) % depth dose for several field sizes
C. Lamp tests	C. gantry and collimator angle indicators	1) % depth dose	2) dose rate for one field size
D. Sidelights	D. field size indicators	2) dose rate	3) output factors
E. ODI	E. output-fixed, arc	3) monitor linearity and end effects	4) applicability of inverse square law
F. Output	F. energy	4) flatness/symmetry in water 30 cm x 30 cm	5) wedge factors
1) fixed	G. flatness/symmetry with film 30 cm x 30 cm		6) tray factors
2) arc	H. light-radiation field congruence		7) monitor linearity and end effects
	I. ODI		8) flatness/symmetry
			a) in water for 10 cm x 10 cm and 30 cm x 30 cm for photon field
			b) in plastic with film for 10 cm x 10 cm and 30 cm x 30 cm for electron fields
			B. Output check and flatness and symmetry check at 0°, 90°, 180°, and 270°

140

Additional Reading

Proceedings of a Symposium on Quality Assurance of Radiotherapy Equipment American Association of Physicists in Medicine Symposium Proceedings No. 3, George Starkschall, ed., (New York, N.Y.: American Association of Physicists in Medicine, 1983).

CLARENCE H. ANNETT, "Program for Periodic Maintenance and Calibration of Radiation Therapy Linear Accelerators," *Appl. Radiol.*, 8(1979), pp. 77–80.

JAMES A. PURDY, "Quality Assurance of Radiation Therapy Treatment Units," *Med. Phys.*, 10(1983), pp. 562–63.

American National Standard Guidelines for Maintaining Cobalt-60 and Cesium-137 Teletherapy Equipment, (New York, N.Y.: American National Standards Institute, 1974).

ARTHUR L. BOYER, "Verification of Mechanical Alignment and Interlock Operation," presented at AAPM Special Workshop for Radiological Physics *Electron Linear Accelerators in Radiation Therapy*, March 1978.

Physical Aspects of Quality Assurance in Radiation Therapy AAPM Report No. 13, Task Group 24, (New York, N.Y.: American Association of Physicists in Medicine, 1984).

Quality Assurance in Radiation Therapy: A Manual for Technologists, Morris J. Wizenberg, M.D., Ed., (Chicago, ILL.: American College of Radiology, 1982).

EIGHT | CALIBRATION OF LOW-ENERGY X-RAY UNITS

8.1 INTRODUCTION

Low energy X-rays (10 to 150 kV) are attenuated quite rapidly by tissue. This property yields a steep depth dose and makes these X-rays ideal for the treatment of superficial lesions. A high dose may be delivered to the tumor while sparing underlying healthy tissue. These benefits may be increased by the simple expedient of employing a short focus-skin distance (FSD) thereby taking advantage of the inverse square law. The use of a short FSD also allows a high dose rate and short treatment times.

8.2 DIFFICULTIES

All of the reasons just mentioned for using this technique present special dosimetric problems in the calibration of these X-ray beams. The walls of the ion chamber attenuate these soft X-rays; the short

FSD demands accurate ion chamber positioning and the high dose rate creates problems of ionic recombination in the ion chamber. Attenuation of the X-ray beam by the air presents an additional problem.

8.2.1 Energy Dependence of Ion Chambers

Most ion chambers exhibit a profound energy dependence for low energy X-rays because of photon attenuation in the wall. The walls of the ion chamber should be as thin as practicable to minimize this dependence. Since electron equilibrium will be established in a few mg/cm^2 of material, mechanical rigidity is the determining factor in the design of an ion chamber to be used for low energy X-ray dosimetry. Several chambers have been designed with minimal energy dependence. These designs are surveyed in *ICRU Report 17*.[1] One type of chamber I have found particularly useful in a clinical setting is a parallel plate design with a small, fixed electrode separation. These chambers are commercially available with an entrance window of either aluminized or graphite-coated mylar. An example is the PTW 0.2 cc chamber sold by Victoreen, which is shown in Figure 8–1. Other suitable chambers are available from Capintec (see Chapter 2). These chambers generally have relatively flat energy response and their volume remains fairly constant over a long period of time.

Before the purchase of one of these chambers, the manufacturer's specifications should be studied to determine the one most suitable for one's particular application. These specifications should be included in a purchase order with the proviso that if the chamber does not meet these specifications as meaured by the National Bureau of Standards (NBS) or an Accredited Dosimetry Calibration Laboratory (ADCL), the manufacturer will pay for these calibrations. These calibration points should be over a range of energies that are used clinically. There should be enough points at intermediate energies to minimize the error resulting from interpolation to a point at the clinically relevant energy.

8.2.2 Ionic Recombination

A second problem with ionometric measurements arises because of the extremely high exposure rate produced by many lightly filtered low energy X-ray units. Ionic recombination may occur in the active volume of the chamber because of inadequate collection voltages at these high exposure rates. Careful measurements of

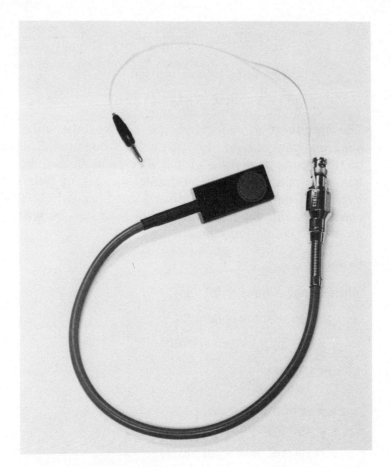

Figure 8–1 PTW chamber model 30–330 used for calibrations of low energy X-ray beams.

these effects are needed. The two-voltage technique[2] discussed in Chapter 10 is a useful method to determine this recombination.

A theoretical analysis should also be performed to compare the calculated collection efficiency to the measured. Following the development of Boag[3] for a parallel plate chamber the collection efficiency f is given by

$$f = \frac{v}{e^v - 1}$$

$$v = \frac{\mu \, p d^2}{V}$$

$$\mu = 1090 \, \frac{V\text{-cm}}{esu}, \text{ an empirical constant}$$

$$p = \text{collected charge per pulse} \left(\frac{\text{esu}}{\text{pulse-cm}^3} \right)$$

$d = \text{plate separation (cm)}$

$V = \text{applied voltage } (V)$

The abbreviation esu stands for electrostatic unit, a quantity of electrical charge equal to 3.336×10^{-10} coulomb. The esu may also be referred to as a statcoulomb. The value of the empirically determined constant μ has been quoted as varying between 1000–1250 V-cm/esu depending on ambient conditions. If 1090 V-cm/esu is chosen for this estimation, the result should be within 1 to 2% of the actual collection efficiency.

Example

$$\text{plate separation } d = 0.1 \text{ cm}$$

$$\text{active volume} = 0.03 \text{ cm}^3$$

$$V = 300 \text{ volts}$$

$$\text{charge collected in one minute} = 100 \text{ nC}$$

$$\text{number of pulses per second} = 60$$

$$p = 100 \text{ nC}/60\text{s} = 1.67 \text{ nC/s}$$

$$= 5.00 \text{ esu/s}$$

$$= 1.67 \times 10^2 \frac{\text{esu}}{\text{s-cm}^3}$$

$$p = 2.78 \frac{\text{esu}}{\text{pulse-cm}^3}$$

$$\nu = \frac{1090 \dfrac{V\text{-cm}}{\text{esu}} \times 2.78 \dfrac{\text{esu}}{\text{pulse-cm}^3} \times (.1\text{cm})^2}{300 \text{ V}}$$

$$\nu = 0.1$$

$$f = \frac{0.1}{e^{0.1} - 1}$$

$$f = 0.95$$

where nC is an abbreviation for nanocoulomb. In this example the expected collection efficiency is 95%.

8.2.3 Chamber Size

For calibration at an ultra short FSD, a small ion chamber is desirable because of the high dose gradient across the chamber arising from inverse square. This geometrical effect has been discussed for conical[4] and cylindrical[5] chambers. For the Victoreen 651, Burlin[4] found a correction factor of 1.07 for an FSD of 1.5 cm and a negligible factor if the FSD were greater than 10 cm. Clark and Brar[5] indicated this error is minimized for cylindrical chambers when the ratio of cylinder height to diameter is 0.75 to 0.80.

8.2.4 Problems with Inverse Square

Many superficial and contact therapy units use cones as well as extremely short FSDs. Because of the construction of the cone or the ion chamber, it may not be possible to position the effective point of measurement at the normal treatment FSD. Calibration at another FSD and use of the inverse square law to calculate the output at the treatment FSD may yield invalid results. Three areas that may cause problems are:

1. Inverse square law may not be applicable because of the short FSD and finite source size
2. Effective FSD may differ from physical FSD
3. Extremely accurate chamber position measurements are necessary because a 1 mm error for a 2 cm FSD can lead to a 10% error in calibration

One method I have found particularly useful in overcoming these problems is to make a series of measurements at a number of FSDs. If the measurements are referenced as to the distance between the end of the cone and the effective point of measurement, a linear regression analysis may be performed with this distance assigned to the x-axis and the reciprocal of the square root of the chamber reading assigned to the y-axis. The correlation coefficient of this analysis is a measure of the applicability of the inverse square law. A correlation coefficient of one indicates perfect agreement with inverse square. If the correlation coefficient is less than 0.97, further work may be required because inverse square may not be applicable. Assuming acceptable agreement with inverse square, the x intercept is the negative of the effective FSD and the reciprocal of the y intercept squared is the ion chamber reading extrapolated to the treatment FSD.

8.2.5 Air Attenuation

In addition to the problems just addressed, air attenuation may be significant for low-energy X-ray calibrations measured at an extended FSD. This effect may be calculated using the table of mass attenuation coefficients found in *ICRU Report 17*.

Example

An X-ray beam with an HVL of 0.1 mm A1 is calibrated 20 cm from the source. For a normal FSD of 2 cm is the air attenuation significant at the extended FSD? The barometric pressure is 745 mm Hg and the temperature is 20°C.

1) *Find the effective energy of the X-ray beam.*

The effective energy of an X-ray beam is the energy of a monoenergetic photon beam that has the same mass attenuation coefficient as the X-ray beam in question. The mass attenuation coefficient of the X-ray beam may be found if one recalls the following relation

$$\frac{\mu}{\rho} = \frac{0.693}{HVL \times \rho}$$

The effective energy may be found from tables in *ICRU Report 17*.

$$\mu)_{Al} = \frac{0.693}{0.01 \text{ cm}}$$

$$= 69.3 \text{ cm}^{-1}$$

$$\rho)_{Al} = 2.7 \text{ g/cm}^3$$

$$\frac{\mu}{\rho}\bigg)_{Al} = \frac{69.3 \text{ cm}^{-1}}{2.7 \text{ g/cm}^3} = 25.7 \frac{\text{cm}^2}{\text{g}}$$

$$\frac{\mu}{\rho}\bigg)_{Al} \quad \text{for 10 keV is } 26.3 \frac{\text{cm}^2}{\text{g}}$$

therefore 10 keV may be taken as an effective energy.

2) *Calculate air density for current temperature and pressure.*

$$\rho_{air} = 1.29 \times 10^{-3} \times \frac{273}{293} \times \frac{745}{760} = 1.18 \times 10^{-3} \frac{g}{cm^3}$$

3) *Look up mass attenuation coefficient for air at 10 keV.*

$$\frac{\mu}{\rho} \quad \text{for air at 10 keV is } 4.96 \frac{cm^2}{g}$$

4) *Calculate percentage of beam transmitted.*

The distance between the calibration distance and the treatment FSD is

$$20 - 2 = 18 \text{ cm}$$

The percentage of beam transmitted is

$$I = Io \, \exp\left(-4.96 \frac{cm^2}{g} \times 1.18 \times 10^{-3} \frac{g}{cm^3} \times 18 \text{ cm}\right)$$

$$I = .9 I_0$$

The air has attenuated this beam 10% over a distance of 18 cm.

8.3 HALF-VALUE LAYER

An ion chamber should be selected with a relatively flat energy response not only for calibration purposes but also for half-value layer (HVL) measurements necessary to establish the effective energy of the beam. Because X-ray tubes designed for low energy X-rays have a low inherent filtration, placing aluminum filters in the beam can significantly alter the X-ray spectrum. If the ion chamber has a rapidly varying energy response then the half-value layer measurements will be affected as the energy of the X-ray beam changes with added filtration.

This may be seen in Figure 8–2. The HVL was measured on a Picker Vanguard Deep Therapy unit at 120 kV with no added filtration. The results from three different ion chambers were compared. The ion chambers were the PTW 0.2 cc Model 30–330, the MDH Industries 3.0 cc pencil chamber model 20X5–103CT designed for CT measurements, and the Exradin 0.5 cc Model A-1 thimble chamber.

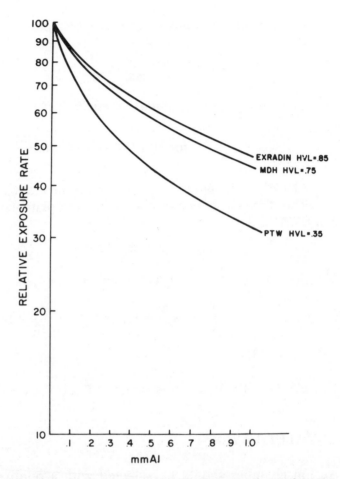

Figure 8–2 Half-value layer measurements of a Picker Vanguard unit at 120 kV with no added filtration made with three different chambers: PTW chamber model 30–330, MDH model 20X5–103 CT, and EXRADIN A-1.

The walls of the Exradin ion chamber are constructed of C-552 "air equivalent" conducting plastic and the conducting properties of this plastic have been achieved by substituting carbon for some of the oxygen and nitrogen. Above 100 keV, the mass energy absorption coefficients are essentially the same; however, below this energy the values for carbon, nitrogen, and oxygen begin to deviate from each other. For this reason C-552 plastic was formulated to have photoelectric absorption equal to air at 20 keV.[6] However, the Exradin chamber still has a greater energy dependence than the PTW chamber that leads to the large difference in HVL measured with the two chambers.

The specification of an X-ray beam using only HVL may not be sufficient. It is helpful to include the generating potential or the homogeneity coefficient which is the ratio of the first to second HVL. However, with low energy X-rays the homogeneity coefficient should be used with caution. For tubes operated below 50 kV with little inherent filtration L-characteristic radiation becomes a significant portion of this spectrum. Transmission of L-characteristic radiation through a 1 mm Be window was reported by Zieler[7] to yield a fairly homogeneous beam. Adding aluminum filters at first decreased and then increased the homogeneity of the beam.

When one measures the HVL for low energy X-ray beams the effect of air attenuation should be investigated. If the beam is lightly filtered, the air will serve as a differential absorber changing the spectral shape. It has been shown[8] for a 8 kV spectrum with 1 mm Be filtration that the HVL changed from 0.013 mm Al to 0.022 mm Al when the measurement distance was increased from 10 to 50 cm. Similar results have been demonstrated at 10 kV when the air path was changed from 15 cm to 27 cm.[9]

One must also recognize that the same HVL may be measured for two completely different spectra. Marshall, et al.[10] have calculated the same HVL for a spectrum generated with a tungsten target at 100 kVcp with no filtration as for a spectrum generated with a tungsten target at 20 kVcp with 0.1 mm Al filtration.

Finally, it must be realized that an HVL measurement requires very high purity aluminum for low energy X-ray beams. Because the photoelectric effect is predominant at these energies, even a small quantity of high Z impurity in the aluminum will yield incorrect results. The aluminum used should be of 1100 grade and can be acquired from either metal supply companies or radiological equipment suppliers.

8.4 COMPREHENSIVE EXAMPLE

The HVL of a Philips RT 50 contact therapy unit is measured to be 0.7 mm Al corresponding to an effective energy of 20 keV. Cones are employed for treatment. The FSD of these cones is approximately 3 cm. A PTW 0.2 cc ion chamber with a plate separation of 1.5 mm is used to make 1-minute readings at distances of 1.5, 3, and 6 mm from the end of the cone. The calibration factor for this chamber at this energy is 114 x 10^8 R/C. The average value of the readings is given below. T = 25°C, BP = 742mm Hg.

Distance (mm)	Reading (10^{-8}C)	(Reading)$^{-1/2}$
1.5	10.60	0.3071
3.0	9.78	0.3198
6.0	8.17	0.3499

1) Air attentuation.

$$\rho = 1.29 \times 10^{-3} \times \frac{273}{298} \times \frac{742}{760} = 1.15 \times 10^{-3} \frac{g}{cm^3}$$

$$\frac{\mu}{\rho} = 0.747 \frac{cm^2}{g}$$

$$I = Io \exp(-0.747 \times 1.15 \times 10^{-3} \times .6) = .999_5 Io$$

therefore no significant air attenuation

2) Expected collection efficiency.

$$106 \frac{nc}{60s} = 4.42 \times 10^{-1} \frac{esu}{pulse - cm^3}$$

$$\nu = \frac{1090 \times 4.42 \times 10^{-1} \times (0.15)^2}{300}$$

$$\nu = 3.61 \times 10^{-2}$$

$$f = \frac{\nu}{e^\theta - 1}$$

$$= \frac{3.61 \times 10^{-2}}{\exp(3.61 \times 10^{-2}) - 1}$$

$$= 0.98$$

The expected collection efficiency is 0.98. In this example we will assume it is born out by other measurements.

3) Linear regression analysis.

Linear regression of the reciprocals of the square roots of the readings versus distance yields

$$\text{correlation coefficient} = 0.999$$

$$x \text{ intercept} = -30.5$$

$$y \text{ intercept} = 0.2921$$

$$\frac{1}{(y - \text{intercept})^2} = 11.72$$

The correlation coefficient demonstrates the output obeys inverse square over the range of measurement. The x intercept indicates an effective FSD of 3.05 cm and the square of the reciprocal of the y intercept yields an ion chamber reading extrapolated to the end of the cone of 11.72×10^{-8} C.

4) *Output determination*.

The exposure rate at the treatment FSD is

$$\dot{X} = 114 \times 10^8 \, \frac{R}{C} \times 11.72 \times 10^{-8} \, \frac{C}{\text{Min}} \times \frac{298}{295} \times \frac{760}{742} \times \frac{1}{0.98}$$

$$= 1411 \, \frac{R}{\text{min}}$$

Notes

1. *Radiation Dosimetry: X Rays Generated at Potentials of 5 to 150 kV ICRU Report 17*, (Washington, D. C.: International Commission on Radiation Units and Measurements, 1970).

2. J. W. Boag and J. Currant, "Current Collection and Ionic Recombination in Small Cylindrical Ionization Chambers Exposed to Pulsed Radiation," *Brit. J. Radiol.*, 53(1980), pp. 471–78.

3. J. W. Boag, "Ionization Chambers," in *Radiation Dosimetry Volume II Instrumentation*, Frank H. Attix and William C. Roesch, eds. (New York, N. Y.: Academic Press, 1966), pp. 1–72.

4. T. E. Burlin, "The Effect of Inverse Square Law Attenuation on the Measurement of Grenz-Ray Exposure with a Cavity Ionisation Chamber," *Brit. J. Radiol.*, 37(1964) pp. 693–95.

5. R. K. Clark and S. S. Brar, "Optimum Shape for Cylindrical Ionization Chambers," *Nucleonics*, 12(1954) pp. 28–29.

6. Francis R. Shonka, John E. Rose, and G. Failla, "Conducting Plastic Equivalent to Tissue, Air, and Polystyrene," *Second UN Conference*

on Peaceful Uses of Atomic Energy, Vol 21, (New York: United Nations, 1958) pp. 184–87.

7. Erich Zieler, "Der Einfluss des Charakteristischen Röntgenspektrums auf die Qualität Weicher Röntgenstrahlen," *Strahlentherapie*, 102(1957) pp. 88–96.

8. D. E. A. Jones and K. Blake, Private Communication Rererenced in ICRU Report 17.

9. F. W. Tranter, "Two Windowless Chambers for the Measurement of Grenz Rays," *Brit. J. Radiol.*, 40(1967), pp. 714–16.

10. M. Marshall, L. H. J. Peaple, G. M. Ardran, and H. E. Crooks, "A Comparison of X-Ray Spectra and Outputs from Molybdenum and Tungsten Targets." *Brit. J. Radiol.*, 48(1975), pp. 31–39.

Additional Reading

J. R. GREENING AND K. J. RANDLE, "The Measurement of Low Energy X-Rays I: General Considerations," *Phys. Med. Biol.*, 13(1968), pp. 159–68.

T. E. BURLIN AND S. R. HUSAIN, "The Saturation Characteristics of a Grenz-Ray Ionisation Chamber," *Brit. J. Radiol.*, 38(1965), pp. 386–89.

J. R. GREENING, "A Compact Free-Air Chamber for Use in the Range 10–50 kV," *Brit. J. Radiol.*, 33(1960), pp. 178–83.

JAMES E. NUNNALLY, "A Method of Calibration for Low Energy X-Ray Beams," *Phys. Med. Biol.*, 18(1973), pp. 878–80.

P. PYCHLAU, "Another Method of Calibration for Low Energy X-Ray Beams," *Phys. Med. Biol.*, 19(1974), p. 386.

J. R. GREENING, "The Derivation of Approximate X-Ray Spectral Distributions and an Analysis of X-Ray 'Quality' Specifications," *Brit. J. Radiol.*, 36(1963), pp. 363–71.

NINE | CALIBRATION OF ORTHOVOLTAGE X-RAY BEAMS

9.1 INTRODUCTION

The calibration of orthovoltage X-ray beams (150 to 500 kV) is somewhat easier than the lower energy X-ray beams discussed in Chapter 8. Problems with air attenuation of the X-ray beam and energy dependence of the ion chamber are not as severe for orthovoltage beams as they are for the lower energy beams. Also, orthovoltage machines usually employ lower dose rates and longer SSDs than low-energy machines. With these comparisons in mind, let's focus on the calibration of orthovoltage X-ray machines.

9.2 ION CHAMBERS

National standards laboratory calibrates X-ray beams in terms of exposure with a free-air ionization chamber. The use of such a chamber for routine clinical calibrations is not practical and other ion chambers have been designed to fill this need. These chambers are calibrated against the free-air ion chamber at a national standard laboratory and a factor is obtained that relates the chamber's ionization reading to the exposure at the center of the chamber *in the absence of the chamber.*

In the previous chapter we saw that X-rays below 150 kV imposed severe restrictions on ion chamber design. Above 150 kV these design restrictions are not as stringent and most thin wall thimble ion chambers may be used. The carbon-wall Farmer chamber has long been the most popular chamber for calibration in this energy regime because it displays a small energy dependence. However, the nylon wall Farmer chamber, several other Farmer-type ion chambers, and a large number of non-Farmer type chambers are also acceptable. It is imperative, though, that the user knows the chamber's energy dependence over the entire range of energies that he or she will be calibrating. The National Bureau of Standards (NBS) or an Accredited Dosimetry Calibration Laboratory (ADCL) will determine the calibration factor at several energies.

The user should plot these values against the energy of an equivalent monoenergetic photon energy. This equivalent energy is defined as the energy of a monoenergetic photon with the same half-value layer (HVL) as the calibration energy. The technique to determine the equivalent or effective energy was discussed in detail in step 1 of the second Example of the previous chapter.

9.3 HALF-VALUE LAYER

Since the ion chamber calibration factor is a function of energy, the quality of the X-ray beam being calibrated must be determined. This may be done by measuring the HVL. A selection of aluminum and copper should be available for this task. The aluminum should be of 1100 grade as described in Chapter 8. To measure the HVL, the ion chamber should be centered in a small field at a distance of approximately 1 meter. The filters should be placed at 50 cm. The attenuation curve of the filters can be measured and plotted to determine the HVL.

9.4 CALIBRATION TECHNIQUES

The International Commission of Radiation Units and Measurements[1] (ICRU) recommends calibration at a depth of 5 cm in water. The ICRU tabulated a set of F-values that were to be used in the conversion from exposure to dose. Because the ion chamber was 5 cm deep in water, these F-values correspond to the photon spectrum at that depth and not to the incident photon spectrum.

In spite of the ICRU's recommendation, most physicists still calibrate 150 to 500 kV X-rays in air. The center of the chamber is placed at the treatment SSD on the central axis of the beam and ionization measurements are made. The ionization reading is converted to the value of the exposure with the chamber calibration factor.,

$$X = N M_C \tag{9–1}$$

where $N =$ chamber calibration factor determined by the standardizing laboratory appropriate for the X-ray energy in question.

$M_C =$ ion chamber reading corrected for temperature, pressure, stem effect, recombination, and polarity effects.

The dose in-air can be calculated from the exposure with the f-factor.

$$D_{air} = fX \tag{9–2}$$

$f = f$-factor for the appropriate X-ray energy.

This f-factor differs from the F-factor of ICRU Report 23 because this factor is for the incident photon spectrum and not for the photon spectrum at 5 cm deep in a phantom.

9.5 APPLICABILITY OF INVERSE SQUARE LAW

Frequently on X-ray machines operating in this energy region, the treated area is defined with metal cones that are placed against the surface of the patient. In this case it may be impossible to place the center of the ion chamber at the position occupied by the surface of the patient. To determine the dose at the treatment distance, one could use the procedure described in Chapter 8 of taking measurements at several distances from the end of the cone. If the X-ray beam conforms to the inverse square law, the distance plotted against the reciprocal of the square root of the ion chamber reading will form a straight line. This line can be extrapolated to the position of the end of the cone to yield the ion chamber reading at that point. Further discussion has been given in Chapter 8.

9.6 FIELD SIZE DEPENDENCE

Calibrations are usually done for one field size; however, the in-air output of an X-ray machine may change with collimator opening. The field size dependence should be determined during the initial calibration and checked periodically. X-ray units that use the fixed metal cones, discussed in Section 9–5, may also display a variation in output with cone size. Therefore, it is essential to quantify the cone ratio.

9.7 SHUTTER CORRECTION

An X-ray machine may have either a positive or negative shutter correction. This should be determined and accounted for in any calculations.

9.8 BACKSCATTER FACTOR

The ratio of the dose on the central axis at the surface of a phantom or patient to the dose in-air at the same point is the backscatter factor. Values of the quantity applicable for orthovoltage beams may be found in British Journal of Radiology (BJR) Supplement 17.[2]

9.9 CENTRAL AXIS PERCENT DEPTH DOSE

To determine the dose at a specified depth in a patient on the central axis of the beam requires a knowledge of the central axis percent depth dose. These quantities are also available in BJR Supplement 17.

9.10 CALCULATION OF DOSE ON THE CENTRAL AXIS

The dose at depth in a patient may be calculated with

$$D_d = D_{air} \, \%dd \, fsd \, B$$

where $D_{air} = fX$ from Equation 9–2

$\%dd$ = central axis percent depth dose $\qquad$ **(9–3)**

fsd = field size dependence

B = backscatter factor.

Notes

1. *Measurement of Absorbed Dose in a Phantom Irradiated by a Single Beam of X or Gamma Rays*, *ICRU Report 23*, (Washington, D. C.: International Commission of Radiation Units and Measurements, 1973).

2. *Central Axis Depth Dose Data for Use in Radiotherapy*, *British Journal of Radiology Supplement 17*., (London: British Institute of Radiology, 1983).

TEN | MEGAVOLTAGE PHOTON CALIBRATION

10.1 INTRODUCTION

Over the years, several national and international organizations have published "protocols" or "codes of practice" to guide the physicist in the calibration of megavoltage photon beams. These organizations include the International Commission on Radiation Units and Measurements (ICRU),[1,2] International Atomic Energy Agency (IAEA),[3] American Association of Physicists in Medicine (AAPM),[4,5,6] Hospital Physicists Association (HPA),[7,8] Nordic Association of Clinical Physcis (NACP),[9,10] German Standards Association (DIN),[11,12,13] and National Council on Radiation Protection and Measurement (NCRP).[14] The aim of these documents has been to assure accurate and consistent measurement of radiation dose.

Prior to 1980, all of the protocols shared a common approach to the problem. This formalism, developed by Greene,[15] employed an air-filled ionization chamber placed at a prescribed depth in a water phantom. This chamber had an exposure calibration factor assigned by a national standards laboratory. The ionization created by photon irradiation of the chamber could be related to dose to water by using a conversion factor referred to as C_λ. The formula for conversion from ionization to dose was

$$D(\text{rad}) = M_c N_x C_\lambda \qquad \qquad (10\text{--}1)$$

where M_c was the meter reading of the ionization chamber corrected for temperature and pressure, stem effect, ion collection efficiency and polarity effect.

             N_x was the exposure calibration factor for cobalt-60 gamma rays or 2 MV X-rays determined by a national standardizing laboratory.

             C_λ was the so-called Roentgen-to-rad conversion factor.

Tables of C_λ as a function of photon energy were supplied in each protocol.

There were a number of shortcomings with this technique. The protocols did not specify what ion chamber was to be used beyond general guidelines on cavity size, usually less than 1 cm internal diameter, and many were not clear on whether or not a buildup cap should be used in phantom. C_λ could be used for any chamber meeting these guidelines regardless of the wall or electrode composition or whether the internal diameter was 3 mm or 10 mm. However, implicit in the formalism used in the development of C_λ was the assumption that the chamber walls were water equivalent.[16] An additional problem was the displacement or replacement factor, which corrected for the water displaced by the ion chamber, was assumed to be independent of cavity size.

10.2 THE NACP PROTOCOL OF 1980

In 1980 the NACP adopted a new code of practice, which abandoned the use of C_λ for megavoltage photon calibrations. There were several motivations for this change. Among the reasons given were:

1. A desire to implement SI units
2. A need to include more recent data elucidating chamber dependent effects

3. A necessary revision of the database to reflect the changing cohort of therapy machines from one that was predominantly betatrons to one that contained a large number of linear accelerators and microtrons

The new procedure was based on an absorbed dose ion chamber factor N_D rather than an exposure factor. This factor was derived from an in-air cobalt-60 calibration. The absorbed dose to water at other photon energies was determined by multiplying the reading of the ion chamber placed at a specified depth in water by this absorbed dose factor and stopping power ratios and perturbation factors furnished in the protocol. The protocol restricted the ion chamber to be one with the walls and central electrode constructed of either air or water/tissue equivalent material with a volume limited to the range of 100 mm³ to 1000 mm.³ If the walls were graphite, the protocol required a thickness of approximately 0.5 mm. Further restrictions were placed on leakage and polarity effects. However, no rigorous definition was given to the terms "air equivalent" or "water/tissue equivalent."

10.3 THE HPA PROTOCOL OF 1983

The HPA revised its protocol for calibration of megavoltage photon beams in 1983. This organization retained the formalism based on C_λ but updated the values of these factors. These new values resulted from revised data used in the calculation, corrections for the percent of ionization arising from the chamber walls as well as the water, a different value for the displacement factor, and a change in the value of W/e.

This document also mandates that the standard calibration system shall be a National Physical Laboratories (NPL) Secondary Standard X-ray Exposure Meter manufactured by Nuclear Enterprises. This calibration system consists of the NE2560 Electrometer and NE2561 graphite-walled ion chamber with Delrin buildup cap. For in-phantom measurements, the chamber must be waterproofed with a sheath constructed of polymethylmethacrylate (PMMA) with the same dimensions as the Delrin buildup cap. The depths of calibration are also specified in the protocol.

10.4 THE AAPM PROTOCOL OF 1983

Late in 1983 Task Group 21 of the AAPM published a protocol
that unified photon and electron calibrations based on the formalism of Loevinger.[17] This document incorporated the most current
data, eliminated the factor C_λ for photon calibrations, and made
explicit chamber dependent factors. The four reasons given for
changing from the previous protocols were:

1. The questionable concept of in-phantom exposure measurements
2. The disagreement between photon (C_λ) and electron (C_E) dose
   conversion factors for comparable in-phantom electron spectra
3. The dubious treatment of the replacement factor as a constant
   for all ion chambers and energies
4. The disregard of differences in composition between the chamber wall and dosimetry phantom

In fairness, it must be pointed out that the HPA protocol that
appeared while the Task Group 21 protocol was in press addressed
the last two motivations. Although the HPA code takes the replacement factor as a constant regardless of energy, the chamber dependent aspect of this factor was eliminated by specifying a particular
ion chamber and for the chamber chosen the energy dependence
varies approximately 0.5% from cobalt-60 to 45 MV. The HPA protocol improved the calculation of C_λ by considering the relative
amount of ionization in the cavity originating in the chamber wall
and in the water. The disagreement between C_λ and C_E values
cannot be addressed as this protocol was limited to photon calibrations.

With this introduction to the latest AAPM protocol, let us
examine the mechanics of it in more detail.

10.4.1 Cavity-Gas Calibration Factor N_{gas}

The AAPM has chosen a technique similar to one used in the NACP
protocol of 1980 to determine the volume of an ion chamber. In
the AAPM protocol a factor referred to as N_{gas} is determined from
the exposure calibration factor N_x. One must be careful though
because N_{gas} is only valid when air fills the ion chamber; if another
gas were to be used, then a different N_{gas} would be required. In
reality N_{gas} is N_{air}.

Equation (6) of the AAPM protocol relates N_{gas} to N_x, the exposure calibration factor.

$$N_{gas} = N_x \; \frac{k \dfrac{W}{e} A_{ion} A_{wall} \beta_{wall}}{\alpha \left(\dfrac{\overline{L}}{\rho}\right)^{wall}_{gas} \left(\dfrac{\overline{\mu}_{en}}{\rho}\right)^{air}_{wall} + (1-\alpha) \left(\dfrac{\overline{L}}{\rho}\right)^{cap}_{gas} \left(\dfrac{\overline{\mu}_{en}}{\rho}\right)^{air}_{cap}} \qquad \textbf{(10–2)}$$

$$k = 2.58 \times 10^{-4} \frac{C}{kg\,R}$$

$$\frac{W}{e} = 33.7 \frac{J}{C}$$

where A_{ion} = ion collection efficiency of the chamber during the standardizing laboratory's cobalt-60 exposure calibration

A_{wall} = correction for attenuation and scatter in the chamber's wall and buildup cap during in-air exposure to cobalt-60

$$\beta_{wall} = \frac{\text{Absorbed dose}}{\substack{\text{collision fraction of kerma in} \\ \text{chamber wall for cobalt-60}}} = 1.005$$

α = fraction of ionization from electrons from chamber wall (see Figure 1, p. 750 of protocol)

$1 - \alpha$ = fraction of ionization from electrons from buildup cap

$\dfrac{\overline{L}}{\rho}$ = restricted mean collision mass stopping power

$\dfrac{\overline{\mu}_{en}}{\rho}$ = mean mass energy-absorption coefficient

After the protocol appeared, two errors were pointed out.[18,19] The first error to be discussed concerned the factors A_{wall} and β_{wall}. Although it is correct to include both of these factors, unfortunately the values of A_{wall}[20] recommended in the protocol were calculated such that β_{wall} was implicitly included. In other words, the values given in the protocol were not for A_{wall} as originally defined in the formalism, but were actually the product of $A_{wall} \beta_{wall}$.

The second error involved the value of W/e. The protocol fails to account for the difference in W/e for dry (33.85 J/c) and

50% humidified air (33.7 J/C). Fortunately, these were compensating mistakes. The first error resulted in values of 0.5% too high, but the second error yielded values 0.5% too low. For this reason it was decided to let the protocol stand as it was.[21]

The use of restricted stopping powers in this protocol rather than unrestricted stopping powers results from the application of the Spencer-Attix[22] theory of cavity ionization. Bragg-Gray theory is based on a continuous slowing down approximation (csda). This approximation assumes that a secondary electron loses its energy at the point of its generation. However, many secondary electrons have enough energy to produce further ionization. These electrons, referred to as delta-rays, are produced in a gas-filled ionization chamber and they frequently are energetic enough to escape the cavity taking some energy with them. This process reduces the energy absorbed in the cavity. To account for the effects of high energy delta-rays, Spencer and Attix divided secondary electrons into two groups, those that are and those that are not energetic enough to cross the cavity of an ion chamber. This cutoff energy is denoted by the symbol Δ and for ion chambers discussed in this protocol Δ is taken as 10 keV. Restricted stopping powers are limited to energy losses less than Δ and δ-rays with energy greater than Δ are added to the spectrum of high energy electrons. Additionally, because the lowest energy of the fast electron spectrum is Δ, the lower limit of the integration to determine the energy deposited in the cavity by the electron flux is Δ rather than zero.

While it is planned that both N_x and N_{gas} will be supplied by the National Bureau of Standards (NBS) or an Accredited Dosimetry Calibration Laboratory (ADCL) at the time of the calibration, the user may calculate N_{gas} for a chamber calibrated prior to the implementation of this protocol with the use of Equation 10–2. This procedure is outlined on Worksheet 1 of the protocol. Values of α, A_{wall}, $\bar{L}/\rho$ and $\bar{\mu}_{en}/\rho$ are available from the protocol, and k, W/e, and β are constants. See the included worksheet that I use to calculate N_{gas}.

Line 3 of this worksheet is for A_{ion}, the ion collection efficiency at the time of the NBS or ADCL calibration. This factor A_{ion} is not stated by the standardizing laboratory and N_x has not been corrected for ion collection efficiency. In most cases the value of A_{ion} will be greater than 0.995 but this should be determined by the user.

One method of measuring A_{ion} is for the user to duplicate the conditions of irradiation used by the standardizing laboratory.

The exposure rate, field size, magnitude, and polarity of the voltage will be given on the calibration certificate. If the user has a cobalt-60 unit, the calibration conditions usually may be reproduced by appropriate choice of source-chamber-distance.

The collection efficiency may then be calculated using the two voltage techniques of Boag.[23] Almond[24] has shown the collection efficiency, f, in a continuous radiation beam at a voltage of V_1 is equal to

$$f = \left(\frac{V_1^2}{V_2^2} - \frac{Q_1}{Q_2} \right) \Big/ \left(\frac{V_1^2}{V_2^2} - 1 \right) \tag{10–3}$$

where $Q_1 =$ charge collected with a bias voltage of V_1
$Q_2 =$ charge collected with a bias voltage of V_2

If V_2 is made equal to one-half V_1 then equation (10–3) reduces to

$$f = \frac{\left(4 - \dfrac{Q_1}{Q_2} \right)}{3} \tag{10–4}$$

Example

A calibration certificate states that a cobalt-60 exposure factor was measured at an exposure rate of 40 $\dfrac{R}{min}$ with -300 V on the thimble. The user has a cobalt-60 unit with an output of 120 $\dfrac{R}{min}$ at 80.5 cm from the source. The output from this unit follows the inverse square law, therefore at 139.5 cm the output will be 40 $\dfrac{R}{min}$.

$$\left(\frac{80.5}{139.5} \right)^2 \times 120 = 40 \, \frac{R}{min}$$

A series of exposures is made with a -300 V on the thimble. The average of these readings is 4.08×10^{-8}C. Then a series of exposures is made with -150 V on the thimble. The average of these readings is 3.98×10^{-8}C. In this case $Q_1/Q_2 = 1.025$. This ratio of Q_1/Q_2

yields a collection efficiency of 0.992 for the voltages used. Therefore $A_{ion} = 0.992$ in this example.

The National Bureau of Standards can provide an absorbed
dose, as well as an exposure calibration factor for the user's ion
chamber at cobalt-60 energy. This calibration factor is measured
by comparing the response of the user's chamber in a water phantom to the response of a graphite chamber at the same point. The
absorbed dose calibration factor is

$$N_D = \frac{D_{water}}{M} \qquad (10\text{--}5)$$

where $D_{water} =$ the absorbed dose to water at the same position
                as the center of the user's chamber when the
                user's chamber is removed and replaced by
                water

      $M =$ the meter reading of the user's chamber, not
                corrected for ionic recombination effects in the
                ion chamber.

The cavity gas factor of the user's chamber is then

$$N_{gas} = N_D \; \frac{A_{ion}\, A_{repl}}{\left(\dfrac{\overline{L}}{\rho}\right)^{wall}_{gas} \left(\dfrac{\overline{\mu}_{en}}{\rho}\right)^{water}_{wall}} \qquad (10\text{--}6)$$

where $A_{repl} =$ replacement correction for the user's chamber at
                cobalt-60 energy
      $A_{ion} =$ correction of ionic recombination

This expression is only valid if the buildup cap is the same
material as the chamber wall. If the materials are different, then
an expression similar to Equation 10–2 above must be used. It
should be pointed out that N_{gas} is valid for all radiation for which
W/e for 50% humidified air is 33.7 J/C. N_{gas} may be derived for
any ion chamber by comparing its response in a phantom in a
megavoltage photon or electron beam to the response of a NBS
or ADCL calibrated chamber at the same point in the same phantom. Further explanation of this procedure will be deferred until
all chamber dependent factors have been fully discussed.

N_{gas} Worksheet

Chamber: _____   Serial number: _____

1. $k \dfrac{W}{e} \beta = 2.58 \times 10^{-4} \times 33.7 \times 1.005 = 8.738 \times 10^{-3}$

2. A_{wall} = _____ from Table II, p. 749 of the protocol
   or if chamber not listed in Table II
   (2a) t = _____ wall + buildup cap thickness in g/cm^2
   (2b) γ = _____ from Table III, p. 749

   (2c) $A_{wall} = 1 - \dfrac{\text{line 2a} \times \text{line 2b}}{100}$ = _____

3. A_{ion} = _____

4. α = _____ from Figure 1, p. 750 ($\alpha = 1$, if buildup cap and wall are same material)

5. $\left(\dfrac{\overline{L}}{\rho}\right)_{air}^{wall}$ = _____ from Table I, p. 749

6. $\left(\dfrac{\overline{\mu}_{en}}{\rho}\right)_{wall}^{air}$ = _____ from Table I, p. 749

7. $1 - \alpha$ = $1 -$ line 4 = _____

8. $\left(\dfrac{\overline{L}}{\rho}\right)_{air}^{cap}$ = _____ from Table I, p. 749

9. $\left(\dfrac{\overline{\mu}_{en}}{\rho}\right)_{cap}^{air}$ = _____ from Table I, p. 749

10. N_x = _____ from calibration certificate

11. $8.738 \times 10^{-3} \times$ line 2 or 2c $\times$ line 3 = _____
12. line 4 $\times$ line 5 $\times$ line 6 = _____
13. line 7 $\times$ line 8 $\times$ line 9 = _____
14. line 10 $\times$ line 11 = _____
15. line 12 + line 13 = _____

16. $N_{gas} = \dfrac{\text{line 14}}{\text{line 15}}$ = _____ Gy/C

10.4.2 Nominal Accelerating Potential

This protocol requires several energy dependent parameters, such as mean stopping power ratios, for the conversion of ionization chamber measurements to the determination of dose in water. The protocol points out that differences in accelerator design may result in different X-ray spectra even though the accelerators are operating at the same voltage. These differences may lead to an incorrect choice of the energy dependent factors and introduce systematic dosimetry errors. In an effort to minimize these errors, the protocol recommends using as an index of beam quality the ratio of readings made at two depths in phantom. These depths depend on the phantom material. The quantity so determined is named the *nominal accelerating potential*.

Measurements may be made in water, polystyrene, or PMMA phantoms at a constant source-detector-distance of 1 meter or the source-axis-distance. The field size should be 10 cm × 10 cm. The depths of measurement, scaled for differences in electron density, are:

	Water	Polystyrene	PMMA
First depth	10 cm	9.9 cm	8.8 cm
Second depth	20 cm	19.8 cm	17.6 cm

The ratio of the ionization at the second depth to the ionization at the first depth can be related to the nominal accelerating potential in Figure 3, p. 752 of the protocol and to mean restricted stopping power ratios in Figure 2 on the same page. This nominal accelerating potential is more closely related to the mean energy than the peak energy. The nominal accelerating potential is also used to determine the depth of calibration, scaling factors for plastic phantoms, corrections for excess scatter for PMMA phantoms, mean mass energy absorption coefficients, and a number of other energy-dependent factors required to calculate dose from the ionization measurements.

This approach to specification of beam quality is similar to the method employed in the NACP protocol of 1980. The NACP limited the measurements to a water phantom, but the ratio of the ionization at 10 cm depth to the ionization at 20 cm depth for a 10 cm × 10 cm field at a 100 cm source-surface-distance was chosen to designate the "acceleration potential." This quantity was then used to determine stopping power ratios and perturbation factors required in the protocol. These protocols chose this approach rather than a measurement of the half-value depth (HVD) because the HVD is critically dependent on the number of contamination electrons in the photon beam at d_{max}.

10.4.3 Dosimetry Phantoms

The protocol recommends that the phantom extend at least 5 cm beyond the radiation field on all sides to provide adequate scattering material. Also, the depth of the phantom should be at least 10 cm greater than the deepest point of measurement. Consequently, a SCRAD phantom with a cross sectional area of 25 cm × 25 cm and a depth of 20 cm could be used to measure field sizes to 15 cm × 15 cm and depths to 10 cm.

In a departure from all previous protocols, this AAPM protocol allows the calibration to be performed in a polystyrene or PMMA phantom as well as a water phantom. The SCRAD protocol[4] did permit polystyrene and PMMA phantoms as a supplement to but not as a replacement for the primary water phantom. However, the Task Group 21 protocol does retain the practice of stating the dose to water regardless of dosimetry phantom used.

Plastic phantoms have several advantages over water phantoms. Ease of handling and positioning are definite benefits. If the phantom is divided into thicknesses of 5 cm or less, the weight of each individual section is considerably less than a water phantom, which may be 30 cm × 30 cm × 40 cm. Another plus is that measurements may be made from any beam direction. This property permits one to verify that the dose per monitor unit of the machine is the same at all four principal angles much more easily than with a water phantom. Exact reproducibility of the detector position is probably the greatest advantage. This is a particularly valuable asset if one wishes to observe the possibility of any change in the machine output over a period of time. The precision of detector positioning is very high when using plastic phantoms. Another important application of plastic phantoms is the derivation of N_{gas} for chambers that do not have a calibration factor from a standardizing laboratory.

There are certain disadvantages, however, of plastic phantoms that must be balanced against the above advantages. Because of differences in electron densities, the attentuation of a photon beam will be different in plastics than in water at the same depth in phantom. Also, a dose transfer from plastic to water is required to state the dose to water. An additional question is the constancy of the composition of plastic. This problem has been studied[25] and it was determined that the only significant difference between the same type of plastic made at different times was in the mass den-

TABLE 10–1. Scaling Factors for Plastic Phantoms

Nominal accelerating potential (MV)	Polystyrene/water	PMMA/water
^{60}Co, 2 to 8	.99	.88
10 to 35	1.00	.88
40 to 50	1.01	.89

Source: "A Protocol for Determination of Absorbed Dose from High-Energy Photon and Electron Beams," *Medical Physics*, 10(741), 1983. Used with permission.

sity. It was recommended that this property be measured for each phantom used. A short time after the adoption of this protocol it was pointed out a problem may exist with plastic phantoms because of insulating properties of plastic.[26] Plastic phantoms may store the charge that results from the ionization created by the photon beam in the phantom. A similar situation exists when an electron beam is stopped in a plastic phantom. Because of these problems Galbraith, Rawlinson, and Munro[26] recommended replacing polystyrene and PMMA phantoms with conducting plastic phantoms. This question is currently unresolved.

The protocol quotes "scaling factors" for both polystyrene and PMMA. With these scaling factors, one may determine the thickness of plastic that yields an equal attenuation of a photon beam as a given thickness of water. These factors are given in Table XIII on p. 761 of the protocol and are reproduced here in Table 10–1.

Example

What depth of PMMA yields equal attentuation of a 18 MV photon beam as 5 cm of water?

Scaling factor $= 0.88$
Depth of PMMA $=$ Scaling factor $\times$ depth of water
$= 0.88 \times 5$ cm
$= 4.4$ cm

10.4.4 Geometry of Calibration

The protocol recommends that the source-detector-distance be the same for a plastic phantom as for a water phantom. The amount of overlying plastic should be scaled as above. If we take a calibration depth of 5 cm in a water phantom, then the calibration depth would be 4.4 cm in a PMMA phantom. However, if the source-surface-distance were 100 cm for a water phantom it would be 100.6 cm for a PMMA phantom. This would result in 105 cm source-detector-distance for both cases.

With this geometry, approximately the same volume of material is irradiated, be it a plastic or a water phantom. However, because of differences of electron densities more photons will be scattered in a plastic phantom than a water phantom. It has been shown[27] that this increase in scattered photons is equal to the TAR of the calibration field size scaled by the ratio of the electron densities of plastic to water divided by the TAR of the calibration field size. A correction for this effect, referred to as an excess scatter correction (ESC), is given in Table XIV on p. 761 of the protocol. ESC factors for ^{60}Co, 2 MV, 4 MV, and 6 MV photons for a variety of field sizes for a PMMA phantom are enumerated. Because the relative electron densities of polystyrene and water are nearly the same any corrections for excess scatter in a polystyrene phantom are negligible.

Example

Calculate the ESC for a cobalt-60 field that is 10 cm × 10 cm at a depth of 5 cm in a PMMA phantom.

The electron density of PMMA relative to water (1.137) is used to scale the field size of 10 cm × 10 cm. Then the ESC is

$$ESC = \frac{TAR\ (10,5)}{TAR\ (11.37,5)}$$

$$= \frac{.905}{.915}$$

$$= .989$$

where TAR (10,5) is the tissue-air ratio for a 10 cm × 10 cm field at 5 cm depth and TAR (11.37,5) is for a 11.37 cm × 11.37 cm field at 5 cm depth. The dose to plastic may be transferred to dose to water with

$$D_{water} = D_{plastic} \left(\frac{\overline{\mu}_{en}}{\rho}\right)^{water}_{plastic} ESC \qquad \textbf{(10–7)}$$

if the geometry used is as outlined above. Values of $\left(\frac{\overline{\mu}_{en}}{\rho}\right)_{\text{plastic}}^{\text{water}}$ are given in Table XII p. 761 of the protocol.

10.4.5 Wall Correction Factor

If a buildup cap is placed on an ion chamber in phantom for mega-voltage calibrations the ionization created in the chamber arises from the phantom material, buildup cap, and chamber wall. The formalism[28] used in the Task Group 21 protocol requires that the percentage of ionization from each material be evaluated and a correction factor determined. To simplify this procedure the protocol has limited the use of a buildup cap to the determination of the exposure calibration factor N_x and the in-air calibration of cobalt-60, unless the buildup cap is the same material as the phantom. With this restriction, only the phantom material and chamber wall contribute to the chamber ionization.

The protocol refers to the fraction of ionization resulting from secondary electrons from the chamber wall as α. Values of α are given in Figure 7 p. 759 of the protocol as a function of the nominal accelerating potential. For ion chambers and dosimetry phantoms specified by the protocol, α is relatively insensitive to the type of material. Alphas may be adequately determined in Figure 7 knowing the wall thickness in areal density, g/cm². This correction factor is named P_{wall} in the protocol and is equal to

$$P_{\text{wall}} = \frac{\alpha(\overline{L}/\rho)_{\text{air}}^{\text{wall}}\left(\frac{\overline{\mu}_{en}}{\rho}\right)_{\text{wall}}^{\text{med}} + (1-\alpha)(\overline{L}/\rho)_{\text{air}}^{\text{med}}}{(\overline{L}/\rho)_{\text{air}}^{\text{med}}} \qquad (10\text{–}8)$$

with symbols the same as are given in the formula for N_{gas} above.

When calibrations are performed in a water phantom, the protocol suggests waterproofing the chamber with a thin rubber sheath rather than a tube of PMMA of the same dimensions as the buildup cap. A rubber sheath of less than 0.5 mm thickness will contribute less than 25% to the ionization and its effect may be ignored. The main motivation behind the recommendation of not using a PMMA cap in water seems to be a desire to reduce Equation 10–8 to a two-component equation as other studies[29,30,31,32] indicate differences of less than 1% for calibrations performed in water with or without a PMMA cap.

10.4.6 Replacement Correction

A cylindrical ion chamber placed in a medium to measure the dose will disturb the electron fluence in that medium. Because of these changes in the fluence, certain correction factors must be included when the dose to medium is calculated from the ionization measurements.

For megavoltage X-ray measurements a gradient correction is required because the protocol recommends that measurements be done on the descending slope of the depth dose curve and that the central axis of the ion chamber be taken as the point of measurements. With these restrictions, it is clear that the surface of the ion chamber nearer the source will experience a higher electron fluence than is present at the point of measurement when the chamber is removed and replaced by medium. This correction is a function of both the size of the chamber and the penetration of the X-ray beam. The protocol furnishes appropriate values of the gradient correction in Figure 5, p. 757 as a function of both these parameters. The correction is referred to as P_{repl} by the protocol. This protocol rejects an alternative method of correction, which is to shift the effective point of measurement some fixed distance forward of the central axis of the ion chamber as was done in the NACP protocol. The reasons stated are that a fixed distance does not account for changes in the gradient of the dose and the possibility also exists of mistakes being made in the specification of the depth. Gradient corrections are not necessary for plane parallel plate chambers with the depth of measurement taken as the inner surface of the electrode closest to the source.

10.4.7 Ionic Recombination Correction

The collection efficiency of an ion chamber is the ratio of the charge collected with a given bias voltage and a certain dose rate to the charge created. Boag has discussed the theory[33] of ion chamber collection efficiency and presented measurement techniques for determining the collection efficiency of an ion chamber exposed to pulsed[23] and pulsed-scanning[34] radiation beams. A similar treatment for continuous radiation has been given by Almond.[24]

Most of the ion chambers that meet the specifications of the protocol and that are biased to 300 V will have collection efficiencies of 99% or higher in continuous or pulsed beams used in radiation therapy. However, the high instantaneous dose rates present in some pulsed-scanning beams may lead to collection efficiencies of less than 90%. The protocol recommends increasing the ion chamber bias if the collection efficiency is less than 0.95.

Regardless of the situation, it is good practice to determine the collection efficiency for each ion chamber in each beam quality at every dose rate employed clinically. The protocol offers a straightforward method based on Boag's two-voltage technique.[23,24,34] As discussed earlier in regard to A_{ion}, the collection efficiency may be determined by making ionization measurements at two voltages, V_1 and $\frac{1}{2} V_1$. The ratio of the charge collected at V_1, referred to as Q_1, and the charge collected at $\frac{1}{2} V_1$, referred to as Q_2, is plotted versus the quantity P_{ion} in Figure 4, p. 757 for continuous, pulsed, and pulsed-scanning radiation beams. P_{ion} is the correction factor that must be applied to the ionization reading at V_1 to correct for incomplete ion collection at that voltage.

10.4.8 Polarity Effects

The protocol recommends measurements be made with both positive and negative polarities on the thimble of a cylindrical chamber or the entrance window of a plane parallel plate chamber. The "true" value is taken as the average of the readings obtained with the two polarities.[35]

10.4.9 Depth of Calibration

The protocol recommends the depth of calibration as a function of the size of the chamber and the energy of the photon beam in Table XI p. 760. This is similar to recommendations made in the SCRAD protocol. These depths are measured to the center of a cylindrical or spherical chamber or the inner surface of the electrode nearest the source for a plane parallel plate chamber. These depths are to be scaled in accordance with the scaling factors discussed in Section 10.4.3.

10.4.10 Review of Factors Necessary for Conversion of Ionization to Dose

Before proceeding further, it might be helpful to review all the factors used in this protocol. There are several factors that depend on the construction of the chamber as well as the energy of the beam. As a result of the rather egalitarian decision that water, polystyrene, and PMMA may all be used as primary phantoms, there are other factors that are required to convert dose in plastic to dose in water. I think of the first group of factors as chamber-energy-dependent-factors and the second as dose-conversion-factors although they are energy dependent also. This rather arbitrary division helps my understanding of the protocol.

In the first group of factors I include the mean restricted stopping power ratio of phantom-medium to air, the wall correction factor, the replacement correction factor, and the recombination correction factor. The dose conversion factors consist of the excess scatter correction and the mean energy absorption coefficient ratio of water to phantom-medium.

The dose to phantom-medium per monitor unit at the point of measurement is

$$D_{\mathrm{med}}(d) = \frac{\overline{M}}{mu} \, N_{\mathrm{gas}} \, C_{\mathrm{cap}} \left(\frac{\overline{L}}{\rho}\right)^{\mathrm{med}}_{\mathrm{air}} P_{\mathrm{wall}} \, P_{\mathrm{ion}} \, P_{\mathrm{repl}} \qquad \textbf{(10–9)}$$

where
$mu =$ number of monitor units. I assume that it has been verified that the monitor system is linear and has no shutter defect (see section on cobalt-60 calibration)

$\overline{M} =$ average ion chamber reading for positive and negative polarities on the collector corrected to standard conditions of temperature and pressure

$N_{\mathrm{gas}} = N_{\mathrm{gas}}$ factor in Gy/C determined at a standardizing laboratory or calculated from exposure calibration factor N_x

$C_{\mathrm{cap}} =$ electrometer correction in C/scale division. This factor is only applicable if the ion chamber and electrometer are calibrated separately. If they are calibrated as a unit N_{gas} will be in terms of Gy/scale division

$\left(\dfrac{\overline{L}}{\rho}\right)^{\mathrm{med}}_{\mathrm{air}} =$ mean restricted stopping power ratio of the phantom medium to air

$P_{\mathrm{wall}} =$ wall correction factor

$P_{\mathrm{ion}} =$ ionization recombination correction factor

$P_{\mathrm{repl}} =$ replacement correction factor

$d =$ depth of measurement

The dose to phantom-medium may be transferred to the dose to water per monitor unit at $d_{\max}$ as

$$D_{\text{water}}(d_{\max}) = D_{\text{med}}(d)\,ESC\left(\frac{\mu_{en}}{\rho}\right)^{\text{water}}_{\text{med}}\frac{1}{\%dd} \qquad (10\text{--}10)$$

where ESC = excess scatter correction, if PMMA phantom is used

$\left(\dfrac{\overline{\mu}_{en}}{\rho}\right)^{\text{water}}_{\text{med}}$ = mean energy absorption coefficient ratio of water to phantom-medium

$\%dd$ = central axis percent depth in water appropriate for the radiation conditions

See the worksheet that I have reproduced that may be helpful in using the Task Group 21 protocol for megavoltage X-ray calibrations.

10.4.11 Derivation of N_{gas} for an Uncalibrated Ion Chamber

Although Task Group 21 recommends deriving N_{gas} for a parallel plate chamber by direct comparison with a cylindrical chamber in a high energy electron beam, it should be possible to derive N_{gas} for any chamber in any radiation beam for which W/e equals $33.7\,J/C$. This would include any megavoltage photon or electron beam used clinically. One should place the calibrated ion chamber at a given depth in phantom. A plastic phantom is particularly useful for this purpose because the irradiation geometry can be accurately reproduced. The response per monitor unit of the calibrated chamber should be determined and compared to the response per monitor unit of the uncalibrated chamber placed in the same phantom at exactly the same depth and source-chamber-distance. If a cylindrical chamber is used, the axis of the cylinder should be oriented perpendicular to the central axis of the beam and the point of measurement taken as the axis of the cylinder. If a parallel plate chamber is used, the point of measurement is taken as the inner surface of the entrance window.

The cavity gas calibration factor of the uncalibrated chamber is

$$(N_{\text{gas}})_u = \frac{(M\,N_{\text{gas}}\,P_{\text{ion}}\,P_{\text{repl}}\,P_{\text{wall}})_c}{(M\,P_{\text{ion}}\,P_{\text{repl}}\,P_{\text{wall}})_u} \qquad (10\text{--}11)$$

where the subscripts u and c refer to the uncalibrated and NBS or ADCL calibrated chambers, respectively. For a plane-parallel plate chamber with a thin entrance window $P_{wall} = P_{repl} = 1$.

The decision to use a megavoltage photon or megavoltage electron beam depends on several considerations. For an electron beam $P_{wall} = 1$, as will be discussed in Chapter 11; however, P_{repl} for cylindrical chambers is generally larger in electron beams than photon beams. Another important consideration with megavoltage electron beams when using a plane parallel plate ion chamber is the backscattered electrons from the plastic support of the ion chamber. The percentage of the total ionization contributed by backscattered electrons is dependent on the atomic number of the material. If the ion chamber support is a different material than the phantom then a mismatch may occur that might result in the ionization being higher or lower than if the ion chamber and phantom were the same material. One should also remember that P_{ion} will usually be greater in a scanned-pulsed beam than in a pulsed beam. As a general rule, one should use the radiation beam that minimizes all three of the corrections, P_{repl}, P_{ion}, and P_{wall}, for both of the ion chambers used.

Worksheet for Megavoltage X-ray Calibration
Date: _____

Machine: _____   Stated energy _____ MV
Ionization ratio: _____
Nominal accelerating potential _____ MV Figure 3 p. 752
Field size: _____ cm × _____ cm   SSD _____ cm
Phantom material: _____ Ion chamber _____ Serial number ____
Depth of calibration _____ cm in water (from Table XI p. 760)
Depth of calibration _____ cm in phantom (Depth of Calibration in water × scaling factor, Table XIII, p. 761)
Inner diameter of ion chamber _____ mm
Wall material _____, wall thickness _____ g/cm²
Electrometer _____   Serial number _____

1. Chamber temperature _____ °C
2. Chamber temperature line (1) + 273 = _____ °K
3. Barometric Pressure = _____ mm Hg
4. Number of monitor units = _____
5. N_{gas} = _____ Gy/C
6. Electrometer factor = _____ C/scale division
7. Fraction of ionization from chamber wall α = _____ from Figure 7, p. 759

8. Restricted stopping power ratio, wall to air $\left(\frac{\overline{L}}{\rho}\right)_{air}^{wall} =$ _____ Table IV, p. 753

9. Energy absorption coefficient, phantom medium to air $\left(\frac{\overline{\mu}_{en}}{\rho}\right)_{air}^{med}$
= _____ Table IX, p. 758

10. Energy absorption coefficient wall to air $\left(\frac{\overline{\mu}_{en}}{\rho}\right)_{air}^{wall} =$ _____ Table IX, p. 758

11. Energy absorption coefficient phantom medium to wall: $\frac{line\ 9}{line\ 10} =$
_____

12. Fraction of ionization from phantom: $1 - line\ 7 =$ _____

13. Restricted stopping power ratio phantom medium to air $\left(\frac{\overline{L}}{\rho}\right)_{air}^{med} =$
_____ Table IV, p. 753

14. Line 7 × line 8 × line 11 = _____

15. Line 12 × line 13 = _____

16. Line 14 + line 15 = _____

17. Line 16 ÷ line 13: $P_{wall} =$ _____

18. Ionization reading at V_1 with collecting electrode positive = _____ C

19. Ionization reading at V_1 with collecting electrode negative
= _____ C

20. $\frac{Line\ 18 + line\ 19}{2} =$ _____ C

21. Ionization reading at $\frac{1}{2} V_1$ with collecting electrode positive
= _____ C

22. Ionization reading at $\frac{1}{2} V_1$ with collecting electrode negative
= _____ C

23. $\frac{Line\ 21 + line\ 22}{2} =$ _____ C

24. Line 20 ÷ line 23: $\frac{Q_1}{Q_2} =$ _____

25. $P_{ion} =$ _____ use line 24 with Figure 4, p. 757

26. $P_{repl} =$ _____ from Figure 5, p. 757

27. Temperature-Pressure Correction $= \frac{line\ 2}{295} \times \frac{760}{line\ 3} =$ _____

28. Ionization at V_1 per monitor unit: $\frac{line\ 20}{line\ 4} =$ _____ C

29. Chamber-Energy Dependent Factors: line 13 × line 17 × line 25 × line 26 = _____

30. Dose per m.u. to phantom material at point of measurement
line 5 × line 6 × line 27 × line 28 × line 29 = _____ Gy/mu

31. If PMMA phantom enter ESC from Table XIV p. 761, otherwise enter
1. _____

32. Energy absorption coefficient water to phantom
medium _____ Table XII, p. 761, enter 1 if water phantom

33. %dd _____

34. *Dose per m.u. to water at d_{max}: line 30 × line 31 × line 32*
÷ line 33 = _____ Gy/mu

10.4.12 Cobalt-60 Calibration

There are three alternative procedures for the calibration of a co-balt-60 unit. These are in-phantom, in-air, and in-phantom using an ion chamber with a dose calibration factor. The in-phantom calibration follows procedures outlined earlier for megavoltage X-ray beams. The in-phantom method using an ion chamber with a dose calibration factor relies on N_D rather than N_{gas}. N_D is the absorbed dose calibration factor available from NBS for cobalt-60 radiation. This factor was discussed in regard to the derivation of N_{gas}. If N_D is used, the center of the chamber is placed 5 cm deep in a water phantom with the surface of the phantom at the treatment SSD. The dose to water at the point of measurement is the product of N_D and the ion chamber reading corrected for temperature and pressure. To find the dose at d_{max}, this product is divided by the appropriate central axis percent depth dose. If iso-centric treatments are used rather than fixed, SSD one may cali-brate with the ion chamber at isocenter, 5 cm deep in a water phantom and use TARs to determine the dose at d_{max}.

The in-air calibration is based on N_x, the exposure calibration factor. The exposure is measured by placing the center of the chamber with its buildup cap at isocenter or the normal SSD plus 0.5 cm. The exposure is equal to

$$X = \bar{M} N_x A_{ion} P_{ion} \qquad (10\text{--}12)$$

with all factors as previously defined. The dose to a small mass of water 0.5 cm in radius at the point of measurement is

$$D_{water} = X f A_{eq} \qquad (10\text{--}13)$$

where $f = 0.967$ cGy/R, Roentgen-to-cGy conversion factor for cobalt-60 photons for water

         $A_{eq} = 0.989$, a factor that accounts for the attenuation and scattering of a cobalt-60 beam in a small mass of water 5 mm in radius

The dose to water at d_{max} in a full scatter phantom is

$$D^{phantom}(d_{max}) = D_{water} PSF \qquad (10\text{--}14)$$

where PSF = appropriate peak scatter factor

Timer linearity and end effects

The most straightforward way to verify the linearity of a cobalt-60 timer or the monitor system of a linear accelerator is to make measurements with an ion chamber for a number of different exposures or monitor units. This data may be fit with a linear regression analysis with time or monitor units assigned to the x–axis and the ion chamber reading assigned to the y–axis. The correlation coefficient should be 0.999 or better if the timer or monitor system is linear. Of course, this measurement assumes the linearity of one's calibrated ion chamber-electrometer system. The Victoreen R-meter with a string electrometer or an early vintage Farmer system, Model 2502, may display nonlinearities and should be checked.[14]

Example

The following chamber readings were recorded for the times indicated on a cobalt-60 unit.

Time (min.)	Ion chamber reading (10^{-8}C)
0.5	0.878
1.0	1.808
1.5	2.740
2.0	3.669
2.5	4.603
3.0	5.528

correlation coefficient = 0.999999

y intercept   = −0.052067

slope   = 1.8608

x intercept   = 0.02798

The correlation coefficient clearly indicates the linearity of the timer. Other important information is also available. The slope represents the ion chamber reading per minute of exposure and the x intercept is a measure of the end effect or shutter correction in minutes.

The end effect is a result of the time required for the shutter to open or to close or for the source to move to the fully exposed position in a cobalt-60 unit. A similar effect might be measured on a linear accelerator because a finite time elapses before the unit reaches its operating dose rate. The monitor chamber in the head of the linac may exhibit a dose rate dependence because of ionic recombination effects. This can result in an end effect in a linac because the first few monitor units recorded may represent a different amount of radiation than all subsequent monitor units.

Orton and Seibert[36] proposed an alternate method of determining the shutter correction. This technique is frequently referred to as the *alpha method* because the symbol α is used to represent the end effect. Used in this context the symbol α is the original notation of Orton and Seibert. It must not be confused with the α of sections 10.4.1 and 10.4.5 where it was used to represent the fraction of ionization from the walls of the ion chamber. With this method, the reading of an ion chamber for a single long exposure is compared to the ion chamber reading for an exposure for the same total time or monitor units that has been interrupted several times. In this case

$$\frac{M_1}{t+\alpha} = \frac{M_n}{t+n\alpha}$$ (10–15)

where $n-1 =$ number of interruptions
$\alpha =$ end effect
$t =$ time or monitor unit setting
$M_1 =$ meter reading when radiation is not interrupted
$M_n =$ meter reading when radiation is interrupted
$n-1$ times

Solving for α we have

$$\alpha = \frac{(M_1 - M_n)t}{M_n - nM_1}$$ (10–16)

Example

An ion chamber recorded a reading of 1.609 for a uninterrupted 1-minute exposure in a cobalt-60 unit and 1.550 for a 1-minute exposure interrupted twice. Solve for α.

$$\alpha = \frac{1.609 - 1.550}{1.550 - 3 \times 1.609}$$

$$\alpha = -0.018 \text{ min}$$

A negative α represents a deficit in actual exposure time compared to the time set for the exposure. In other words in the above example 0.018 minutes should be added to all exposure times. This is clear by noting that the ion chamber reading of the uninterrupted 1-minute exposure is larger than the ion chamber reading of the twice interrupted 1-minute exposure.

It is important to point out that if a linear regression analysis is used to find the end effect then a positive x intercept corresponds to a negative α and a negative x intercept corresponds to a positive α.

Both the α method and the linear regression method should be used to determine end effects and the two values should agree within a few tenths of a second.

Nuclear Regulatory Commission requirements for cobalt-60

The Nuclear Regulatory Commission (NRC) requires output measurements to be performed once a month for one set of operating conditions of a cobalt-60 unit; that is, one field size at one treatment distance.[37] These measurements must include verification of timer accuracy and linearity, light-radiation field congruence, and accuracy of all distance-measuring devices used in treating humans. The difference between the measured dose rate and the dose rate obtained by mathematically correcting for physical decay since the last full calibration must be recorded as a percentage in the data book.

A full calibration is required

1. prior to first human application
2. prior to human application
   (a) when the spot check differs from the anticipated value by more than 5%
   (b) following source replacement or reinstallation of the unit at a new location
   (c) following any major repair requiring source removal or major repair of components of source exposure assembly
3. at intervals not exceeding a year

A full calibration requires measurements of:

"1. The exposure rate or dose rate to an accuracy within ± 3 percent for the range of field sizes and for the range of distances (or for the axis distance) used in radiation therapy;

2. The congruence between the radiation field and the field indicated by the light beam localizing device;

3. The uniformity of the radiation field and its dependence upon the orientation of the useful beam;

4. Timer accuracy; and

5. The accuracy of all distance measuring devices used for treating humans."[37]

The NRC requires a full calibration to be performed by a qualified radiation expert and to conform to the procedures of the SCRAD Protocol.[4] The dosimetry system used for a full calibration must have been calibrated by the National Bureau of Standards or an Accredited Dosimetry Calibration Laboratory within the last two years or after any servicing that may have changed the calibration.

For monthly spot checks it is acceptable to use a dosimetry system that has a calibration factor derived within the last year by direct intercomparison to a system with a NBS or ADCL factor that has been determined within the last two years. The monthly spot checks do not have to be performed by a qualified expert but must be reviewed by one within 15 days.

A qualified expert is defined to be one who

"a. Is certified by the American Board of Radiology in Therapeutic Radiological Physics, Radiological Physics, Roentgen-Ray and Gamma-Ray Physics, or X-ray and Radium Physics, or

b. Has the following minimum training and experience:

1. A Master's or Doctor's degree in physics, biophysics, radiological physics, or health physics.

2. One year of full-time training in therapeutic radiological physics; and

3. One year of full-time experience in a radiotherapy facility including personal calibration and spot check of at least one teletherapy unit."[37]

Record-keeping requirements

For medical–legal purposes records of all calibrations should be maintained in a log book. This book should have bound, consecutively-numbered pages. Each entry should be dated and all essential information recorded, for instance, temperature, pressure, field size, dosimetry system, SSD, and so on. If an institution has more than one machine it is most convenient to have a log book for each machine. Records of all dosimetry system calibrations by the NBS or ADCL should be kept in a file. These records should be maintained indefinitely. In addition, the NRC has the following record-keeping requirements:

"The licensee shall maintain, for inspection by the Commission, records of the measurements, tests, corrective actions, and instrument calibrations . . . and records of the licensee's evaluation of the qualified expert's training and experience . . ."[37] and

"a. Records of (1) full calibration measurements . . . and (2) calibration of the instruments used to make these measurements . . . shall be preserved for five years after completion of the full calibration.

b. Records of (1) spot-check measurements and corrective actions . . . and (2) calibration of instruments used to make spot-check measurements . . . shall be preserved for two years after completion of the spot-check measurements and corrective actions.

c. Records of the licensee's evaluation of the qualified expert's training and experience . . . shall be preserved for five years after the qualified expert's last performance of a full calibration on the licensee's teletherapy unit."[37]

Notes

1. *Radiation Dosimetry: X-Rays and Gamma-Rays with Maximum Photon Energies Between 0.6 and 50 MeV.*, ICRU Report 14., (Washington, D. C.: International Commission on Radiation Units and Measurements, 1969).

2. *Measurement of Absorbed Dose in a Phantom Irradiated by a Single Beam of X or Gamma Rays.*, *ICRU Report 23.*, (Washington, D. C.: International Commission on Radiation Units and Measurements, 1973).

3. John B. Massey, *Manual of Dosimetry in Radiotherapy*, *Technical Report Series No. 110.* (Vienna: International Atomic Energy Agency, 1970).

4. American Association of Physicists in Medicine, Scientific Committee on Radiation Dosimetry, "Protocol for the Dosimetry of X- and Gamma-Ray Beams with Maximum Energies Between 0.6 and 50 MeV," *Phys. Med. Biol.*, 16(1971), pp. 379–96.

5. American Association of Physicists in Medicine, Task Group 10, "Code of Practice for X-Ray Therapy Linear Accelerators," *Med. Phys.*, 2(1975), pp. 110–21.

6. American Association of Physicists in Medicine, Task Group 21, "A Protocol for the Determination of Absorbed Dose from High-Energy Photon and Electron Beams," *Med. Phys.*, 10(1983), pp. 741–71.

7. Hospital Physicists Association, "A Code of Practice for the Dosimetry of 2 to 35 MV X-ray and Caesium-137 and Cobalt-60 Gamma-Ray Beams," *Phys. Med. Biol.*, 14(1969), pp. 1–8.

8. Hospital Physicists Association, "Revised Code of Practice for the Dosimetry of 2 to 35 MV X-ray, and of Caesium-137 and Cobalt-60 Gamma-ray Beams," *Phys. Med. Biol.*, 28(1983), pp. 1097–104.

9. Nordic Association of Clinical Physics, "Procedures in Radiation Therapy Dosimetry with 5 to 50 MeV Electrons and Roentgen and Gamma Rays with Maximum Photon Energies Between 1 and 50 MeV," *Acta Radiol. Ther. Phys. Biol.*, 11(1972), pp. 603–24.

10. Nordic Association of Clinical Physics, "Procedures in External Radiation Therapy Dosimetry with Electron and Photon Beams with Maximum Energies Between 1 and 50 MeV," *Acta Radiol. Oncol.*, 19(1980), pp. 55–79.

11. "Klinische Dosimetrie: Therapeutische Anwendung gebündelter Röntgen-, Gamma-, und Elektronenstrahlung," Deutsches Institut für Normung, DIN 6809, Teil 1, 1976.

12. "Dosismessverfahren in der Radiologischen Technik: Ionisationsdosimetrie," Deutsches Institut für Normung DIN 6800, Teil 2, 1980.

13. "Dosismessverfahren in der Radiologischen Technik: Allgemeines zur Dosimetrie von Photonen–und Elektronenstrahlung nach der Sondenmethode," Deutsches Institut für Normung DIN 6800, Teil 1, 1980.

14. *Dosimetry of X-Ray and Gamma-Ray Beams for Radiation Therapy in the Energy Range 10 keV to 50 MeV, NCRP Report No. 69*. (Washington, D. C.: National Council on Radiation Protection and Measurements, 1981).

15. David Greene, "The Use of an Ethylene-Filled Polythene Chamber for Dosimetry of Megavoltage X-rays," *Phys. Med. Biol.*, 7(1962), pp. 213–24.

16. Harold Elford Johns and John Robert Cunningham, *The Physics of Radiology, Third Edition*., (Springfield, ILL.: Charles C. Thomas, 1974) pp. 288–90.

17. Robert Loevinger, "A Formalism for Calculation of Absorbed Dose to a Medium from Photon and Electron Beams," *Med. Phys.*, 8(1981), pp. 1–12.

18. A. C. McEwan and V. G. Smyth, "Comments on 'Calculated Response and Wall Correction Factors for Ionization Chambers Exposed to ^{60}Co Gamma-Rays,'" *Med. Phys.*, 11(1984), pp. 216–18.

19. B. J. Mijnheer and J. R. Williams, "Comments on Dry Air or Humid Air Values for Physical Parameters Used in the AAPM Protocol for Photon and Electron Dosimetry," *Med. Phys.*, 12(1985), pp. 656–58.

20. Ravinder Nath and R. J. Schulz, "Calculated Response and Wall Correction Factors for Ionization Chambers Exposed to ^{60}Co Gamma-Rays," *Med. Phys.*, 8(1981), pp. 85–93.

21. R. J. Schulz, "Reply to Comments of Mijnheer and Williams," *Med. Phys.*, 12(1985), p. 658.

22. L. V. Spencer and F. H. Attix, "A Theory of Cavity Ionization," *Radiat. Res.*, 3(1955), pp. 239–54.

23. J. W. Boag and J. Currant, "Current Collection and Ionic Recombination in Small Cylindrical Ionization Chambers Exposed to Pulsed Radiation," *Brit. J. Radiol.*, 53(1980), pp. 471–78.

24. Peter R. Almond, "Use of a Victoreen 500 Electrometer to Determine Ionization Chamber Collection Efficiencies," *Med. Phys.*, 8(1981), pp. 901–4.

25. R. J. Schulz and Ravinder Nath, "On the Constancy in Composition of Polystyrene and Polymethylmethacrylate Plastics," *Med. Phys.*, 6(1979), pp. 153–56.

26. Duncan M. Galbraith, J. Alan Rawlinson, and Peter Munro, "Dose Errors Due to Charge Storage in Electron Irradiated Plastic Phantoms," *Med. Phys.*, 11(1984), pp. 197–203.

27. Harvey Casson, "Correction of Measurements in Plastic Phantoms to Obtain Dose in Water," *Med. Phys.*, 5(1978), p. 321.

28. P. R. Almond and H. Svensson, "Ionization Chamber Dosimetry for Photon and Electron Beams. Theoretical Considerations," *Acta Radiol. Ther. Phys. Biol.*, 16(1977), pp. 177–86.

29. M. J. Day, D. Greene, and J. B. Massey, "Use of a Perspex Sheath for Ionization Chamber Measurements in a Water Phantom," *Phys. Med. Biol.*, 10(1965), pp. 111–12.

30. G. Kutcher, K. Strubler, and N. Suntharalingam, "High-Energy-Photon Dose Measurements Using Exposure-Calibrated Ionization Chambers," *Med. Phys.*, 4(1977), pp. 414–18.

31. Michael T. Gillin, Robert W. Kline, Azam Niroomand-Rad, and Daniel F. Grimm, "The Effect of the Thickness of the Waterproofing Sheath on the Calibration of Photon and Electron Beams," *Med. Phys.*, 12(1985), pp. 234–36.

32. William F. Hanson and J. Antonio Dominguez Tinoco, "Effects of Plastic Protective Caps on the Calibration of Therapy Beams in Water," *Med. Phys.*, 12(1985), pp. 243–48.

33. J. W. Boag, "Ionization Chambers," in *Radiation Dosimetry Volume II Instrumentation*, ed. Frank H. Attix and William C. Roesch (New York, N. Y.: Academic Press 1966), pp. 1–72.

34. J. W. Boag, "The Recombination Correction for an Ionisation Chamber Exposed to Pulsed Radiation in a 'Swept Beam' Technique I. Theory," *Phys. Med. Biol.*, 27(1982), pp. 201–11.

35. Jasper E. Richardson, "Effect of Chamber Voltage on Electron Buildup Measurements," *Radiol.*, 62(1954), pp. 584–88.

36. C. G. Orton and Joan B. Seibert, "The Measurement of Teletherapy Unit Timer Errors," *Phys. Med. Biol.*, 17(1972), pp. 198–205.

37. U. S. Nuclear Regulatory Commission, "Calibration of Teletherapy Units," *Federal Register*, 44(1979), pp. 1722–24.

ELEVEN

MEGAVOLTAGE ELECTRON CALIBRATION

11.1 INTRODUCTION

In addition to the numerous megavoltage photon calibration protocols discussed in the previous chapter, a variety of protocols have been published by international and national organizations for the calibration of megavoltage electron beams. Some of the protocols[1,2,3], are applicable only to electron beams with energy greater than 5 MeV, others[4,5,6], extend the energy range as low as 1 MeV, while a few[7,8] are addressed specifically to low energy electrons. The primary calibration technique discussed in these documents is measurement with an ion chamber in a water phantom. The geometry of the calibration, depth of measurement, and factors necessary to convert ionization to dose in water are given in the protocols.

In a manner similar to megavoltage photon calibrations, an equation to calculate dose from ionization measurement was presented in these protocols. Prior to 1980 the equation used to convert ionization measurements to dose to water was

$$D = M_C N_X C_E \, p_{w,g} \tag{11-1}$$

where M_C was the ionization chamber reading corrected for polarity, displacement, saturation, stem, temperature and pressure effects

   N_X was the cobalt-60 or 2MV X-ray exposure calibration factor determined by a national standards laboratory

   $p_{w,g}$ was the perturbation factor

   C_E was referred to as a Roentgen-to-rad conversion factor

The perturbation factor $p_{w,g}$ accounts for the perturbation of the electron fluence by the introduction of a cavity into a water phantom. This perturbation effect is the result of two simultaneously occurring phenomena. The first results from the density of the gas in the cavity being lower than the density of water. Because of this density difference, more electrons are scattered into the ion chamber than out of it. This causes a higher ionization in the cavity than would occur if no density differences existed. However, this increased ionization is partially offset because the electrons experience fewer collisions in the lower density material and their overall track length is shorter than in a similar volume of water. These two effects are referred to as *in-scattering* and *obliquity*. For a plane-parallel plate chamber, these effects essentially cancel each other and the perturbation factor is taken to be one. For cylindrical chambers, though, the in-scattering effect is predominant and the ionization reading must be corrected by a factor less than unity. The perturbation factor has been discussed by Harder[9] and Svensson and Brahme[10] and measured in PMMA phantoms by Johansson.[11]

The factor C_E is equal to

$$C_E = 0.869 \, A_{eq} \left(\frac{S}{\rho}\right)_{air}^{water} \tag{11-2}$$

$$A_{eq} = 0.985$$

where $\left(\dfrac{S}{\rho}\right)_{air}^{water}$ is the collisional mass stopping power ratio of water to air for the mean electron energy at the point of measurement

C_E may be approximated to within 1% with the empirical relation

$$C_E = 0.97\, E_z{}^{-0.048} \tag{11-3}$$

where E_z = the mean electron energy at the point of
measurement

11.2 THE NACP PROTOCOL OF 1980

As discussed in Chapter 10, the NACP revised its calibration procedure for megavoltage photon and electron beams in 1980.[5] In the
process, the factors C_E and N_X were abandoned. The absorbed
dose to air chamber calibration factor, N_D, was introduced to replace the exposure calibration factor N_X. C_E was superseded by
two factors $(s_{w,air})_u$ and p_u. The factor $(s_{w,air})_u$ was defined as the
mass stopping power ratio of water to air at the user's radiation
quality and p_u was the total perturbation factor including a correction for lack of water equivalence in the wall of the ion chamber.
Tables of $(s_{w,air})_u$ and p_u were given in the protocol as a function
of the mean electron energy at the point of measurement.

11.3 THE AAPM PROTOCOL OF 1983

In late 1983, Task Group 21 of the AAPM published a unified
protocol[6] for both megavoltage photon (see Chapter 10) and megavoltage electron calibrations using calibrated ion chambers. The
reasons for this new protocol and several of the technical aspects
have been discussed in the previous chapter and will not be repeated here. In this chapter I will address only those aspects applicable to electron calibrations.

11.3.1 Energy Determination

To convert ionization measurements to absorbed dose requires the
determination of several energy dependent parameters. These parameters are given in the protocol as a function of the mean electron
energy. The symbol $\bar{E}_0$ denotes the mean electron energy incident
on the phantom and it may be determined by measuring d_{50}, the
depth in a water phantom at which the ionization reading is reduced
to one-half of its maximum value. $\bar{E}_0$ is related to d_{50} by

$$\bar{E}_0(\text{MeV}) = 2.33\, d_{50}(\text{cm}). \tag{11-4}$$

The factor 2.33 MeV/cm was determined by analyzing depth dose curves of plane parallel monoenergetic electron beams impinging on semi-infinite water phantoms. Therefore the measurements of d_{50} must be made in field sizes for which the depth of d_{50} is maximum. The $\bar{E}_0$ determined with this procedure is applicable for all field sizes.

The protocol also permits the measurement of d_{50} in polystyrene and PMMA phantoms. If these phantoms are used

$$\bar{E}_0 \text{ (MeV)} = 2.33 \, d_{50}(\text{cm})f \qquad (11\text{--}5)$$

where f is a scaling factor that is equal to 0.965 for polystyrene and 1.11 for PMMA.[12]

If d_{50} is expressed in terms of g/cm² then f must be divided by the density. In this case

$$\bar{E}_0 \text{ (MeV)} = 2.33 \, d_{50} \, (\text{g/cm}^2) \frac{f}{\rho} \qquad (11\text{--}6)$$

11.3.2 Dosimetry Phantom

In a manner similar to photons, the protocol requires that dose be expressed in terms of cGy to water but allows measurements to be made in PMMA and polystyrene phantoms as well as in water. The phantom should extend at least 5 cm outside the field on all sides and should be at least 1 cm deeper than the electron range.

11.3.3 Ion Chamber

Either a cylindrical or plane parallel plate chamber may be used to calibrate electron beams. If cylindrical chambers are used, the correction P_{repl}, which we will discuss soon must be included. The buildup cap should not be employed unless it is the same material as the dosimetry phantom. If it is necessary to waterproof the ion chamber a thin rubber sheath should be used as suggested in Chapter 10. The correction factor P_{repl} is taken as unity for plane parallel plate chambers, but these chambers should be used with care if the dosimetry phantom is of a different material than the support of the ion chamber. This mismatch in materials may result in higher or lower ionization measurements because of differences between

electron backscatter of the disparate materials. For either cylindrical or plane parallel plate chambers the correction factor P_{wall},
discussed in Chapter 10, is unity for electron beams. The protocol
recommends plane parallel plate chambers with minimal plastic
construction, to reduce electron backscatter, in a water phantom
as an optimal choice.

11.3.4 Depth of Calibration

This protocol restricts all electron calibrations to d_{max}. For plastic
phantoms the depth of d_{max} should be measured because the scaling
factors of 0.965 and 1.11 used for polystyrene and PMMA at d_{50}
may not be valid at d_{max}.

11.3.5 Replacement Correction

The replacement factor correction is necessary because a cylindrical ion chamber placed in a phantom will disturb the electron fluence. This factor was referred to as the perturbation correction
in previous protocols and has been discussed in Section 11.1. The
replacement factor is denoted as P_{repl} in this protocol. Values for
this factor, measured by Johansson et al,[11] are given in Table VIII,
p. 758 of the protocol. These numbers appear as a function of the
inner diameter of the ion chamber and the mean energy of the
electron beam at the point of measurement, $\bar{E}_z$. The P_{repl} values
in Table VIII may be calculated within 0.5% with the following
relations.

$$P_{repl} = (a\bar{E}_z - 20a)d + 1 \qquad (11\text{--}7)$$

$$a = 3.7 \times 10^{-4} \qquad (11\text{--}8)$$

where d is the inner diameter of the chamber.

The energy, $\bar{E}_z$, is found by assuming a linear decrease in
energy with depth,

$$\bar{E}_z = \bar{E}_0\left(1 - \frac{z}{R_p}\right) \qquad (11\text{--}9)$$

where z = depth of measurement
R_p = practical range

The practical range is determined by measuring the depth ionization curve in phantom with an ionization chamber. It is the depth at which a straight line drawn through the linearly decreasing slope of the depth ionization curve intercepts a straight line drawn through the bremsstrahlung background. This point is illustrated in Figure 11–1. If a cylindrical chamber is used, the effective point of measurement is closer to the electron source than the central axis of the cylinder by an amount equal to three-fourths of the inside radius of the cylinder. The point of measurement of a plane parallel plate chamber is taken as the inner surface of the entrance window.

The geometry of the measurement may be either a constant source-surface-distance or a constant source-detector-distance. When one is measuring in a plastic phantom the constant source-detector-distance technique is generally easier to use because plastic can be added to the top of the phantom. However, if one chooses to measure in a water phantom, one typically maintains a constant source-surface-distance and moves the ion chamber to greater depths.

The practical range and HVD are more correctly measured in a geometry of constant-source-detector-distance than in a geometry of constant-source-surface-distance because Equation 11–4, re-

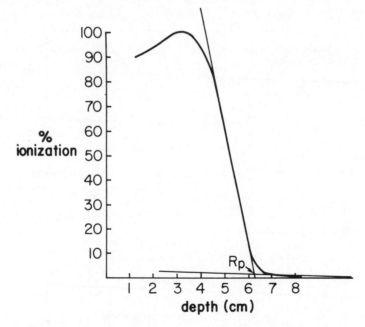

Figure 11–1   Illustration of the technique to determine R_p.

lating mean electron energy to HVD, is based on an analysis of plane-parallel, infinitely wide beams of monoenergetic electrons impinging on a semi-infinite water phantom. Additionally the term "range" is generally used to refer to measurements made with a constant source-detector-distance. In spite of these points, Task Group 21 does not recommend correcting the data for beam divergence. However, if one wishes to transform data measured in constant source-surface-distance geometry to constant source-detector-distance geometry, this may be accomplished by multiplying the ionization at each depth by

$$\left(\frac{S+z}{S}\right)^{2} \tag{11-10}$$

where S = effective source-surface-distance
z = effective depth

11.3.6 Ionic Recombination Correction

The correction for ionization recombination effects is discussed in Chapter 10.

11.3.7 Wall Correction Factor

Johansson, et al.[11] found the response to the electron beams of thin-walled ionization chambers to be independent of the composition of the wall for low atomic number materials. On the basis of this data the wall correction factor P_{wall} is taken as unity for electron beams. However, one should note that the behavior of thick-walled chambers and chambers with large central electrodes has not been investigated and these type chambers should be used for electron calibration with caution.

11.3.8 Application of the Factors to Determine Dose to Water

The equation to calculate dose to phantom from ionization chamber measurement is

$$D_{med} = \frac{\overline{M}}{mu} N_{gas} \ C_{cap} \left(\frac{\overline{L}}{\rho}\right)_{air}^{med} P_{ion} P_{repl} \tag{11-11}$$

where $\overline{M}$ = average electrometer reading for both bias
                 polarities on the thimble corrected for
                 temperature and pressure

              mu = number of monitor units

              N_{gas} = ion chamber factor (see Chapter 10)

              C_{cap} = capacitor factor (see Chapter 10)

              $\dfrac{\overline{L}}{\rho}\Big)^{med}_{air}$ = mean restricted stopping power ratio of
                 phantom medium to air

              P_{ion} = correction for ionic recombination

              P_{repl} = replacement correction factor

The mean restricted stopping power ratios for water to air, polystyrene to air, and PMMA to air appear in the protocol on pp. 754, 755, and 756 as Tables V, VI, and VII. These ratios are given as a function of $\bar{E}_0$ and depth of d_{max} in g/cm^2.

From Equation (11–11), one may calculate dose to water with

$$D_{water} = D_{med} \frac{\overline{S}}{\rho}\Big)^{water}_{med} \phi\Big)^{water}_{med} \qquad (11\text{–}12)$$

where $\dfrac{\overline{S}}{\rho}\Big)^{water}_{med}$ is the mean unrestricted stopping power ratio for water to medium

The ratio is relatively constant over the electron energy range of this protocol. Values of this factor, given in Table XV p. 762 of the protocol, are

$$\frac{\overline{S}}{\rho}\Big)^{water}_{PMMA} = 1.033 \qquad (11\text{–}13)$$

$$\frac{\overline{S}}{\rho}\Big)^{water}_{polystyrene} = 1.030. \qquad (11\text{–}14)$$

The factor $\phi)^{water}_{med}$ is the ratio of the electron fluence at d_{max} in water to d_{max} in plastic. Hogstrom and Almond[13] have presented data expressing electron fluence at d_{max} as a function of the mass angular scattering power of the material. Electron fluence corrections for polystyrene are given in Table XVI, p. 762 of the protocol. This table covers the electron energy range of $\bar{E}_0$ from 5 to 16 MeV. The data presented in the table may be fit with the equation

$$\phi)^{\text{water}}_{\text{polystyrene}} = 1.052 - 0.00271\,\bar{E}_0 \qquad (11\text{--}15)$$

to within 0.1%. The protocol recommends that the value of $\phi)^{\text{water}}_{\text{PMMA}}$ be taken as unity.

See the worksheet prepared for your use during electron calibration.

Worksheet for Megavoltage Electron Calibrations
Date: _____

Machine: _____   Nominal Energy: _____ MeV

Field Size: _____ cm x _____ cm   SSD: _____ cm

Phantom Material _____

HVD: _____ cm R_p: _____ cm

Depth of Measurement (z): _____ cm

$\bar{E}_0$ _____ MeV $\bar{E}_z$: _____ MeV

(1 for water)
$\bar{E}_0 = 2.33\,f\,HVD$ where $f =$ (0.965 for polystyrene)
(1.11 for PMMA)

$$\bar{E}_z = \bar{E}_0\left(1 - \frac{z}{R_p}\right)$$

Ion Chamber: _____   Serial Number: _____

Inner Diameter in mm: _____

Electrometer: _____   Serial Number: _____

1. Chamber temperature = _____ °C
2. Chamber temperature: line (1) + 273 = _____ °K
3. Barometric Pressure = _____ mm Hg
4. Number of monitor units = _____
5. N_{gas} = _____ Gy/C
6. Electrometer factor = _____ C/scale division
7. $\dfrac{\bar{L}}{\rho}\Big)^{\text{med}}_{\text{air}}$ (for $\bar{E}_0$ at depth z) = _____ Table V p. 754, Table VI p. 755 or Table VII p. 756 for water, polystyrene or PMMA
8. P_{repl} = _____ Table VIII p. 758
9. Electrometer reading at V_1 with collecting electrode positive = _____ C
10. Electrometer reading at V_1 with collecting electrode negative = _____ C
11. $\frac{1}{2}$ (Line 9 + Line 10) = _____ C
12. Electrometer reading at $\frac{1}{2}$ V_1 with collecting electrode positive = _____ C
13. Electrometer reading at $\frac{1}{2}$ V_1 with collecting electrode negative = _____ C
14. $\frac{1}{2}$ (Line 12 + Line 13) = _____ C

15. Line 11 ÷ Line 14: $\dfrac{Q_1}{Q_2} =$ _____

16. $P_{ion} =$ _____ use Line 15 and Figure 4, p. 757

17. Ionization per monitor unit at V_1 Line 11 ÷ Line 4 = _____ C/mu

18. Temperature-Pressure Correction: $\dfrac{\text{Line 2}}{295} \times \dfrac{760}{\text{Line 3}} =$ _____

19. Dose per monitor unit to phantom material at d_{max}
    Line 5 × Line 6 × Line 17 × Line 18 × Line 7 × Line 8 × Line 16 = _____ Gy/mu

20. If polystyrene phantom used enter $\phi)_{med}^{water}$ from Table XVI, p. 762, otherwise enter 1 _____

21. Unrestricted stopping power ratio water to phantom medium, Table XV p. 762, enter 1 for water phantom = _____

22. Dose per monitor unit to water at d_{max}:
    Line 19 × Line 20 × Line 21 = _____ Gy/mu

11.4 ICRU REPORT 35

In 1984 the ICRU issued Report 35, which addressed the calibration of electron beams with energies between 1 and 50 MeV. This report is similar in many respects to the NACP protocol of 1980 in that calibrations with ion chambers are based on the absorbed dose to air calibration factor N_D. This factor is multiplied by the ion chamber reading, a stopping power ratio of water to air, and a perturbation factor. Tables of stopping power ratios and perturbation factors are given in the Report. The Report recommends water as the primary calibration medium. The Report also recommends converting measurements made in plastic to "in-water data" with a procedure discussed in the Report.

11.5 CALIBRATION OF LOW-ENERGY ELECTRONS

The AAPM, NACP, and HPA caution that special problems are associated with the calibration of low-energy electrons. The principal problems associated with the use of a cylindrical ion chamber for low energy electron calibrations are:

1. its walls are relatively thick
2. the perturbation or replacement factor associated with the size of the cavity is large

3. the increase in the proportion of electrons absorbed in the collector as the electron energy decreases results in an increasing polarity effect

The HPA and NACP have formulated separate protocols addressing these problems. The AAPM has not formulated a special protocol, but warns against using a cylindrical chamber in a plastic phantom below 10 MeV incident electron energy. The HPA considers electrons of 5 MeV incident energy and below as requiring special attention, whereas the NACP extends this energy up to 15 MeV.

11.5.1 The HPA Low-Energy Electron Protocol

The HPA protocol recommends the use of a specially designed parallel plate chamber in a polystyrene phantom for electrons with $\bar{E}_0$ less than 5 MeV.[14] The incident energy is determined from the HVD in polystyrene by

$$\bar{E}_0 \, (MeV) = 2.37 HVD(g/cm^2) + 0.19 \qquad (11\text{--}16)$$

The calibration factor for the parallel plate chamber is found by comparing its response in a PMMA phantom irradiated by a cobalt-60 beam to the response of a calibrated cylindrical chamber under identical irradiation conditions. The electron beam is calibrated at the depth of the maximum ionization in a phantom. The absorbed dose to water is taken to be the product of the reading at maximum ionization, corrected for temperature, pressure, recombination and polarity effects, and the chamber's calibration factor determined in the PMMA phantom times the appropriate C_E value given in the protocol. The protocol specifies the phantom used for low-energy electron calibrations should be similar to the one recommended by the HPA protocol for electrons with incident energies of 5 to 35 MeV. The phantom in that document was described as polystyrene or polystyrene-water composite.

The implementation of this protocol requires both a PMMA and a polystyrene phantom. The protocol does not rule out using a water phantom also. However, if a water phantom is used, the protocol does not indicate how the ion chamber should be waterproofed nor does it warn of possible deformation of the thin entrance window due to hydrostatic pressure.

11.5.2 The NACP Low-Energy Electron Protocol

The NACP protocol of 1980 did not address the calibration of electron beams below 10 MeV incident electron energy. A supplement
to the protocol appeared in 1981 that provided a means to calibrate
electron beams below 15 Mev[8]. This protocol is based on a plane
parallel plate ion chamber[15] that met the design requirements of
the 1980 Nordic protocol. This chamber had an entrance window
of 0.5 mm graphite and a collector of graphite deposited onto a
thin layer of rexolite used as an insulator. This rexolite is embedded
in graphite that is connected to the guard.

   This protocol permits electrons below 15 MeV incident energy
to be calibrated in phantoms of polystyrene, PMMA, or A-150 plastic. Factors to convert from ionization in plastic to ionization in
water are given for each of these plastics. Measurement of the
depth ionization curve in plastic is also permitted. Factors to convert the depth ionization curve to range in water are enumerated
in the protocol.

   The protocol details a technique to determine N_D, the absorbed
dose calibration factor for the plane parallel plate chamber. This
is performed by comparing its response to that of a calibrated
cylindrical chamber in a PMMA phantom irradiated by an electron
beam of energy of at least 18 MeV at the phantom surface. An
alternative technique of determining N_D is also explained. With
this alternate method, the chamber is placed at d_{max} in a PMMA
phantom and irradiated by a cobalt-60 beam. If this technique is
used a factor k_{pp} must be known. This factor accounts for the
cobalt-60 backscatter, the attenuation and scatter in the buildup
material and the lack of air equivalence of the ion chamber and
buildup material. This factor has been experimentally determined
for the parallel plate chamber described in this protocol but is
not known for one other parallel plate chambers.

   The absorbed dose to water at the reference point is

$$D_{water} = N_D \, M \, (s_{w,air})_u \qquad\qquad (11\text{--}17)$$

where
N_D = absorbed dose calibration factor
M = meter reading corrected for temperature,
pressure, polarity, and recombination effects
$(s_{w,air})_u$ = water to air mass stopping power ratio at user's
radiation quality

Values of $(s_{w,air})_u$ are tabulated in the protocol as a function of energy and depth of calibration.

11.5.3 AAPM Recommendations for the Calibration of Low Energy Electrons

The AAPM has not formulated specific protocols for the calibration of low-energy electrons, and furthermore no strong recommendations are given in the 1983 protocol. The recommendations presented are ambiguous. The protocol states that the uncertainty in the measurement of any parameter is reduced as the correction factors become smaller. With this questionable rationale the protocol proceeds to recommend a plane parallel plate chamber over a cylindrical chamber when both are used in the same phantom. This statement is qualified by saying that a cylindrical chamber in a water phantom may be comparable to a plane parallel plate chamber in a plastic phantom when both are irradiated by low-energy electrons. The reason for this statement is that the cylindrical chamber will require a replacement correction and use of the plastic phantom requires a fluence correction. The reader is cautioned to wisely choose the phantom and ion chamber for low-energy electron dosimetry. The reader is further advised that a water phantom and a plane parallel plate chamber with minimum amount of plastic construction to minimize any dosimetric mismatch are an optimal choice because neither fluence nor replacement corrections are required. However, as in the HPA low-energy electron protocol, no advice is given on waterproofing the chamber or warning on the possible deformation of the entrance window due to hydrostatic pressure. The last recommendation of the protocol is to avoid cylindrical chambers in plastic phantoms for electron beam energies below 10 MeV.

A further warning should be given on the use of plane parallel plate chambers for low energy electron beams. Williams and Jordan[16] have reported an extra-cameral volume that developed in the HPA designed low energy-electron chamber.[14] This extra-cameral volume occurred in the plastic support of the chamber at a depth beyond the range of 5 MeV electrons. This volume will not change the chamber's response to low-energy electrons, however its response to cobalt-60 gamma rays will be modified. Therefore calibration of a chamber with this defect in a cobalt-60 beam will lead to an incorrect calibration factor and possible overdosages of low-energy electrons.

11.6 CENTRAL AXIS PERCENT DEPTH DOSE

The electron central axis percent depth dose is not identical to the central axis percent ionization because the restricted stopping power ratio $\dfrac{\bar{L}}{\rho}\Big)^{med}_{air}$ depends on the electron energy, which depends on the depth of measurement. The 1983 AAPM protocol does not discuss techniques for measuring electron central axis percent depth dose.

The NACP protocol of 1980 suggests ion chambers, semiconductor detectors, liquid-ionization chambers, and ferrous sulfate dosimeters for the measurement of electron percent depth dose. For ion chamber measurements it recommends shifting the effective point of measurement by one-half the inside radius toward the source and multiplying the measured ionization by the stopping power ratios, $(s_{w,air})_u$, furnished in the protocol. The stopping power used should be appropriate for the electron energy at the point of measurement. This energy is found by using Equation 11–9.

The HPA protocol of 1971 incorporates the change in chamber response relative to its response at d_{max} into a graph. This graph contains curves for the ratio of chamber response per rad at the calibration point to the chamber response at depth for incident electron energies of 5, 10, 20, and 35 MeV as a function of depth.

Prior to implementation of the 1983 AAPM protocol, Almond[17] described a method of measurement of the central axis percent depth dose using a thimble ion chamber. This technique involved several steps summarized below:

1. measure depth ionization curve

2. shift effective point of measurement forward of central axis of ion chamber 3/4 the inside radius

3. correct for beam divergence with Equation 11–10

4. find the practical range

5. determine the energy at the surface of the phantom with the Markus equation

$$E_o = \frac{R_p + 0.376}{0.521} \qquad (11\text{–}18)$$

6. find the energy at each depth z with the equation 11–9
7. calculate the perturbation factor at each depth

$$p_{w,g} = \frac{1}{1 + \dfrac{Jgp}{Jg}} \tag{11–19}$$

where $\dfrac{Jgp}{Jg} = \dfrac{2}{5} \dfrac{br^{1/2}}{\pi}$ (11–20)

$$b = \frac{1.096(E_z + 0.511)}{E_z \, (E_z + 1.022)} \text{ for water} \tag{11–21}$$

$r =$ inner radius of ion chamber in centimeters

8. calculate C_E for each depth with Equation 11–3
9. multiply the ionization at each depth corrected for the $3/4 \, r$ shift but not corrected for beam divergence by C_E and $p_{w,g}$
10. normalize each value to the maximum value

This method remains viable except C_E and $p_{w,g}$ are no longer meaningful quantities in the 1983 AAPM protocol. These quantities have been replaced by the factors contained in N_{gas} and $\left(\dfrac{\bar{L}}{\rho}\right)^{med}_{air}$ and by P_{repl}. Since N_{gas} is a constant and percent depth dose values are relative numbers the ionization at each depth multiplied by $\left(\dfrac{\bar{L}}{\rho}\right)^{med}_{air}$ will account for the energy dependence previously accounted for by C_E, but P_{repl} is only valid at d_{max}. One can then adopt one of three stratagems. The first of these is to note that $p_{w,g}$ and P_{repl} both change slowly with energy, therefore ignoring them will shift the percent depth dose curve less than 1 mm. Second, the ratio of $p_{w,g}$ to P_{repl} changes less than 1% over a wide range of energies and chamber sizes, therefore for the percent depth dose curve one could use $p_{w,g}$. Finally, one could assume P_{repl} is valid at other depths and use P_{repl} for each depth. Since all data are normalized in Step 10, any of these alternatives should yield the same percent depth dose curve to within the precision of measurement.

One final caution should be mentioned about measuring percent depth dose values in plastic. The protocol warns against using the scaling factors given in Equation 11–5 for any depth except the HVD. Also the fluence corrections, $\phi)_{air}^{med}$, are only valid at d_{max}. Because of two restrictions, one is limited to measuring central axis percent depth dose in water.

Notes

1. Hospital Physicists' Association, *A Practical Guide to Electron Dosimetry* (5–35 MeV), *HPA Report Series No 4*, (London: Hospital Physicists' Association, 1971).

2. American Association of Physicists in Medicine, Sub-committee on Radiation Dosimetry, "Protocol for the Dosimetry of High Energy Electrons," *Phys. Med. Biol.*, 11(1966), pp. 505–20.

3. Nordic Association of Clinical Physics, "Procedures in Radiation Therapy Dosimetry with 5 to 50 MeV Electrons and Roentgen and Gamma Rays with Maximum Photon Energies Between 1 and 50 MeV," *Acta Radiol. Ther. Phys. Biol.*, 11(1972), pp. 603–24.

4. *Radiation Dosimetry: Electron Beams with Energies Between 1 and 50 MeV. ICRU Report No. 35*, (Washington, D. C.: International Commission on Radiation Units and Measurements, 1984).

5. Nordic Association of Clinical Physics, "Procedures in External Radiation Therapy Dosimetry with Electron and Photon Beams with Maximum Energies Between 1 and 50 MeV," *Acta Radiol. Oncol.*, 19(1980), pp. 55–79.

6. American Association of Physicists in Medicine, Task Group 21, "A Protocol for the Determination of Absorbed Dose from High-Energy Photon and Electron Beams," *Med. Phys.*, 10(1983), pp. 741–71.

7. Hospital Physicists' Association, *A Practical Guide to Electron Dosimetry Below 5 MeV for Radiotherapy Purposes, HPA Report Series No. 13*, (London: Hospital Physicists' Association, 1975).

8. Nordic Association of Clinical Physics, "Electron Beams with Mean Energies at the Phantom Surface Below 15 MeV," *Acta Radiol. Oncol.*, 20(1981), pp. 401–15.

9. Dietrich Harder, "Einfluss der Vielfachstreuung von Elektronen auf die Ionisation in gasgefüllten Hohlräumen," *Biophysik*, 5(1968), pp. 157–64.

10. H. Svensson and A. Brahme, "Ferrous Sulphate Dosimetry for Electrons. A Re-evaluation," *Acta Radiol. Oncol.*, 18(1979), pp. 326–36.

11. K-A. Johansson, L. O. Mattsson, L. Lindborg, and H. Svensson, "Absorbed-Dose Determination with Ionization Chambers in Electron

and Photon Beams Having Energies Between 1 and 50 MeV," *National and International Standardization of Radiation Dosimetry, Volume II*, IAEA-SM-222/35, (Vienna, International Atomic Energy Agency, 1978), pp. 243–70.

12. R. Loevinger, C. J. Karzmark, and M. Weissbluth, "Radiation Therapy with High-Energy Electrons. Part I. Physical Considerations, 10 to 60 MeV," *Radiol.*, 77(1961), pp. 906–27.

13. K. R. Hogstrom and P. R. Almond, "The Effect of Electron Multiple Scattering on Dose Measured in Non-Water Phantoms," *Med. Phys.*, 9(1982), p. 607.

14. W. T. Morris and B. Owen, "An Ionization Chamber for Therapy-level Dosimetry of Electron Beams," *Phys. Med. Biol.*, 20(1975), pp. 718–27.

15. L. O. Mattsson, K-A. Johansson, and H. Svensson, "Calibration and Use of Plane-Parallel Ionization Chambers for the Determination of Absorbed Dose in Electron Beams," *Acta Radiol. Oncol.*, 20(1981), pp. 385–99.

16. P. C. Williams and T. J. Jordan, "Extra-Cameral Volume Effects in Ionization Chambers for Electron Beam Dosimetry," *Phys. Med. Biol.*, 29(1984), pp. 277–79.

17. Peter R. Almond, "Radiation Physics of Electron Beams," in *Clinical Applications of the Electron Beam*, ed. Norah du V. Tapley, (New York, N. Y.: John Wiley and Sons, 1976), pp. 7–80.

TWELVE | CALIBRATION OF MEGAVOLTAGE NEUTRON BEAMS

12.1 INTRODUCTION

The American Association of Physicists in Medicine (AAPM),[1] International Commission of Radiation Units and Measurements (ICRU),[2] and European Clinical Neutron Dosimetry Group (EC-NEU),[3] have each published protocols addressing the problems of neutron dosimetry. These protocols all use similar philosophy and techniques. All of these documents recommend ionometric methods for calibration.

The dose is calculated from ionization measurements explicitly from first principles with the Bragg–Gray equation. This method is similar to the AAPM megavoltage photon and electron protocol and contrasts with the HPA megavoltage photon protocol, which uses the dose conversion factor C_λ, which itself is calculated from Bragg–Gray theory.

12.2 APPLICATION OF THE BRAGG-GRAY EQUATION TO NEUTRON DOSIMETRY

Bragg-Gray theory originally developed for photon dosimetry[4,5] was extended to neutron dosimetry[6] with the same assumptions as used for photons. These assumptions were that the number and energy distribution of the secondary charged particles in the gas is the same as in the walls of the chamber. This is true if either the atomic composition of the gas is the same as the walls[7] or the cavity is small enough not to perturb the charged particle flux; that is, all charged particles cross the cavity without significant loss of energy.

For X-ray and gamma ray dosimetry, it is generally possible to fulfill the second condition by using a small air-filled cavity, however, for neutron dosimetry this is not true. A significant portion of the charged particle flux generated in the walls by the neutrons will be heavy ions with extremely short ranges. The charged particle flux may be divided into four categories,[8] "crossers," "starters," "stoppers," and "insiders." The crossers are those that are generated in the walls and cross the cavity; the starters start in the cavity and stop in the walls; the stoppers start in the wall and stop in the cavity; and the insiders start and stop in the cavity. For an inhomogeneous chamber-gas system, Bragg–Gray theory is only applicable to the crossers. The percentage of ionization due to starters, stoppers, and insiders will depend on size of the gas cavity. The validity of using Bragg–Gray theory for inhomogeneous chamber-gas system thus depends on cavity size. Bischel and Rubach[9,10,11] have investigated this effect and have presented values for kerma, stopping power ratios and W-values as a function of cavity size. With this introduction to the caveats involved, let's proceed assuming Bragg–Gray theory is applicable.

The general relationship between dose and ionization is

$$D_{wall} = \frac{100\, Q\, \dfrac{W}{e}\, S_{gas}^{wall}}{M} \qquad (12\text{--}1)$$

where D_{wall} = dose to the wall of the ion chamber in cGy
    Q = charged collected in C

$\dfrac{W}{e}$ = average energy required to create an ion pair divided by the electron charge in $\dfrac{J}{C}$

S_{gas}^{wall} = mass stopping power ratio between the wall of
the ion chamber and gas in the cavity

M = mass of the gas in the cavity in kg

The determination of dose requires a knowledge of the mass of the gas in the cavity. One method to determine this would be with shop drawings. It may be difficult, however, to determine the sensitive volume accurately enough with shop drawings. A second technique that is recommended in the neutron protocols is to expose the chamber in a known gamma field. Equation 12–1 may be inverted to determine the mass of the gas.

$$M = \frac{100\, Q_c \left(\dfrac{W}{e}\right)_c (S_{gas}^{wall})_c}{D_{wall,c}} \qquad (12\text{--}2)$$

where all quantities are the same as before and the subscript c represents the calibration gamma field

Also

$$D_{wall,c} = D_{muscle,c} \left(\frac{\mu_{en}}{\rho}\right)_{muscle,c}^{wall} \qquad (12\text{--}3)$$

where $\left(\dfrac{\mu_{en}}{\rho}\right)_{muscle,c}^{wall}$ = ratio of mass energy absorption coefficients between the wall of the ion chamber and muscle at the calibration gamma energy

If a ^{60}Cobalt teletherapy unit with a known output is used to determine the mass of the gas

$$M = \frac{100\, Q_c \left(\dfrac{W}{e}\right)_c (S_{gas}^{wall})_c \, C_{tp}}{X_c f_c A_{eq,c} \left(\dfrac{\mu_{en}}{\rho}\right)_{muscle,c}^{wall}} \qquad (12\text{--}4)$$

with C_{tp} = factor that corrects for temperature-pressure differences from standard conditions

X_c = exposure in Roentgen

$$f_c = f\text{-factor for muscle at cobalt-60 energy}$$
$$A_{eq,c} = \text{attenuation and scattering correction}$$
$$\text{factor for cobalt-60}$$

$$\left(\frac{\mu_{en}}{\rho}\right)^{\text{wall}}_{\text{muscle},c} = \text{mass energy absorption coefficient ratio}$$
$$\text{of wall to muscle for cobalt-60}$$

We may combine Equations 12–1 and 12–4 to yield the dose to muscle from a neutron irradiation.

$$D_{\text{muscle},n} = \frac{100\, Q_n \left(\dfrac{W}{e}\right)_n (S^{\text{muscle}}_{\text{gas}})_n\, (K^{\text{muscle}}_{\text{wall}})_n\, C_{tp,n} X_c f_c A_{eq,c} \left(\dfrac{\mu_{en}}{\rho}\right)^{\text{wall}}_{\text{muscle},c}}{100\, Q_c \left(\dfrac{W}{e}\right)_c (S^{\text{wall}}_{\text{gas}})_c\, C_{tp,c}} \qquad (12\text{–}5)$$

where $(K^{\text{muscle}}_{\text{wall}})_n$ = kerma ratio for neutrons for muscle to wall

As discussed in Chapters 10 and 11 and in Section 12–7, an ion chamber introduced into a phantom displaces phantom material and changes the radiation field. To correct for this perturbation, it is necessary to include a displacement factor, d_n. In this case, the equation relating ionization to dose is

$$D_{muscle,n} = \frac{\left(\dfrac{W}{e}\right)_n (S^{\text{wall}}_{\text{gas}})_n\, (K^{\text{muscle}}_{\text{wall}})_n\, C_{tp,n}\, Q_n d_n X_c f_c A_{eq,c}}{\left(\dfrac{W}{e}\right)_c (S^{\text{wall}}_{\text{gas}})_c \left(\dfrac{\mu_{en}}{\rho}\right)^{\text{muscle},c}_{\text{wall}} C_{tp,c}\, Q_c} \qquad (12\text{–}6)$$

where d_n = displacement factor

12.3 DETERMINATION OF PARAMETERS IN BRAGG–GRAY EQUATION

In Equation 12–6, the photon parameters are for ^{60}Co. To calculate the neutron parameters, a knowledge of the neutron spectrum is required. There are several methods to measure the neutron spectrum. These methods include time-of-flight, foil activation analysis, and proton recoil counters. Because of scattering and absorption processes, the neutron spectrum will change with depth in the phantom, which implies the parameters may change.

In addition to the neutron spectrum, the equilibrium-charged particle spectrum generated in the chamber walls is necessary. Limited information exists in this area although some computer generated information is available.[11,12,13] As the neturon energy increases, the percentage of heavy ions increases with the concommitant problems with Bragg–Gray theory discussed earlier.

Although the problem is difficult, it is not intractable and several investigators have proposed sets of parameters to be used for neutron dosimetry. The dose determined with ionometric techniques using these parameter sets has been compared to the dose measured with calorimetry and the two methods generally agree within 2%. This agreement gives validity to the parameters chosen.

12.4 ION CHAMBERS

Differing philosophies on ion chambers emerged between the U. S. and European physics groups initially. All the U. S. centers chose a spherical 1 cc ion chamber[14] constructed with walls of A-150 tissue equivalent plastic[15] for calibrations and a cylindrical 0.1 cc chamber[14] of A-150 plastic for relative dose measurements. In Europe each institute used an ion chamber of its own design. Because each chamber had its own characteristics, dosimetry intercomparisons revealed variations that were attributed to ion chamber design differences.[16] Subsequently the European centers have adopted an ion chamber[17] of common design and manufacture.

The properties of the A-150 plastic used in the construction of these ion chambers have been discussed in detail.[18,19] Its elemental composition is not identical to ICRU muscle[20] because carbon has been substituted for oxygen to make it electrically conducting. For photons it is relatively tissue equivalent down to an energy of about 100 keV; however, this is not true for neutrons. This is the reason for the kerma factor $(K_{\text{wall}}^{\text{muscle}})_n$ in Equation 12–6, which corrects from dose in plastic to dose in tissue. For most neutron therapy centers this correction is on the order of 5%.

12.5 TISSUE EQUIVALENT GAS VS. AIR IN THE CAVITY

The obvious choice of gas to use in the ion chamber is one that makes the chamber-gas system homogeneous so Bragg–Gray theory is applicable. A methane-based gas[21] with an atomic composition the same as tissue has been chosen. This gas, however, does not have the same formulation as A-150 so the stopping power ratio is not unity. After these protocols were written, a gas[22] with the same composition as A-150 was developed. However, this gas has not found wide acceptance.

The use of TE gas requires it to flow through the ion chambers. When this is done care must be taken that the chamber response is independent of the flow rate. One must evaluate the response versus flow rate and operate in a region where this response does not change. Each bottle of TE gas should be analyzed for impurities

TABLE 12–1. Neutron Parameters used in Equation 12–6 for Calculations of Neutron Dose at Neutron Therapy Centers in the United States

Reaction producing neutron beam (institution)	Chamber/gas combination	$\left(\dfrac{W}{e}\right)_n$	$(S_{gas}^{wall})_n$
1) 8.3 MeV deuterons on deuterium (University of Chicago) and	TE/Air	35.8	1.188
2) 21 MeV deuterons on beryllium target (16 MeV thick) (University of Washington)	TE/TE C/CO_2 Mg/Ar	30.5 34.9 26.4	1.013
3) 35 MeV deuterons on beryllium target (Naval Research Laboratory)	TE/Air TE/TE	34.98 30.5	1.174 0.995
4) 25 MeV deuterons on beryllium target (Cleveland Clinic)	TE/Air TE/TE	35.8 30.5	1.164 1.012
5) 50 MeV deuterons on beryllium target (M. D. Anderson Hospital)	TE/Air	35.8	1.157
6) 66 MeV protons on beryllium target (49 MeV thick) (Fermilab)	TE/TE	30.5	1.020
7) 42 MeV protons on beryllium target (16 MeV thick) (M. D. Anderson Hospital)			
8) 43 MeV protons on beryllium target (21 MeV thick) (Cleveland Clinic)			
9) 50 MeV protons on beryllium target (20 MeV thick) (University of Washington)			
10) Deuterons on tritium target (Fox Chase Cancer Center)	TE/TE	31.0	1.0

Source: "Protocol for Neutron Beam Dosimetry," *AAPM Report No. 7*, by Task Group 18. Used with permission.

as these may affect the results. Because of this, many U. S. facilities originally calibrated with air as the cavity gas. This meant one did not have a homogeneous chamber-gas system, but worries about flow rate and impurities were alleviated. More recently U. S. facilities have agreed to perform primary calibrations with TE gas; however, it is permissible to use either air or TE gas for relative dose measurements. A table of parameters that are used at neutron therapy centers currently or have been used in the past are given in Tables 12–1, 12–2, and 12–3.

TABLE 12–2. Photon parameters used in Equation 12–6 for Calculation of Neutron Dose at Neutron Therapy Centers in the United States

Institution	Chamber/gas combination	$\left(\dfrac{W}{e}\right)_c$	$(S_{\text{gas}}^{\text{wall}})_c$
M. D. Anderson Hospital	TE/Air	33.7	1.142
Fermilab	TE/TE	29.2	1.001
Cleveland Clinic	C/CO_2	32.9	1.009
	Mg/Ar	26.2	1.14
Naval Research Laboratory	TE/Air	33.7	1.140
	TE/TE	29.2	0.995
	C/CO_2	32.9	—
	Mg/Ar	26.2	—
University of Washington	TE/Air	33.7	1.133
University of Chicago	TE/TE	29.2	0.994
	C/CO_2	32.9	—
	Mg/Ar	26.2	—

Source: "Protocol for Neutron Beam Dosimetry," *AAPM Report No. 7*, by Task Group 18. Used with permission.

TABLE 12–3. Kerma Correction Factor Used in Equation 12–6 by Neutron Therapy Centers in the United States

Reaction indicated in Table 12–1	$K_{\text{wall}}^{\text{muscle}}$
1	0.962
2	0.954
3 and 4	0.955
5, 6, 7, 8, 9	0.952
10	0.987

Source: "Protocol for Neutron Beam Dosimetry," *AAPM Report No. 7*, by Task Group 18. Used with permission.

12.6 PHANTOM

These protocols recommend a cubic phantom 30 cm on a side with walls made of polymethylmethacrylate 6 mm thick but with the entrance window no more than 3 mm thick. A general rule to follow is to use a phantom that has at least a 5 cm margin of scattering material outside the beam. The effects of phantom size on central axis depth dose measurements have been discussed by Wootton, et al.[23] and Awschalom, et al.[24]

Originally, the U. S. and European centers disagreed on the choice of liquid to be used in the phantom. Water is used by the Europeans. In the U. S. a concern was expressed that water and ICRU muscle do not have the same elemental composition or density. With photons and electrons this is not a problem because the interactions are occurring with the atomic electrons; however, with neutrons the interactions occur with the nuclei. The U. S. facilities used either Frigerio tissue equivalent liquid[25] or a similar formulation by Goodman.[26] The Goodman liquid reproduces the elemental abundances of C, H, O, and N but not the trace elements that are duplicated by the Frigerio liquid. These trace elements have not been shown to be of dosimetric importance. However, the tissue equivalent liquid was formulated with a density of 1.07 g/cc, which is close to the density of fat-free muscle (1.066 g/cc), whereas the density of ICRU muscle is 1.04 g/cc. Awschalom, et al.[27] have shown that measurements made in water or tissue equivalent liquid of 1.04 g/cc would yield nearly identical values because water has a shorter neutron mean free path and a lower density. In light of this information the U. S. facilities have changed from tissue equivalent liquid to water.

12.7 DISPLACEMENT FACTOR

As discussed in the chapters on megavoltage photon and electron dosimetry, the displacement of liquid in the phantom by the ion chamber changes the attenuation and scattering of the radiation field. In the U. S., a displacement factor is used to correct this effect. Shapiro[28] and Awschalom[29] have studied the displacement factor for the ion chambers used in the U. S. Based on these data, Task Group 18 of the AAPM decided on values of 0.98 of the 1 cc spherical chamber and 0.995 for the 0.1 cc cylindrical chamber. A factor of 0.985 was adopted for the Exradin 0.5 cc T-2 chamber.[30]

In Europe, since ion chambers of different design were in use, each chamber had its own unique displacement factor. Zoetelief, et al[31,32] have recommended that the value of the displacement factor is

$$d = 1 - 2.5 \times 10^{-3} r \tag{12-7}$$

where $\quad d =$ displacement factor
$\quad\quad\quad r =$ inside radius in mm

From the magnitude of these factors, one sees the need to use ion chambers as small as practicable.

12.8 GEOMETRY OF CALIBRATION

Beam calibration should be performed with the surface of the phantom at the normal SSD. Calibration measurements should not be made at d_{max} but in the exponential decay portion of the depth dose curve. As most neutron beams used for therapy have a penetration similar to X-rays in the 2 to 10 MV range, a calibration depth of 5 cm is recommended to conform with the photon practice. However, it should be verified this depth lies on the exponential decay portion of the depth dose curve.

12.9 GAMMA CONTAMINATION

Tables 12-1 and 12-2 include stopping power ratios and W/e values of Mg-Ar and C-CO_2 chamber-gas combinations. These systems are used to measure the amount of gamma contamination of the neutron field. Since neutrons and gammas have very different biological effects, the percentage of the dose due to photons must be determined.

The gamma contamination may be ascertained with a proportional counter by separating events caused by protons and heavy ions from those resulting from electrons.[33,34,35,36,37] An alternate method is a two-chamber technique.[38] With the second method, one chamber is equally sensitive to neutrons and photons and the other chamber is relatively insensitive to neutrons. The A-150 chamber with TE gas filling is the one sensitive to both components and a non-hydrogenous system such as Mg-Ar or C-CO_2 is the one less sensitive to neutrons. However, the C-CO_2 combination is not recommended by the protocols because the porosity of the C allows diffusion of air through the walls[39,40,41] into the chamber.

If one uses the two-chamber technique, two equations may be generated

$$R_t = k_t D_n + h_t D_g \tag{12--8}$$

$$R_u = k_u D_n + h_u D_g \tag{12--9}$$

where D_n and D_g are the dose due to neutron and the dose due to gamma respectively

The subscripts t and u refer to the neutron sensitive and neutron insensitive chamber respectively

The ks are the sensitivities to neutrons divided by the sensitivity to photons in the photon calibration beam of each chamber

The hs are the sensitivities of each chamber to photons in the neutron beam divided by the sensitivities to the photons in the photon calibration beam. The values of the hs are usually taken to be in unity

The Rs are the chamber responses in the mixed neutron-photon beam divided by their sensitivities in the photon calibration beam

These equations may be solved for D_n and D_g to yield

$$D_n = \frac{h_u R_t - h_t R_u}{h_u k_t - h_t k_u} \tag{12--10}$$

$$D_g = \frac{k_t R_u - k_u R_t}{h_u k_t - h_t k_u} \tag{12--11}$$

The relative neutron sensitivity of the neutron sensitive chamber can be calculated with

$$k_t = \frac{\left(\dfrac{W}{e}\right)_c (S_{\text{gas}}^{\text{wall}})_c \left(\dfrac{\mu_{en}}{\rho}\right)_{\text{wall},c}^{\text{muscle}}}{\left(\dfrac{W}{e}\right)_n (S_{\text{gas}}^{\text{wall}})_n (K_{\text{wall}}^{\text{muscle}})_n} \tag{12--12}$$

The relative neutron sensitivity of the neutron insensitive dosimeter, k_u, must be determined for each neutron beam studied. ICRU[2] gives the value of k_u for a number of devices at a number of energies. Additional measurements have been made by Waterman, et al.[42] and Mijnheer, et al.[43,44] and Kuchnir, et al.[45] Attix, et al.[38] and Ito[46] have reported on measurement techniques for k_u and Waterman, et al.[47] have given precautions necessary when using the lead filtration method of Attix, et al.[38] Stinchcomb, et al.[36] have reported on difficulties with the technique of Ito.[46]

12.10 UNIFICATION OF THE U. S. AND EUROPEAN PROTOCOLS

Recently, Task Group 18 and ECNEU have drafted a unified neutron dosimetry protocol.[30] As a result of these meetings, slightly different terminology and parameters have been suggested. The quantity A_{eq} is now referred to as A_{wall} and its value is taken as 0.983. The f-factor for tissue at the energy of cobalt-60 is 9.62×10^{-3} Gy/R.

Individual values are no longer quoted for the stopping power ratios and W-values but they have been combined in a factor

$$\frac{(S^{wall}_{gas})_n \left(\dfrac{W}{e}\right)_n}{(S^{wall}_{gas})_c \left(\dfrac{W}{e}\right)_c}$$

which for neutrons above 15 MeV has a value of 1.06 for a TE chamber-TE gas system. A value of 0.95 has been adopted for $(K^{muscle}_{wall})_n$ for all high energy neutron beams generated by protons on beryllium targets. The mass energy absorption coefficient $\left(\dfrac{\mu_{en}}{\rho}\right)^{muscle, c}_{wall}$ is taken to be 1.001 for cobalt-60.

With these values, Equation 12–6 simplifies for high energy neutron beams to

$$D_{muscle, n} = 1.06 \left(\frac{.95}{1.001}\right) (9.62 \times 10^{-3}) (0.983) \frac{X_c Q_n d_n}{Q_c}$$

$$D_{muscle, n} = 9.51 \times 10^{-3} \frac{X_c Q_n d_n}{Q_c}$$

with $D_{muscle, n}$ expressed in Gy, Q_n, and Q_c in C, and X_c in R

12.11 EFFECT OF GAMMA CONTAMINATION ON DOSE MEASUREMENTS

In Equation 12–6 it was implicitly assumed all the ionization was created by neutrons and the conversion to dose was performed using neutron parameters. However, the ionization collected is actually the sum of a component due to neutrons and one resulting from photons. This may be written as

$$Q_t = Q_n + Q_g \tag{12–13}$$

then the total dose in cGy is

$$D_{\text{muscle}, t} = 100 \frac{\left[Q_n \left(\dfrac{W}{e} \right)_n (S_{\text{gas}}^{\text{wall}})_n (K_{\text{wall}}^{\text{muscle}})_n + Q_g \left(\dfrac{W}{e} \right)_g (S_{\text{gas}}^{\text{wall}})_g \left(\dfrac{\mu_{en}}{\rho} \right)_{\text{wall}, g}^{\text{muscle}} \right.}{M} \tag{12–14}$$

or

$$D_{\text{muscle}, t} = 100 \frac{(K_{\text{wall}}^{\text{muscle}})_n (S_{\text{gas}}^{\text{wall}})_n \left(\dfrac{W}{e} \right)_n Q_t \left\{ 1 - \left(1 - \dfrac{k_t}{h_t} \right) \dfrac{Q_g}{Q_t} \right\} C_{tp} d_n}{M} \tag{12–15}$$

$$\frac{Q_g}{Q_t} = \text{percentage of photon contamination, \% PC}$$

Examining the factor in the bracket in Equation 12–15 we have

$$1 - \left(1 - \frac{k_t}{h_t} \right) (\% \text{ PC})$$

Typical values of k_t, h_t, and % PC are

$$k_t = 0.994$$

$$h_t = 1.000$$

$$\% \text{ PC} = 0.20$$

If we substitute these values we have

$$1 - (1 - 0.994)(.2) = 0.999$$

The factor in the bracket in Equation 12–15 may be approximated as one yielding

$$D_{\text{muscle},t} = \frac{100\, Q_t \left(\dfrac{W}{e}\right)_n (S_{\text{gas}}^{\text{wall}})_n\, (K_{\text{wall}}^{\text{muscle}})_n\, C_{tp}d_n}{M} \qquad (12\text{–}16)$$

which reduces to Equation 12–6 when the right-hand side of equation 12–4 is substituted for M. Therefore, the assumption that all ionization is created by neutrons leads to a negligible error.

Notes

1. Task Group 18 of American Association of Physicists in Medicine, *Protocol for Neutron Beam Dosimetry*, *AAPM Report No. 7*, (New York: American Association of Physicists in Medicine, 1980).

2. *Neutron Dosimetry for Biology and Medicine*, *ICRU Report No. 26.*, (Washington, D. C.: International Commission on Radiation Units and Measurements, 1977).

3. J. J. Broerse, B. J. Mijnheer, and J. R. Williams, "European Protocol for Neutron Dosimetry for External Beam Therapy," *Brit. J. Radiol.*, 54(1981), pp. 882–98.

4. L. H. Gray, "The Absorption of Penetrating Radiation," *Proc. Roy. Soc.*, A122(1929), pp. 647–68.

5. L. H. Gray, "An Ionization Method for the Absolute Measurement of Gamma Ray Energy," *Proc. Roy. Soc.*, A156(1936), pp. 578–96.

6. L. H. Gray, "The Ionization Method of Measuring Neutron Energy," *Proc. Cambridge Phil. Soc.*, 40(1944), pp. 72–102.

7. U. Fano, "Note on the Bragg–Gray Cavity Principle for Measuring Energy Dissipation," *Radiat. Res.*, 1(1954), pp. 237–40.

8. Randall S. Caswell, "Deposition of Energy by Neutrons in Spherical Cavities," *Radiat. Res.*, 27(1966), pp. 92–107.

9. Antje Rubach and Hans Bichsel, "Neutron Dosimetry with Spherical Ionization Chambers I. Theory of the Dose Conversion Factors r and W_n," *Phys. Med. Biol.*, 27(1982), pp. 893–904.

10. Hans Bichsel and Antje Rubach, "Neutron Dosimetry with Spherical Ionization Chambers II. Basic Physical Data," *Phys. Med. Biol.*, 27(1982), pp. 1003–13.

11. Antje Rubach and Hans Bichsel, "Neutron Dosimetry with Spherical Ionization Chambers III. Calculated Results for Tissue-equivalent Chambers," *Phys. Med. Biol.*, 27(1982), pp. 1231–43.

12. Randall S. Caswell and J. Joseph Coyne, "Interaction of Neutrons and Secondary Charged Particles with Tissue: Secondary Particle Spectra," *Radiat. Res.*, 52(1972), pp. 448–70.

13. Alan H. Wells, "Calculation of Dosimetry Parameters for Fast Neutron Radiotherapy," Los Alamos Scientific Laboratory of the University of California, LA-7288-T, Thesis 1978.

14. M. Awschalom, "The USA Fast Neutron Beam Dosimetry Physics Group Experience with Ionization Chambers," *Ion Chambers for Neutron Dosimetry* J. J. Broerse, ed. (London: Harwood Academic Publishers Ltd., 1980), pp. 97–106.

15. Francis R. Shonka, John E. Rose, and G. Failla, "Conducting Plastic Equivalent to Tissue, Air, and Polystyrene," *Second United Nations Conference on Peaceful Uses of Atomic Energy*, Volume 21, (New York: United Nations, 1958), pp. 184–87.

16. J. R. Williams, J. J. Broerse, B. J. Mijnheer, C. J. Parnell, "Experience with Ionization Chambers by the European Clinical Neutron Dosimetry Group (ECNEU)," *Ion Chambers for Neutron Dosimetry*, J. J. Broerse, ed., (London: Harwood Academic Publishers Ltd., 1980), pp. 107–11.

17. H. Schraube, "Summary of the Concluding Discussions on Ion Chambers for Neutron Dosimetry," *Ion Chambers for Neutron Dosimetry*, J. J. Broerse, ed., (London: Harwood Academic Publishers Ltd., 1980), pp. 345–50.

18. Leon J. Goodman, "Density and Composition Uniformity of A-150 Tissue Equivalent Plastic," *Phys. Med. Biol.*, 23(1978), pp. 753–58.

19. James B. Smathers, Victor A. Otte, Alfred R. Smith, Peter R. Almond, Frank H. Attix, John J. Spokas, William M. Quam, and Leon J. Goodman, "Composition of A-150 Tissue-Equivalent Plastic," *Med. Phys.*, 4(1977), pp. 74–77.

20. Physical Aspects of Irradiation, ICRU Report No 10b, 1962, Published as *National Bureau of Standards Handbook 85*. (Washington, D. C., U.S. Government Printing Office, 1964).

21. Harald H. Rossi and G. Failla, "Tissue-Equivalent Ionization Chambers," *Nucleonics*, 14(1956), pp. 32–37.

22. M. Awschalom and F. H. Attix, "A-150 Plastic-Equivalent Gas," *Phys. Med. Biol.*, 25(1980), pp. 567–69.

23. P. Wootton, K. Weaver, and J. Eenmaa, "Treatment Planning for Neutron Radiation Therapy," *Int. J. Radiat. Oncol. Biol. Phys.*, 3(1977), pp. 177–83.

24. M. Awschalom, I. Rosenberg, and R. K. Ten Haken, "The Effect of Missing Backscatter on the Dose Distribution of a p(66)Be(49) Neutron Therapy Beam," *Med. Phys.*, 9(1982), pp. 559–62.

25. N. A. Frigerio, R. F. Coley, and M. J. Sampson, "Depth Dose Determinations I. Tissue-equivalent liquids for Standard Man and Muscle," *Phys. Med. Biol.*, 17(1972), pp. 792–802.

26. L. J. Goodman, "A Modified Tissue-Equivalent Liquid," *Health Physics*, 16(1969), p. 763.

27. M. Awschalom, I. Rosenberg, and R. K. Ten Haken, "Scaling Neutron Absorbed Dose Distributions from One Medium to Another," *Med. Phys.*, 10(1983), pp. 436–43.

28. P. Shapiro, F. H. Attix, L. S. August, R. B. Theus, and C. C. Rogers "Displacement Correction Factor for Fast-neutron Dosimetry in a Tissue-equivalent Phantom," *Med. Phys.*, 3(1976), pp. 87–90.

29. M. Awschalom, I. Rosenberg, and R. K. Ten Haken, "A New Look at Displacement Factor and Point of Measurement Corrections in Ionization Chamber Dosimetry," *Med. Phys.*, 10(1983), pp. 307–13.

30. B. J. Mijnheer, P. Wootton, J. R. Williams, J. Eenmaa, and C. J. Parnell, "Uniformity in Dosimetry Protocols for Therapeutic Applications of Fast Neutron Beams," to be published in *Medical Physics*.

31. J. Zoetelief, A. C. Engels, J. J. Broerse, and B. J. Mijnheer, "Effect of Finite Size of Ion Chambers Used for Neutron Dosimetry," *Phys. Med. Biol.*, 25(1980), pp. 1121–31.

32. J. Zoetelief, A. C. Engels, and J. J. Broerse, "Displacement Correction Factors for Spherical Ion Chambers in Phantoms Irradiated with Neutrons of Different Energies," *Phys. Med. Biol.*, 26(1981), pp. 513–14.

33. R. S. Caswell, "Neutron-insensitive Proportional Counter for Gamma-ray Dosimetry," *Rev. Scient. Instrum.*, 31(1960), pp. 869–71.

34. K. Weaver, H. Bichsel, J. Eenmaa, and P. Wootton, "Measurement of Photon Dose Fraction in a Neutron Radiotherapy Beam, *Med. Phys.*, 4(1977), pp. 379–86.

35. L. S. August, R. B. Theus, and P. Shapiro, "Gamma Measurements with a Non-hydrogenous Rossi Counter in a Mixed Field," *Sixth Symposium on Microdosimetry*, J. Booz and H. G. Ebert, eds., (London: Harwood Academic Publishers, 1978), pp. 441–49.

36. T. G. Stinchcomb, F. T. Kuchnir, and L. S. Skaggs, "Comparison of the Microdosimetric Event-size Method and the Twin-chamber Method of Separating Dose into Neutron and Gamma Components," *Phys. Med. Biol.*, 25(1980), pp. 51–64.

37. J. Fidorra and J. Booz, "Microdosimetric Investigations on Collimated Fast-neutron Beams for Radiation Therapy: I. Measurements of Microdosimetric Spectra and Particle Dose Fractions in a Water Phantom for Fast Neutrons from 14 MeV Deuterons on Beryllium," *Phys. Med. Biol.*, 26(1981), pp. 27–41.

38. F. H. Attix, R. B. Theus, and C. C. Rogers, "Measurements of Dose Components in an n-γ Field," *Proceedings of the Second Symposium on Neutron Dosimetry in Biology and Medicine*, G. Burger and H. G. Ebert, eds., (Luxembourg: Commission of the European Communities, 1975), p. 329.

39. F. H. Attix, D. W. Pearson, S. J. Goetsch, P. M. DeLuca, Jr., and R. P. Torti, *Wisconsin Medical Physics Report*, No. WMP-101, Section COO-1105–259., (Madison, Wisconsin, 1978).

40. E. Maier and G. Burger, "Experimental Correction Factors for Chamber Dosimetry," *Proceedings of the Third Symposium on Neutron Dosimetry in Biology and Medicine*, G. Burger and H. G. Ebert, eds., (Luxembourg: Commission of the European Communities, 1978), pp. 165–80.

41. D. W. Pearson, F. H. Attix, P. M. DeLuca, Jr., S. J. Goetsch, and R. P. Torti, "Ionization Error due to Porosity in Graphite Ionization Chambers," *Ion Chambers for Neutron Dosimetry*, J. J. Broerse, ed., (London: Harwood Academic Published, Ltd., 1980), pp. 325–26B.

42. F. M. Waterman, F. T. Kuchnir, L. S. Skaggs, R. T. Kouzes, and W. H. Moore, "Energy Dependence of the Neutron Sensitivity of C-CO_2, Mg-Ar, and TE-TE Ionization Chambers," *Phys. Med. Biol.*, 24(1979), pp. 721–33.

43. B. J. Mijnheer, P. A. Visser, V. E. Lewis, S. Guldbakke, H. Lesiecki, J. Zoetelief, and J. J. Broerse, "The Relative Neutron Sensitivity of Geiger-Müller Counters," *High LET Radiations in Clinical Radiotherapy*, Suppl. Eur. J. Cancer (Oxford, Pergamon Press, 1979), pp. 162–63.

44. B. J. Mijnheer, "The Relative Neutron Sensitivity, k_u, for Non-hydrogeneous Detectors," *Ion Chambers for Neutron Dosimetry*, J. J. Broerse, ed., (London: Harwood Academic Publishers Ltd., 1980), pp. 307–19.

45. F. T. Kuchnir, M. Awschalom, L. E. Grumboski, and M. N. Sabau, "Determination of the Sensitivity of a Mg-Ar Chamber to High Energy Neutrons by the Use of Two Independent Methods," *Ion Chambers for Neutron Dosimetry*, J. J. Broerse, ed., (London: Harwood Academic Publishers, Ltd., 1980), pp. 327–32.

46. A. Ito, "Neutron Sensitivity of C-CO_2 and Mg-Ar Ionization Chamber," *Proceedings of the Third Symposium on Neutron Dosimetry in Biology and Medicine*, G. Burger and H. G. Ebert, eds., (Luxembourg: Commission of the European Communities, 1978), pp. 605–18.

47. F. M. Waterman, F. T. Kuchnir, and L. S. Skaggs, "Comparison of Two Independent Methods for Determining the Neutron/Gamma Sensitivity of a Dosemeter," *Phys. Med. Biol.*, 22(1977), pp. 880–88.

THIRTEEN

RADIATION PROTECTION

13.1 WHAT'S WUT

The radiation therapy physicist may well be called upon at some point in his or her career to design a treatment room for a new therapy unit. To perform this task the physicist must know what's WUT.

The letters W, U, T are used in barrier design calculations to indicate workload, use factor, and occupancy factor respectively. The workload is the amount of exposure produced by the therapy unit in the course of a week's treatment. For X-ray equipment operated below 4 MV, workload is expressed in terms of milliampere-minutes. For gamma beam teletherapy units and X-ray units of 4 MV and above, workload is stated in units of Roentgen per week at 1 meter. The use factor is the percentage of the time the therapy unit is directed at the barrier under consideration. The occupancy factor is the percentage of time the area considered is occupied while the radiation beam is activated. These three factors can generally be determined at each institution on the basis of past experience. However, if this information is not readily obtainable, the National Council of Radiation Protection and Measurements (NCRP) provides values in Report 49.[1] These numbers are reproduced in Tables 13–1, 13–2, and 13–3.

13.2 BARRIER DESIGN

13.2.1 Permissible Radiation Levels

Once the physicist has determined what's WUT, he or she may begin the barrier calculations. The amount of radiation penetrating a barrier must be "as low as reasonably achievable" (ALARA). If the general public has access to the area—for instance a sidewalk outside a therapy facility—it is considered an "uncontrolled area" and the exposure levels must be limited to 10 mR or less per week. *2 mR/wk* Additionally, the exposure rate in an uncontrolled area may not exceed 2 mR in any one hour. If the area is not open to the public, but is occupied only by radiation workers, the exposure levels may be 100 mR per week. Areas with radiation levels this high are referred to as "controlled areas" because they are under the control of the Radiation Safety Officer. Many treatment rooms, however, are designed to limit the exposure levels in controlled

TABLE 13–1. Estimate of Typical Workloads from NCRP Report 49.
May Be Used for Planning in Absence of Other Data

Therapy	Patients/day	Weekly workload (W)
Superficial (up to 150 kV)	32	3,000 mA min
Orthovoltage (200 to 500 kV)	32	20,000 mA min
Megavoltage (0.5 MV to 10 MV)	50	100,000 R at a meter
Cesium		
50 cm SSD	16	8,000 R at a meter
50 cm SSD	32	15,000 R at a meter
60 cm SSD	32	24,000 R at a meter
Cobalt		
70 cm SSD	32	30,000 R at a meter
80 cm SSD	32	40,000 R at a meter
100 cm SSD	32	60,000 R at a meter

Source: "Structural Shielding Design and Evaluation for Medical Use of X-rays and Gamma Rays of Energies Up to 10 MeV," *NCRP Report 49*. Used with permission.

TABLE 13–2. Typical Use Factors from NCRP Report 49 to Be Used for Planning in Absence of Other Data

Floor	1
Walls	$\frac{1}{4}$
Ceilings	$\frac{1}{4}$

Source: "Structural Shielding Design and Evaluation for Medical Use of X-rays and Gamma Rays of Energies Up to 10 MeV," NCRP Report 49. Used with permission.

TABLE 13–3. Typical Occupancy Factors from NCRP Report 49 for Planning in Absence of Other Data

Full Occupancy ($T = 1$)

Work areas such as offices, laboratories, shops, wards, nurses' stations; living quarters; children's play areas; and occupied space in nearby buildings

Partial Occupancy ($T = \frac{1}{4}$)

Corridors, rest rooms, elevators using operators, unattended parking lots

Occasional Occupancy ($T = \frac{1}{16}$)

Waiting rooms, toilets, stairways, unattended elevators, janitors' closets, outside areas used only for pedestrians or vehicular traffic

Source: "Structural Shielding Design and Evaluation for Medical Use of X-rays and Gamma Rays of Energies Up to 10 MeV," NCRP Report 49. Used with permission.

areas to 10 mR per week on the grounds that the cost of an additional tenth value layer (TVL) of shielding is not great during the construction phase and may pay future dividends. Some advantages accrued from this philosophy are that greater flexibility may be acheived if the facility is expanded in the future or if the currently mandated exposure levels for controlled areas are reduced to correspond to uncontrolled areas.

13.2.2 Shielding Materials

Frequently, radiation therapy departments are placed below ground level to permit the use of earth as a shielding material. Other factors, such as proximity of other services, easy patient access, excavation costs, or watertight sealing, may preclude this possibility though. For therapy facilities located on ground level, it may be necessary to shield the outside walls and ceiling if the nearby areas may be occupied. The location of therapy departments located on the second floor or higher might require that floors, as well as ceilings and walls, be shielded, which may also increase the cost of the needed structural support.

When earth cannot be used for shielding, several other materials are available. Steel, lead, or heavy concrete may be appropriate when space is a problem, otherwise normal concrete is usually the second best choice after earth.

13.2.3 Types of Barriers

Three types of radiation must be considered in barrier design; primary, leakage, and scatter. The primary radiation is the radiation of the main beam. This radiation will require the greatest shielding thickness, and barriers struck by this radiation are designated "primary barriers." The leakage radiation is the radiation that penetrates the shielding in the head of the treatment unit around the gamma ray source or X-ray target when the beam is "on." The scatter radiation is the radiation that has been scattered at least once by either the patient or another barrier. Barriers against leakage and scatter radiation are referred to as "secondary barriers."

Primary barriers

Now that we understand not only WUT, but also controlled and uncontrolled areas and primary and secondary barriers, let's calculate the thickness required for a primary barrier.

Example

Calculate the thickness of concrete required for a primary barrier wall against 6 MV X-rays. The distance from the source to the area of interest is 5 meters, the workload is 120,000 Roentgen per week at a meter (Rwm), and the adjacent area is an uncontrolled corridor.

If there were no barrier, the anticipated exposure of a nonoccupationally exposed individual could be calculated by multiplying the amount of radiation produced by the machine at one meter (workload) by the percentage of time the machine is aimed at the point under consideration (use factor), and by the percentage of time the individual might be expected to be in the area (occupancy factor), and then dividing this product by the square of the distance to the point of interest (inverse square law). Mathematically this may be written as

$$\dot{X} = WUT/(d_{pri}^2)$$ (13–1)

where W = workload
U = use factor
T = occupancy factor
d_{pri} = distance in meters to point of interest

W and d_{pri} were given to be 120,000 Rwm and 5 m respectively. NCRP Report 49 suggests for both U and T a value of 1/4 for these conditions. Then

$$\dot{X} = \frac{120,000 \times \frac{1}{4} \times \frac{1}{4}}{25}$$

$$\dot{X} = 300 \text{ Roentgen per week}$$

The permissible exposure rate, P, is 10 mR per week. This implies a barrier transmission factor for the useful X-ray beam, B_{ux}, of

$$B_{ux} = \frac{P}{\dot{X}}$$

$$B_{ux} = \frac{0.01}{300}$$

$$B_{ux} = 3.3 \times 10^{-5}$$

This is the maximum fraction of the useful beam that the barrier may transmit. The barrier thickness of concrete corresponding to B_{ux} of 3.3×10^{-5} is equal to 155 cm from Figure 13–1.

If the therapy unit has a beamstopper intercepting the primary beam an additional factor may be included in Equation 13–1. This factor is T_B, the transmission through the beamstopper. Then Equation 13–1 becomes

$$\dot{X} = \frac{WUTT_B}{d_{pri}^2}$$

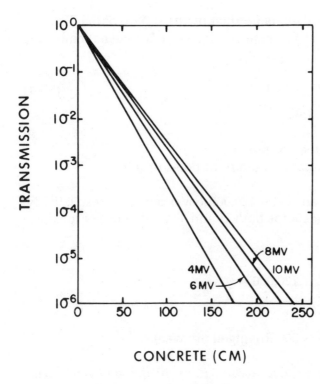

Figure 13–1 Transmission through concrete of 4 to 10 MV X-rays. From "Structural Shielding Design and Evaluation for Medical Use of X-rays and Gamma Rays of Energies up to 10 MeV," *NCRP Report 49*. Used with permission.

However, one must be careful with this approach because beamstopper design requirements vary with each manufacturer. Some beamstoppers may reduce the primary beam by a factor of 1000, while others may reduce it by a factor of only 100. The angles of scattered radiation that are intercepted by the beamstopper also depend on the manufacturer.

Secondary barriers—leakage

Let's proceed to a calculation of a secondary barrier for leakage radiation. Calculations for barriers against leakage radiation are similar to primary barrier calculations in that the energy of leakage radiation is assumed to be the same as the primary beam. This assumption is made for radiation protection calculation purposes in spite of the fact that the leakage radiation is generally a lower energy than the primary beam (Section 5.3.4 describes a method to measure the energy of leakage radiation). This assumption results in calculated barriers being slightly thicker than necessary if the true energy of the leakage were known, but permits one to calculate barrier thicknesses erring on the side of safety. Otherwise one would have to determine the energy of the leakage radiation before the machine is installed in one's clinic. This is usually not practical.

The workload may be reduced by a factor of 1000 because head shielding provides this degree of attenuation for X-ray units above 500 keV. Therapy units below 500 keV have housings that limit the leakage to 1 R per hour at meter; therefore, it is necessary to know the number of hours the unit will be used. For further discussion of leakage calculations for units below 500 keV the reader is referred to NCRP Report 49.

Example

Calculate the concrete barrier required to shield against leakage radiation from an 8 MV X-ray beam with a workload of 160,000 Roentgen per week at a meter. The distance from the source to the barrier, which is a wall against a corridor in a controlled area, is 3 meters.

Solution

Without a barrier, the weekly exposure rate at 3 meters is

$$\dot{X}_{LX} = \frac{0.001\,WUT}{d_{LX}^2} \qquad (13\text{--}2)$$

where
$W = 160,000$

$U = 1$, use factor for leakage radiation is taken to be one

$T = 1$, occupancy factor for controlled area is one

$d_{LX} = 3$ m

$$\dot{X} = \frac{0.001 \times 160,000 \times 1 \times 1}{3^2}$$

$$= 18 \text{ R/week}$$

The permissible exposure rate for a controlled area is 100 mR per week so the leakage barrier transmission factor must be

$$B_{LX} = \frac{P}{\dot{X}_{LX}}$$

$$B_{LX} = \frac{0.1 \text{ R}}{18 \text{ R}}$$

$$= 5.6 \times 10^{-3}$$

From Figure 13–1, this transmission factor requires a concrete thickness of 87 cm. However, if we wish to limit controlled areas to the same exposure as uncontrolled areas, we must add 1 tenth value layer (TVL) to this number. The TVL from Table 13–4 is 37.8 cm of concrete, which results in a wall thickness of 87 + 38 = 125 cm.

TABLE 13–4. Approximate HVL and TVL Values of Lead, Concrete and Iron Measured in Broad Beam Conditions

	Attenuation material					
	Lead (mm)		Concrete (cm)		Iron (cm)	
Peak voltage (kV)	HVL	TVL	HVL	TVL	HVL	TVL
50	0.06	0.17	0.43	1.5		
70	0.17	0.52	0.84	2.8		
100	0.27	0.88	1.6	5.3		
125	0.28	0.93	2.0	6.6		
150	0.30	0.99	2.24	7.4		
200	0.52	1.7	2.5	8.4		
250	0.88	2.9	2.8	9.4		
300	1.47	4.8	3.1	10.4		
400	2.5	8.3	3.3	10.9		
500	3.6	11.9	3.6	11.7		
1,000	7.9	26	4.4	14.7		
2,000	12.5	42	6.4	21		
3,000	14.5	48.5	7.4	24.5		
4,000	16	53	8.8	29.2	2.7	9.1
6,000	16.9	56	10.4	34.5	3.0	9.9
8,000	16.9	56	11.4	37.8	3.1	10.3
10,000	16.6	55	11.9	39.6	3.2	10.5
Cesium-137	6.5	21.6	4.8	15.7	1.6	5.3
Cobalt-60	12	40	6.2	20.6	2.1	6.9
Radium	16.6	55	6.9	23.4	2.2	7.4

Source: "Structural Shielding Design and Evaluation for Medical Use of X-Rays and Gamma Rays of Energies Up to 10 MeV," *NCRP Report 49*. Used with permission.

Secondary barriers—scatter

The calculation of barriers against scattered radiation requires more factors than the above calculations because scattered radiation is lower in intensity and in energy than the primary and leakage radiation.

Report 49 of the NCRP tabulates the ratio of the scattered to incident exposures as a function of photon energy and scattering angle. This factor, designated "a," in the report is valid for a field area of 400 cm² at 1 meter. To correct this ratio to other field sizes, it must be multiplied by the factor $F/400$ where F is the field area under consideration. This procedure leads to an exposure rate from scatter radiation at 1 meter when the scatterer is 1 meter from the source of

$$\dot{X}_{sc\,1} = a\,\dot{X}_u\,\frac{F}{400} \qquad (13\text{--}3)$$

where $\dot{X}_{sc\,1} =$ exposure rate from scatter radiation at 1 meter when scatterer is 1 meter from source
$a =$ ratio of scatter to incident exposure
$\dot{X}_u =$ exposure rate from useful beam at 1 meter
$F =$ field area of interest in cm,² specified at 1 meter

Then the exposure rate at the point of interest is

$$\dot{X}_{sc} = \frac{a\,\dot{X}_u}{d_{\text{sec}}^2}\,\frac{F}{400} \qquad (13\text{--}4)$$

where $\dot{X}_{sc} =$ exposure rate at point of interest
$d_{\text{sec}} =$ distance to point of interest

This equation must be modified if the scatterer is not 1 meter from the source. This modification yields

$$\dot{X}_{sc} = \frac{a\,\dot{X}_u}{d_{\text{sec}}^2}\,\frac{1}{d_{\text{sca}}^2}\,\frac{F}{400} \qquad (13\text{--}5)$$

$$\dot{X}_{sc} = \frac{a\,WT}{d_{\text{sec}}^2}\,\frac{1}{d_{\text{sca}}^2}\,\frac{F}{400} \qquad (13\text{--}6)$$

where $\dot{X}_u = WT$ because U is taken as 1 for scatter radiation

Graphs of the attenuation of scattered 6MV X-rays through concrete as a function of angle are given in NCRP Report 49 and are reproduced in Figure 13–2. With this information, the barrier thickness for scatter radiation may be calculated.

Example

Calculate the thickness of concrete required for a 6 MV X-ray unit with the following conditions: $d_{sca} = 1$, $d_{sec} = 6$, $W = 160{,}000$ Rwm, $T = 1$, angle of scatter = 90°, $F = 1600$.

Solution

The weekly exposure rate in the absence of a barrier at the point of interest is

$$\dot{X}_{sc} = \frac{a\ WT}{d_{sec}^2} \frac{1}{d_{sca}^2} \frac{F}{400}$$

from Table 13–5

$$a = 0.0006$$

then
$$\dot{X}_{sc} = \frac{0.0006 \times 160{,}000 \times 1600}{6^2 \times 1^2 \times 400}$$

$$\dot{X}_{sc} = 10.7\ \text{R/week}$$

If we limit the exposure to 10 mR/week the barrier transmission factor must be

$$B_{sc} = \frac{P}{\dot{X}_{sc}}$$

$$B_{sc} = \frac{0.01}{10.7}$$

$$B_{sc} = 9.3 \times 10^{-4}$$

In Figure 13–2 we see that our barrier penetration factor is beyond the range of the graph. However, we observe that the thickness of 2 TVL for 90° scattered 6 MV X-rays is 34.5 cm of concrete. We also know that 1 HVL equals approximately 0.3 TVL, which implies that 1 HVL is approximately 5.2 cm. Now 3 TVL + 1 HVL will result in a reduction factor of 5×10^{-4}. Therefore a barrier of 3 TVL + 1 HVL or approximately 58 cm of concrete will be more than adequate.

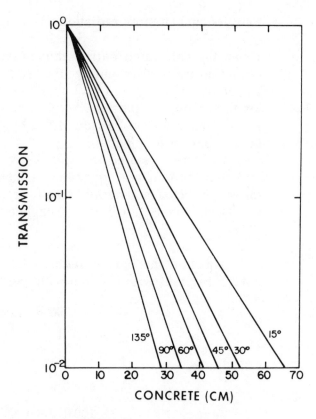

Figure 13–2 Transmission through concrete of 6 MV X-rays scattered by unit density cylindrical phantom 27 cm in diameter 1 meter from source, as a function of angle. From "Structural Shielding Design and Evaluation for Medical Use of X-rays and Gamma Rays of Energies up to 10 MeV," *NCRP Report 49*. Used with permission.

TABLE 13–5. Ratio of Scattered Exposure to Incident Exposure as a Function of X-ray Energy and Scattering Angle for a 400 cm² Field

Source	Scattering angle (from central ray)					
	30	45	60	90	120	135
X-rays						
50 kV	0.0005	0.0002	0.00025	0.00035	0.0008	0.0010
70 kV	0.00065	0.00035	0.00035	0.0005	0.0010	0.0013
100 kV	0.0015	0.0012	0.0012	0.0013	0.0020	0.0022
125 kV	0.0018	0.0015	0.0015	0.0015	0.0023	0.0025
150 kV	0.0020	0.0016	0.0016	0.0016	0.0024	0.0026
200 kV	0.0024	0.0020	0.0019	0.0019	0.0027	0.0028
250 kV	0.0025	0.0021	0.0019	0.0019	0.0027	0.0028
300 kV	0.0026	0.0022	0.0020	0.0019	0.0026	0.0028
4 MV	—	0.0027	—	—	—	—
6 MV	0.007	0.0018	0.0011	0.0006	—	0.0004
Gamma Rays						
137Cs	0.0065	0.0050	0.0041	0.0028	—	0.0019
60Co	0.0060	0.0036	0.0023	0.0009	—	0.0006

Source: "Structural Shielding Design and Evaluation for Medical Use of X-rays and Gamma Rays of Energies up to 10 MeV," *NCRP Report 49*. Used with permission.

Barriers against stray radiation

When the calculated barrier thicknesses for scatter and leakage radiation are approximately the same, then the larger thickness should be increased by 1 HVL to obtain the total thickness required for the secondary barrier. If the thicknesses for the leakage and the scatter radiation barriers differ by more than 1 TVL, then the thicker barrier is adequate.

It has been stated that for X-ray units of 4 MV and above that barriers that are adequate for leakage are usually adequate for scatter. This is generally true for radiation that has been scattered 45° or more. For forward angle scatter this may not be true.

Example

Calculate the barrier required for leakage radiation from a 6MV X-ray unit with the following parameters

$$W = 160,000 \text{ Rwm}$$

$$T = 1$$

$$U = 1$$

$$d_{lx} = 6\text{m}$$

$$\dot{X}_{lx} = \frac{160,000 \times 1 \times 1 \times .001}{6^2}$$

$$= 4.444 \text{ R/W}$$

$$B_{lx} = \frac{0.01}{4.444} = .00225$$

From Figure 13–1 a leakage barrier penetration factor, B_{lx}, of 2.25×10^{-3} will require a barrier thickness of 92.5 cm of concrete.

Now calculate the barrier required for 30° scatter radiation from a 6 MV X-ray unit with a maximum field size at 1 meter of 40 cm x 40 cm and

$$d_{sca} = 1$$

$$d_{sec} = 6$$

$$W = 160,000$$

$$U = 1$$

$$T = 1$$

From Table 13–5

$$a = 0.007$$

then $\quad \dot{X}_{sc} = 0.007 \times \dfrac{160{,}000 \times 1 \times 1}{6^2} \times \dfrac{1600}{400}$

$$= 124.4 \ R/W$$

$$B_{sc} = \dfrac{0.01}{124.4}$$

$$= 8.0 \times 10^{-5}$$

The required barrier thickness is found from Figure 13–2. In that figure 2 TVLs for 30° scatter equal 52.6 cm and 1 TVL equals 26.3 cm. A barrier penetration factor of 8 x 10^{-5} means the barrier must equal 4.1 TVLs. Then the required barrier thickness is 4.1 x 26.3 cm or 108 cm.

Now consider all the same facts, but for 45° scatter where the ratio of scattered to incident exposure is equal to 0.0018 from Table 13–5.

$$\dot{X}_{sc} = 0.0018 \times \dfrac{160{,}000 \times 1 \times 1}{6^2} \times \dfrac{1600}{400}$$

$$= 32 \ R/W$$

$$B_{sc} = \dfrac{.01}{32}$$

$$= 3.125 \times 10^{-4}$$

A barrier penetration factor of 3.125×10^{-4} implies that a barrier of 3.5 TVLs is required. From Figure 13–2, the TVL for 45° scatter is 23 cm. The required barrier thickness is 3.5 cm x 23 cm or 81 cm.

To summarize the results

Type of secondary irradiation	Required barrier thickness
leakage	92.5 cm
30° scatter	108 cm
45° scatter	81 cm

In this example, a barrier for leakage radiation is inadequate for 30° scatter, but is adequate for 45° scatter. It is inadequate for stray radiation in both cases. An additional HVL for stray radiation should be added to the larger barrier thickness in each case.

Barriers for scattered radiation from machines of less than 4 MV

The discussion on scatter radiation was addressed to X-ray energies of 4 MV and above. For energies of 500 kV and below, the penetrating ability of the scatter radiation should be taken to be

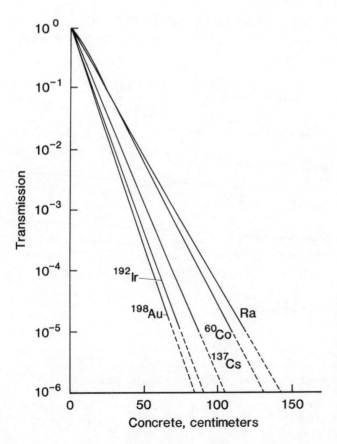

Figure 13–3 Transmission through concrete of gamma rays of gold-198, iridium-192, cesium-137, cobalt-60, and radium 226. From "Structural Shielding Design and Evaluation for Medical Use of X-rays and Gamma Rays of Energies up to 10 MeV," *NCRP Report 49*. Used with permission.

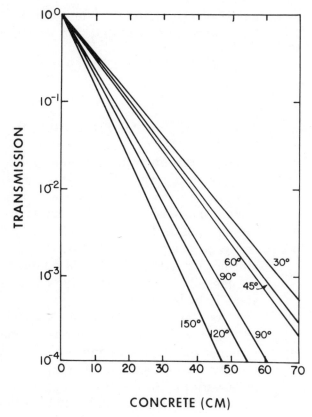

Figure 13–4 Transmission through concrete of cobalt-60 gamma rays scattered by unit density phantom 20 cm in diameter 1 meter from source, as a function of angle. From "Structural Shielding Design and Evaluation for Medical Use of X-rays and Gamma Rays of Energies up to 10 MeV," *NCRP Report 49*. Used with permission.

the same as the primary. For X-rays of 1, 2, or 3 MV energy, the transmission of the 90° scatter radiation is taken to be the same as 500 keV. However, Equation 13–6 must be multiplied by 20, 300, or 700 when calculating scatter radiation for 1, 2, or 3 MV X-rays respectively. This is because of the higher output per milliampere-minute at these higher voltages.

Barriers for radiation from radioisotopes

Figures 13–3 and 13–4 may be used for calculation of barriers for radioisotopes. Transmission through concrete for the gamma rays of several radioisotopes is given in Figure 13–3. Figure 13–4 displays the transmission through concrete for cobalt-60 gamma rays that have been scattered by a unit density phantom, which is 1 meter from the source. The data for several scattering angles are given in this figure.

13.3 MAZES, DOORS, AND THRESHOLDS

From a radiation protection standpoint, the longer a radiation maze and the more turns it has, the better, because each time radiation is scattered it suffers a loss of energy and intensity. However, certain concessions must be made to personnel who must walk the maze 70 to 80 times a day. Generally a maze with a 90° turn is a good compromise. The door will require some lead but it can still be opened by a 5′2″, 98 pound technologist. Additionally, if the gap between the floor and the door is minimized, lead thresholds should not be necessary.

As discussed in Chapter 5, accelerators operating at 10 MV or above will produce neutrons. Primary and secondary barriers designed for the X-ray beam are adequate to attenuate the neutrons; however, a problem may exist at the door. In this case it may be necessary to add a hydrogenous material to the door to attenuate the neutrons. Borated polyethylene is a particularly good choice. The hydrogen in the polyethylene will thermalize the neutrons and the boron has a particularly large cross section for capturing thermal neutrons. Neutron capture in the boron will produce a 478 keV gamma ray. The thermal neutrons will be captured by the hydrogen also. A deuteron will be formed as a result of this capture and a 2.23 MeV gamma ray will be emitted. Other capture gammas will range up to 10 MeV. Lead may be required in the door downstream to provide shielding for these capture gamma rays.

13.4 CONDUITS AND DUCTS

Conduits to carry cables from the treatment room to the outside world are required for a variety of reasons. First and foremost the machine must be connected to the control panel. Second, audio and visual contact must be maintained with the patient during treatment. Audio contact is usually accomplished with an intercom and closed-circuit TV cameras are frequently used for visual observation. Third, physics measurements may be greatly facilitated with cables that reside permanently in conduits. Air ducts will be required as well. The design of these conduits and ducts should leave no unacceptable voids in the walls or paths through which scattered radiation could pass. Serpentine conduits and angled ducts will generally accomplish this purpose, but the reader is referred to the extensive details in NCRP Report 49.

13.5 BRACHYTHERAPY CONSIDERATIONS

Specially designed rooms are usually not required for brachytherapy sources. They are usually stored in a shielded safe and personnel usually work with them behind a shielded L-block. Barrier transmission factors to reduce the exposure of 1 curie sources of various isotopes to 100 mR per week at several distances are given in Table 13–6. These factors are reproduced from NCRP Report 49. When the brachytherapy sources are in place during treatment NCRP Report #48[2] recommends that the patient be separated from other patients by at least 6 feet in all directions and patients in

TABLE 13–6. Barrier Transmission Factor Per Curie to Reduce Exposure to 100 mR per Week for Cobalt-60, Radium-226, Iridium-192, Cesium-137, and Gold-198

Distance m	^{60}Co	^{226}Ra	^{192}Ir	^{137}Cs	^{198}Au
0.5	0.00048	0.00076	0.00114	0.00188	0.0027
1	0.00192	0.00303	0.00455	0.0075	0.0107
1.5	0.0043	0.0068	0.0102	0.0169	0.024
2	0.0077	0.012	0.0182	0.0301	0.043
2.5	0.012	0.019	0.028	0.047	0.067
3	0.0173	0.027	0.0404	0.068	0.096

Source: "Structural Shielding Design and Evaluation for Medical Use of X-rays and Gamma Rays of Energies Up to 10 MeV," *NCRP Report 49*. Used with permission.

adjoining beds should be past child-bearing age. Further details are available in NCRP Reports 39,[3] 40,[4] and 48.[2]

13.6 PERSONNEL MONITORING

Maximum permissible doses (MPD) for occupational exposure are given in Table 13-7. The NCRP[5] recommends that any individual with a probability of receiving more than 25% of the limit for occupational exposure should wear a monitoring device. This monitor should be worn on the part of the body most likely to receive the highest percentage of the MPD. The amount of time the monitor is worn before being read depends on the situation, although in a radiation therapy department one month is generally a reasonable time. In certain instances a pocket ion chamber dosimeter may be useful as a secondary monitor. NCRP Report 49 states that all exposures recorded by the primary radiation monitor should enter the person's permanent record except if the monitor failed, the monitor was not being worn when it was exposed, or other indicators show the exposure was different than that recorded by the monitor.

TABLE 13-7. Maximum Permissible Dose Levels for Occupationally Exposed Workers

	Weekly dose	Maximum calendar quarter dose	Maximum yearly dose	Maximum accumulated dose
	rem	rem	rem	rem
Whole body, gonads, red bone marrow, lens of eye	0.1	3	5	5(N − 18)
Skin of whole body	—	—	15	—
Hands	—	25	75	—
Forearms	—	10	30	—
	N = age in years			

Source: "Structural Shielding Design and Evaluation for Medical Use of X-rays and Gamma Rays of Energies up to 10 MeV," *NCRP Report 49*. Used with permission.

Notes

1. *Structural Shielding Design and Evaluation for Medical Use of X-rays and Gamma Rays of Energies up to 10 MeV NCRP Report No. 49.*, (Washington, D. C.: National Council on Radiation Protection and Measurements, 1976).

2. *Radiation Protection for Medical and Allied Health Personnel NCRP Report No. 48.*, (Washington, D. C.: National Council on Radiation Protection and Measurements, 1976).

3. *Basic Radiation Protection Criteria NCRP Report No. 39.*, (Washington, D. C.: National Council on Radiation Protection and Measurements, 1971).

4. *Protection Against Radiation From Brachytherapy Sources NCRP Report No. 40.*, (Washington, D. C.: National Council on Radiation Protection and Measurements, 1972).

5. *Operational Radiation Safety Program NCRP Report No. 59.*, (Washington, D. C.: National Council on Radiation Protection and Measurements, 1978).

Additional Reading

Medical X-ray and Gamma-Ray Protection for Energies Up to 10 MeV—Equipment Design and Use NCRP Report No. 33, (Washington, D. C.: National Council on Radiation Protection and Measurments, 1968).

Precautions in the Management of Patients Who Have Received Therapeutic Amounts of Radionuclides NCRP Report No. 37., (Washington, D. C.: National Council on Radiation Protection and Measurements, 1970).

Protection Against Neutron Radiation NCRP Report No. 38, (Washington, D. C.: National Council on Radiation Protection and Measurements, 1971).

Review of the Current State of Radiation Protection Philosophy NCRP Report No. 43., (Washington, D. C.: National Council on Radiation Protection and Measurements, 1975).

Radiation Protection Design Guidelines for 0.1–100 MeV Particle Accelerator Facilities NCRP Report No. 51., (Washington, D. C.: National Council on Radiation Protection and Measurements, 1977).

Review of NCRP Radiation Dose Limit for Embryo and Fetus in Occupationally Exposed Women NCRP Report No. 53., (Washington, D. C.: National Council on Radiation Protection and Measurements, 1977).

Medical Radiation Exposure of Pregnant and Potentially Pregnant Women NCRP Report No. 54., (Washington, D. C.: National Council on Radiation Protection and Measurements, 1977).

Instrumentation and Monitoring Methods for Radiation Protection NCRP Report No. 57., (Washington, D. C.: National Council on Radiation Protection and Measurements, 1978).

A Handbook of Radioactivity Measurements Procedures NCRP Report No. 58., (Washington, D. C.: National Council on Radiation Protection and Measurements, 1978).

FOURTEEN | CLINICAL EXTERNAL BEAM DOSIMETRY

14.1 INTRODUCTION

Radiation therapy equipment demands a tremendous expenditure of personnel and financial resources. Many hours are devoted to equipment selection, followed by weeks of acceptance tests, and months of commissioning measurements. This manpower commitment is protected by a continuing program of quality assurance. All of these costs are paid to achieve a singular result—the proper application of radiation to the patient. Careful planning by the therapist and physicist resulting in a plan that must be scrupulously adhered to by dedicated staff technologists is required to achieve this goal. However, all this effort may be squandered by a careless, incorrect calculation of "beam-on time." The beam-on time must be calculated to deliver the prescribed dose to the prescribed depth or isodose level. These calculations are straightforward mathematical operations that may be accomplished with a simple four-function calculator but they must be performed in a logical, consistent manner to transfer a treatment plan to a patient.

14.2 TERMINOLOGY

Let's begin our discussion of clinical dosimetry with a terminology review.

14.2.1 Calibrated Output

A treatment unit is generally calibrated for one standard set of conditions. A cobalt-60 unit may be calibrated in-air, but a supervoltage unit must be calibrated in phantom. Typical conditions for a cobalt-60 calibration might be the in-air dose rate on the central axis of a 10 cm x 10 cm field at 80.5 cm from the source. The output of an 18 MV X-ray beam might be stated as the dose per monitor unit delivered by a 10 cm x 10 cm field at d_{max} on the central axis in a water phantom positioned at 100 cm SSD. All other beam conditions are normalized to this calibrated output.

14.2.2 Output Factor and Field Size Dependence

The output factor is a measure of the machine output (dose per monitor unit) for various field sizes at d_{max} relative to the standard conditions for the calibrated output. For a high energy X-ray or electron beam, this factor is measured in a water phantom positioned at the same SSD as that used to determine the calibrated output.

For cobalt-60 this factor might be measured in-air, in which case it is referred to as the *field size dependence*. Because of the difference in measurement techniques, the output factor includes the scatter component, but the field size dependence does not.

14.2.3 Peak Scatter Factor

The term *backscatter factor* was introduced for orthovoltage X-rays and is the ratio of the absorbed dose at the surface of a phantom to the absorbed dose from primary photons alone measured at the same point on the beam axis. The term *peak scatter factor* has been proposed for the same concept for megavoltage photons; that is, the ratio of the absorbed dose at d_{max} on the central axis in a phantom to the absorbed dose from primary photons at the same point. Although this is the more correct terminology, one frequently encounters the term backscatter factor rather than the peak scatter factor applied to megavoltage photon beams.

14.2.4 Central Axis Percent Depth Dose

The central axis percent depth dose is the ratio of the dose at a given depth on the central axis to the dose at d_{max} on the central axis expressed as a percentage. The central axis percent depth dose is a function of the beam energy, field size, SSD, and depth.

14.2.5 Mayneord's Factor

This factor permits the conversion of the central axis percent depth dose values from one SSD to another SSD. This factor equals

$$F = \left(\frac{SSD_{orig} + d}{SSD_{orig} + d_{max}}\right)^2 \left(\frac{SSD_{new} + d_{max}}{SSD_{new} + d}\right)^2$$

where SSD_{orig} is the original SSD
SSD_{new} is the SSD to which the change is made
d is the depth of interest

The new percent depth dose value equals

$$\%dd)_{new} = \%dd)_{orig} \, F$$

14.2.6 Tissue-Air Ratio

The tissue-air ratio (TAR)[1] is the ratio of the dose at a given depth in phantom to the dose at that same point in-air. The TAR is a function of field size, beam energy, and depth. Note the peak scatter factor is the TAR at d_{max}.

14.2.7 Tissue-Maximum Ratio

The tissue-maximum ratio (TMR)[2] was introduced to replace the tissue-air ratio for high energy X-ray beams because of the difficul-

ties of making in-air measurements on these beams. The TMR is
the ratio of the dose at a specified depth on the central axis to
the dose at the same distance from the source but at a depth of
d_{max}. The TMR is a function of beam energy, field size, and depth.

14.2.8 Tissue-Phantom Ratio

The tissue-phantom ratio (TPR)[3] is similar to the TMR except that
reference depth is not necessarily d_{max}. For instance, 5 cm may
be specified as the reference depth and all values normalized to

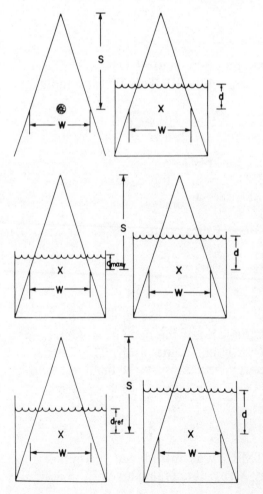

Figure 14–1 The concepts of TAR,
TMR, and TPR are schematically
illustrated in the upper, middle, and
lower diagrams respectively. The
TAR is the ratio of the dose at a
depth d pictured in the upper right
to the dose in-air diagrammed in
the upper left. Note the reference
point is a distance S from the
source and the field width is W for
both cases. The TMR is similarly
diagrammed in the middle panel.
The difference being that in the left-
hand illustration the dose is measured at d_{max} rather than in-air. The
lower panel displays the TPR,
which is similar except that the dia-
gram on the left side is for dose
at some reference depth d_{ref}.

this depth. Like the TMR and TAR, the TPR is a function of beam energy, field size, and depth. The difference between TAR, TMR, and TPR may be clarified by reference to Figure 14–1.

14.2.9 Wedge Factor

The wedge factor is the ratio of the dose at a specified point on the central axis with a wedge in the beam to the dose at the same point with no wedge in the beam (see Chapter 6).

14.2.10 Tray Factor

The tray factor is the ratio of the dose at a specified point on the central axis with a secondary blocking tray in the beam to the dose at the same point without the tray in the beam (see Chapter 6).

14.2.11 Equivalent Square

The equivalent square is the square field that has the same central axis percent depth dose characteristics as a given rectangular or irregular field. The equivalent square of rectangular fields may be approximated with tables given in British Journal of Radiology Supplement 17.[4] The equivalent square of blocked fields may be estimated by dividing four times the area by the perimeter $(4A/P)$.

14.2.12 Beam Weighting

Beam weighting or beam loading refers to the amount of radiation delivered by a particular port relative to another port. For instance, a right and left lateral parallel-opposed-pair that delivered twice as much radiation from the right port as from the left port, would be referred to as weighted 2 to 1 (or 1 to 0.5). Fixed SSD treatments are weighted by given dose, whereas isocentric treatments are weighted by tumor dose.

14.3 CENTRAL-AXIS CALCULATIONS

The simplest and most common "treatment plan" requires the delivery of a prescribed dose at a prescribed depth. Possibly 80 to 90% of all patients are treated in this manner. Frequently, the therapist will prescribe a certain dose to be delivered at mid-depth with equally-loaded parallel-opposed ports. The calculation of beam-on time for this situation might be accomplished with a simple table look up. Many institutions have tables with the beam-on time required to deliver 100 cGy for a number of field sizes at a number of depths. If the therapist prescribes 200 cGy with an equally-weighted parallel-opposed pair, then it is clear that each port should deliver 100 cGy. The beam-on time is determined simply by looking up the time under the appropriate depth and field size.

This technique yields satisfactory results and is very time-efficient but departmental personnel are removed from all the factors that are involved in the calculation and may encounter difficulty in determining the time for a more complex plan. A calculation sheet, such as illustrated in Figure 14–2, provides a menu making all factors explicit and serving as a constant reminder of the details of a calculation. The disadvantage is that this technique requires more time.

Let's examine this menu in detail. This calculation sheet is for calculation of beam-on time for SSD treatments on a linear accelerator. The top of the sheet provides spaces for the patient's name, hospital number, date and treatment area. There are also places to indicate if the radiation is X-ray or electron and the energy of the radiation. Then spaces are provided for SSD and depth. This is followed by information on the open field size and its equivalent square, which is determined from tables published in British Journal of Radiology Supplement 17. The equivalent square of the blocked field is calculated with $4A/P$.

The machine output for a 10 cm x 10 cm field at d_{max} in a water phantom positioned at 100 cm SSD is entered in the first line of the calculation section. This value is multiplied by the output factor for the open field in Line 2. For this particular machine, the output factor is determined by finding the equivalent square of the open field. Some linear accelerators will exhibit a different output for rectangular fields depending on whether the upper or lower collimator jaw forms the short side of the field. For instance, a 10 cm x 30 cm field with the upper jaw forming a 10 cm side may have a different output factor than a 10 cm x 30 cm field with a lower jaw forming the 10 cm side. If this occurs, it will be necessary to correlate output factors to collimator opening during commissioning measurements. The open field rather than the blocked field was chosen to determine the output factor because the output is more dependent upon the collimator opening than

LINEAR ACCELERATOR _____   PATIENT'S NAME _____
SSD CENTRAL AXIS DOSE CALCULATIONS   CLINIC # _____
- -
DATE _____   TREATMENT AREA _____
X-RAY _____   ELECTRON _____   ENERGY _____
- -
SSD = _____   Depth = _____   Area/Perimeter Blocked Field ____
Open Field Size at SSD = _____ cm   Eq. Sq. Blocked Field _____
Equivalent Square Open Field _____

CALCULATIONS:
1) Output at 10 cm × 10 cm = _____ cGy/mu.
2) Multiplied by Output factor for Eq. Sq. for open field _____ equals _____ cGy/mu.
3) Multiplied by Wedge Transmission _____ (1.0 if no wedge used) equals _____ cGy/mu.
4) Multiplied by Tray Transmission _____ (1.0 if no tray used) equals _____ cGy/mu at d_{max}.
5) Multiplied by %dd for Blocked Field _____ % equals _____ cGy/mu. at depth.

TUMOR DOSE/PORT:

$$\underline{\hspace{3cm}} = \frac{\text{cGy req.}}{\text{cGy/mu at depth}} = \underline{\hspace{3cm}} \text{ mu set.}$$

MAX DOSE/PORT:

_____ mu X _____ cGy/mu at max _____ cGy.
                                    Given Dose

Calculated by: _____
Checked by: _____
Physics ck: _____
Date: _____

Figure 14–2 Sheet for calculation of beam-on time for fixed SSD treatments on a linear accelerator. This sheet is used when the dose is delivered at a prescribed depth.

on secondary blocking. At this point we have the output at d_{max} for the open field defined by the collimators. This value is multiplied by the wedge factor and tray factor in Lines 3 and 4. This yields the output at d_{max} with any beam modifying devices in the field.

To calculate the dose rate at the depth of interest we multiply the product in Line 4 by the central axis percent depth dose for the equivalent square of the blocked field. The blocked field is used because the central axis percent depth dose is more dependent upon the actual area irradiated than upon the collimator opening. The dose rate at depth is divided into the tumor dose required from this port to yield the number of monitor units required. The given dose is found by multiplying the monitor units delivered by the output at d_{max} from Line 4. Finally, lines are provided for the date and the initials of the individuals who calculated and checked the values.

The calculation sheet for isocentric treatments is shown in Figure 14–3. The heading is similar with spaces for name, clinic number, date, treatment area, SSD, and depth, but this is followed with a space for source-axis-distance (SAD). Beneath these spaces is an area to calculate the equivalent square of the open and blocked fields. Then we enter the calculation section of the sheet. The first line is the output for a 10 cm x 10 cm field. For the isocentric case this value is stated at the SAD. To clarify, for a 6 MV X-ray beam the output for the isocentric case would be measured at 100 cm in a water phantom positioned at an SSD of 98.5 cm. The output for fixed SSD treatments would be measured at 101.5 cm with the water phantom positioned at an SSD of 100 cm. This value is multiplied by the output factor, wedge and tray factors in the following lines. This is the output at SAD at d_{max}. This output is multiplied by the TAR or TMR to yield the output at treatment depth. This number is divided into the prescribed dose to give the required number of monitor units. The given dose is found by multiplying the number of monitor units by the dose per monitor unit calculated in Line 4, peak scatter factor, and an inverse square factor $\left(\dfrac{SAD}{SSD + d_{max}}\right)^2$. The inverse square factor corrects the dose per monitor unit at d_{max} at SAD to the dose per monitor unit at d_{max} at the point of the given dose. The peak scatter factor is taken as one for X-rays above 4 MV. This procedure is not entirely valid, but the measurement of the PSF above 4 MV is fraught with difficulties.

The cobalt-60 calculation sheet shown in Figure 14–4, is similar to the sheet used for linear accelerators except for minor modifications that are necessary because this unit is calibrated in-air. The headings are the same as on the linear accelerator sheets. In the calculation section Line 1 refers to the dose rate to a miniphantom centered at 80.5 cm in a 10 cm x 10 cm field.

ISOCENTRIC CENTRAL AXIS DOSE   PATIENT'S NAME _____
  CALCULATIONS
THERAPY UNIT _____ ENERGY ____ CLINIC # _____

- -

DATE _____   TREATMENT AREA _____

- -

SSD = _____ cm   Depth = _____   SAD = _____ cm
Open Field Size at SAD = _____ cm   Area/Perimeter = _____
Eq. Sq. = _____ cm   Eq. Sq. of Blocked Field = _____

CALCULATIONS:
1) Output at 10 cm × 10 cm at SAD = _____ cGy/mu.
2) Multiplied by Output factor for Eq. Sq. of Open Field _____ equals _____ cGy/mu.
3) Multiplied by Wedge Transmission _____(1.0 if no wedge used) equals _____ cGy/mu per _____ °Wedge.
4) Multiplied by Tray Transmission _____(1.0 if no tray used) equals _____ *cGy/mu.
5) Multiplied by TMR/TAR of Blocked Field _____ equals _____ cGy/mu at SAD.

TUMOR DOSE/PORT:

$$\frac{\text{cGy Required}}{\text{cGy/mu. at SAD}} = \text{_____} = \text{_____ mu. preset}$$

MAX DOSE/PORT:

$$\left(\frac{\text{SAD}}{\text{SSD} + d_{max}}\right)^2 \quad \text{(mu preset)} \quad \text{(*cGy/mu)} \quad \text{(PSF)} \quad = \quad \text{max dose}$$

$$\left(\frac{}{\quad + \quad}\right)^2 \quad (\text{_____}) \quad (\text{_____}) \quad (\text{_____}) \quad = \quad \text{\_\_\_\_ cGy}$$

Calculated by: _____
Checked by: _____
Physics ck: _____
Date: _____

Figure 14–3 Sheet for calculation of beam-on time for isocentric treatments on a linear accelerator. This sheet is used when the dose is delivered at a prescribed depth.

COBALT TELETHERAPY
CENTRAL AXIS DOSE CALCULATIONS

PATIENT'S NAME _____

CLINIC # _____

- -

DATE _____

TREATMENT AREA _____

- -

SSD = _____ cm   Depth = _____ cm

Area/Perimeter Blocked Field ____

Open Field Size at SSD = _____ cm

Eq. Sq. Blocked Field _____

Eq. Sq. Open Field _____ cm

CALCULATIONS:

1) Output at 10 cm × 10 cm = _____ cGy/min.
2) Multiplied by Field Size Dependence for open field _____ equals _____ cGy/min.
3) Multiplied by Wedge Transmission _____(1.0 if no wedge used) equals _____ cGy/min.
4) Multiplied by Tray Transmission _____ (1.0 if no tray used) equals _____ cGy/min.
5) Multiplied by P.S.F. for blocked field _____ equals _____ cGy/min at max.
6) Multiplied by %dd for blocked field _____ equals _____ cGy/min at depth.

TUMOR DOSE PORT:

$$\text{_____} = \frac{\text{cGy req.}}{\text{cGy/min. at depth}} = \text{_____ min.} + \frac{.02}{} \text{_____ min shutter}$$

time = ____ min. TX time.

MAX DOSE PORT:

_____ min. X _____ cGy/min. at max _____ cGy given dose.

Calculated by: _____
Checked by: _____
Physics ck: _____
Date: _____

Figure 14–4 Sheet for calculation of beam-on time for fixed SSD treatments on a cobalt-60 unit. This sheet is used when the dose is delivered to a prescribed depth.

Field size dependence replaces output factor in Line 2. The wedge and tray factors follow in Lines 3 and 4. Line 5 is the peak scatter factor of the blocked field. This factor multiplied by the product in Line 4 yields the dose rate at d_{max} for the treatment-field. This is multiplied by the percent depth dose to find the dose rate at treatment depth in Line 6. This value is divided into the prescribed dose to give the treatment time. For this particular cobalt-60 unit, the shutter correction is -0.02 min, therefore 0.02 min is added to the calculated treatment time to yield the required time setting. The given dose is found by multiplying the time calculated without the shutter correction by the dose rate at d_{max} in Line 5.

The alternative to prescribing the dose at a given depth or point is to prescribe the dose to a volume or area enclosed by a given isodose surface or line of a treatment plan. In this case one must relate the prescribed dose at the isodose surface to the weights of the beams. A systematic method of achieving this is shown in Figure 14–5 and might best be illustrated with a comprehensive example. Consider the treatment plan diagrammed in Figure 14–6. This plan is a four field prostate treatment. The anterior and posterior ports are parallel-opposed 14 cm x 12 cm fields weighted 43%. The right and left lateral ports are parallel opposed 9 cm x 12 cm fields weighted 57%.

A completed calculation sheet for the anterior and posterior fields is shown in Figure 14–7 and for the right and left laterals in Figure 14–8. The dose rate for the calibration field is entered in Line 1 and multiplied by appropriate values of output factor, wedge factor, and tray factor in lines 2, 3, and 4 which yields the dose rate at d_{max} for the treated field. The total prescribed dose and the prescribed isodose level are entered in Lines 5 and 6. The total dose delivered to the 100% level is calculated on Line 7 where Line 5 is divided by Line 6. The weight of the port is given in Line 8 and the total given dose of the port is calculated in Line 9 by taking the product of Line 8 and Line 7. This dose is divided into the total number of fractions (Line 10). The irradiation time is equal to the given dose per fraction from Line 11 divided by the dose rate at d_{max} from Line 4.

A similar plan treated isocentrically is shown in Figure 14–9. Recall the weightings are at isocenter and not at d_{max} for isocentric treatments. In this plan each port has been weighted to 50 at isocenter. The beam-on time for each port is calculated in Figures 14–10 and 14–11. The calibrated output is entered on Line 1 of the calculation section. The output factor and wedge and tray factors follow on Lines 2, 3, and 4. This gives the output at the SAD at a depth of d_{max}. This value is multiplied by the TAR or TMR on Line 5 to find the output at the SAD at the treatment depth.

FIXED SSD TREATMENTS
FOR ISODOSE LINE PRESCRIPTIONS ONLY
THERAPY UNIT _____ ENERGY _____

PATIENT'S NAME: _____

CLINIC #: _____

- -

DATE: _____

TREATMENT AREA: _____

- -

SSD = _____ cm
Open Field Size at SSD = _____ cm
Eq. Sq. for Open Field = _____ cm

Area/Perimeter Blocked Field: ____
Eq. Sq. for Blocked Field: _____

CALCULATIONS:
1) Output at 10 cm × 10 cm = _____ cGy/mu.
2) Multiplied by Output Factor for Open Field _____ equals _____ cGy/mu.
3) Multiplied by Wedge Transmission _____(1.0 if no wedge used) equals _____ cGy/mu.
4) Multiplied by Tray Transmission _____(1.0 if no tray used) equals _____ cGy/mu.
5) Total Prescribed Dose: _____ cGy.
6) At Isodose Level: _____.
7) Dose at 100% Isodose $\left(\dfrac{\text{Line 5}}{\text{Line 6}} \times 100\right)$ _____ cGy.
8) Weight of Port: _____.
9) Total Given Dose of Port (line 7 × 8) _____ cGy.
10) Number of Fractions This Port Treated: _____
11) Given Dose Per Fraction $\left(\dfrac{\text{Line 9}}{\text{Line 10}}\right)$ _____ cGy.
12) Mu Required $\left(\dfrac{\text{Line 11}}{\text{Line 4}}\right)$ _____ mu.

Calculated by: _____
Checked by: _____
Physics ck: _____
Date: _____

Figure 14–5 Sheet for calculation of beam-on time for fixed SSD treatments on a linear accelerator. This sheet is used when the dose is prescribed to an isodose surface.

Line 6 is the total prescribed dose and Line 7 is the isodose level to which this dose is prescribed. The 100% isodose level equals the quotient of Line 6 divided by Line 7. The weight of the port is entered on Line 9 and the total tumor dose delivered by this

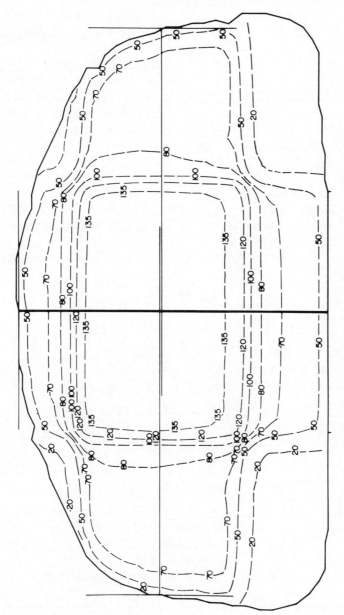

Figure 14–6 Four-field fixed SSD treatment plan for prostate treatment. The anterior and posterior ports are weighted 43% and the lateral ports are weighted 57%.

FIXED SSD TREATMENTS   PATIENT'S NAME: __Jack Dough__
FOR ISODOSE LINE PRESCRIPTIONS ONLY
THERAPY
UNIT: __THERAC__ ENERGY: __18 MV__   CLINIC #: _____555–1212_____

- -

DATE: __February 28, 1987__   TREATMENT AREA: __AP + PA__
                                                 Prostate

- -

SSD = _____100_____ cm   Area/Perimeter Blocked Field: __N/A__
Open Field Size at SSD = __12 × 14__ cm Eq. Sq. for Blocked Field: __N/A__
Eq. Sq. for Open Field = _____12.9_____ cm

CALCULATIONS:
1) Output at 10 cm × 10 cm = _____.85_____ cGy/mu.
2) Multiplied by Output Factor for Open Field __1.034__ equals __.879__ cGy/mu.
3) Multiplied by Wedge Transmission __1.0__ (1.0 if no wedge used) equals
   __.879__ cGy/mu.
4) Multiplied by Tray Transmission __1.0__ (1.0 if no tray used) equals
   __.879__ cGy/mu.
5 Total Prescribed Dose: _____6000_____ cGy.
6) At Isodose Level: _____135%_____.
7) Dose at 100% Isodose $\left(\dfrac{\text{Line 5}}{\text{Line 6}} \times 100\right)$ _____4444_____ cGy.
8) Weight of Port: _____43%_____.
9) Total Given Dose of Port (line 7 × 8) _____1911_____ cGy.
10) Number of Fractions This Port Treated: _____30_____.
11) Given Dose Per Fraction $\left(\dfrac{\text{Line 9}}{\text{Line 10}}\right)$ _____64_____ cGy.
12) Mu Required $\left(\dfrac{\text{Line 11}}{\text{Line 4}}\right)$ _____72_____ mu.

Calculated by: _____
Checked by: _____
Physics ck: _____
Date: _____

Figure 14–7 Completed calculation sheet for the anterior and posterior
ports for the treatment plan in Figure 14–6. The prescribed dose is 6000
cGy to the 135% isodose surface.

FIXED SSD TREATMENTS
FOR ISODOSE LINE PRESCRIPTIONS ONLY
THERAPY
UNIT: ___THERAC___ ENERGY: ___18 MV___

PATIENT'S NAME: __Jack Dough__

CLINIC #: _____555–1212_____

- -

DATE: February 28, 1987

TREATMENT AREA: __R + L Lat.__
Prostate

- -

SSD = ____100____ cm
Open Field Size at SSD = ___12 × 9___ cm
Eq. Sq. for Open Field = ____10.3____ cm

Area/Perimeter Blocked Field: N/A
Eq. Sq. for Blocked Field: __N/A__

CALCULATIONS:

1) Output at 10 cm × 10 cm = ____.85____ cGy/mu.
2) Multiplied by Output Factor for Open Field _1.006_ equals __.855__ cGy/mu.
3) Multiplied by Wedge Transmission ___1.0___ (1.0 if no wedge used) equals __.855__ cGy/mu.
4) Multiplied by Tray Transmission ___1.0___ (1.0 if no tray used) equals __.855__ cGy/mu.
5) Total Prescribed Dose: ____6000____ cGy.
6) At Isodose Level: ____135%____.
7) Dose at 100% Isodose $\left(\dfrac{\text{Line 5}}{\text{Line 6}} \times 100\right)$ ____4444____ cGy.
8) Weight of Port: ____57%____.
9) Total Given Dose of Port (Line 7 × 8) ____2533____ cGy.
10) Number of Fractions This Port Treated ____30____.
11) Given Dose Per Fraction $\left(\dfrac{\text{Line 9}}{\text{Line 10}}\right)$ ____84____ cGy.
12) Mu Required $\left(\dfrac{\text{Line 11}}{\text{Line 4}}\right)$ ____99____ mu.

Calculated by: _____
Checked by: _____
Physics ck: _____
Date: _____

Figure 14–8 Completed calculation sheets for the right and left lateral ports for the treatment plan in Figure 14–6.

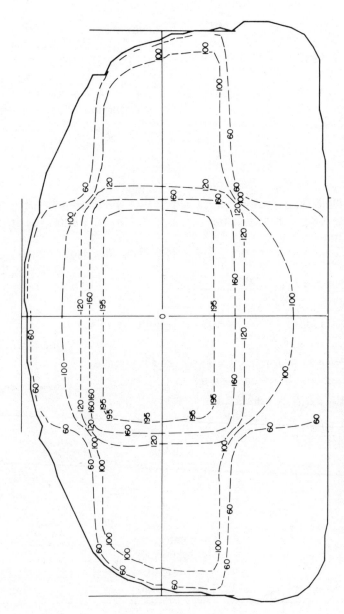

Figure 14–9 Isocentric four-field treatment plan for prostate cancer. The isocenter is a 8.5 cm from the anterior, 10 cm from the posterior, and 16.5 cm from both right and left lateral surfaces. All beams are weighted 50% at isocenter.

ISOCENTRIC TREATMENTS   PATIENT'S NAME __Jack Dough__
FOR ISODOSE LINE PRESCRIPTIONS ONLY
THERAPY
UNIT: __THERAC__ ENERGY: __18 MV__   CLINIC #: _____555–1212_____

- -
DATE February 28, 1987   TREATMENT AREA: _AP Prostate_
- -

SSD = ____91.5____ cm   DEPTH = ____8.5____   SAD = ____100____ cm
Open Field Size at SAD = __14 × 12__ cm   Eq. Sq. for Blocked Field _____
Eq. Sq. for Open Field = ____12.9____ cm   Area/Perimeter Blocked Field ____

CALCULATIONS:
1) Output at 10 cm × 10 cm at SAD = _____.90_____ cGy/mu.
2) Multiplied by Output Factor for Open Field _1.035_ equals __.932__ cGy/mu.
3) Multiplied by Wedge Transmission __1.0__ (1.0 if no wedge used) equals
   __.932__ cGy/mu per _____ °wedge.
4) Multiplied by Tray Transmission __1.0__ (1.0 if no tray used) equals __.932__
   cGy/mu.
5) Multiplied by TAR/TMR for Blocked Field __.93__ equals __.866__ cGy/mu at
   depth.
6) Total Prescribed Dose _____6000_____ cGy.
7) At Isodose Level ____195%____.

8) Dose at 100% Isodose Level $\left(\dfrac{\text{Line 6}}{\text{Line 7}}\right) \times 100$ _____3077_____ cGy.

9) Weight of Port _____50%_____.
10) Total Tumor Dose Delivered by This Port (Lines 8 × 9) _____1538_____ cGy.
11) Number of Fractions This Port Treated _____30_____.

12) Tumor Dose per Fraction $\left(\dfrac{\text{Line 10}}{\text{Line 11}}\right)$ _____51_____ cGy.

13) Mu Required $\left(\dfrac{\text{Line 12}}{\text{Line 5}}\right)$ _____59_____ mu.

14) Given Dose per Fraction

$$\left[\text{Line 13} \times \text{Line 4} \times \left(\frac{\text{SAD}}{\text{SSD} + d_{\max}}\right)^2 \times \text{PSF}\right]$$ _____62_____ cGy.

Calculated by: _____
Checked by: _____
Physics ck: _____
Date: _____

Figure 14–10 Completed calculation for the anterior port in Figure
14–9.

ISOCENTRIC TREATMENTS   PATIENT'S NAME __Jack Dough__
FOR ISODOSE LINE PRESCRIPTIONS ONLY
THERAPY
UNIT: __THERAC__ ENERGY: __18 MV__   CLINIC #: _____555–1212_____

- -

DATE __February 28, 1987__   TREATMENT AREA: __R & L Lateral__
                                                   Prostate

- -

SSD = ___83.5___ cm   DEPTH = ___16.5___   SAD = ___100___ cm
Open Field Size at SAD = ___9 × 12___ cm   Eq. Sq. for Blocked Field _____
Eq. Sq. for Open Field = ___10.3___ cm   Area/Perimeter Blocked Field ____

CALCULATIONS:

1) Output at 10 cm × 10 cm at SAD = ___.90___ cGy/mu.
2) Multiplied by Output Factor for Open Field __1.006__ equals __.905__ cGy/mu.
3) Multiplied by Wedge Transmission __1.0__ (1.0 if no wedge used) equals __.905__ cGy/mu per _____ °wedge.
4) Multiplied by Tray Transmission __1.0__ (1.0 if no tray used) equals __.905__ cGy/mu.
5) Multiplied by TAR/TMR for Blocked Field __.762__ equals __.690__ cGy/mu at depth.
6) Total Prescribed Dose ___6000___ cGy.
7) At Isodose Level ___195%___.
8) 100% Isodose Level $\left(\dfrac{\text{Line 6}}{\text{Line 7}}\right)$ × 100 ___3077___ cGy.
9) Weight of Port ___50%___.
10) Total Tumor Dose Delivered by This Port (Lines 8 × 9) ___1538___ cGy.
11) Number of Fractions This Port Treated ___30___.
12) Tumor Dose per Fraction $\left(\dfrac{\text{Line 10}}{\text{Line 11}}\right)$ ___51___ cGy.
13) Mu Required $\left(\dfrac{\text{Line 12}}{\text{Line 5}}\right)$ ___74___ mu.
14) Given Dose per Fraction
$$\left[\text{Line 13} \times \text{Line 4} \times \left(\frac{\text{SAD}}{\text{SSD} + d_{max}}\right)^2 \times \text{PSF}\right] \underline{\hspace{1cm} 90 \hspace{1cm}} \text{cGy.}$$

Calculated by: _____
Checked by: _____
Physics ck: _____
Date: _____

Figure 14–11 Completed calculation sheet for the lateral ports in Figure 14–9.

port is the product of Lines 8 and 9, which is calculated at Line 10. The tumor dose per fraction is found by dividing the total tumor dose (Line 10) by the number of fractions this port will be treated (Line 11). The irradiation time equals the tumor dose per fraction divided by the dose rate at the SAD at the treatment depth (Line 5). The given dose can then be calculated by multiplying the irradiation time by the dose rate in Line 4 and by an inverse square factor and peak scatter factor as was described for Figure 14–3.

14.4 IRREGULAR FIELD CALCULATIONS

The $4A/P$ approximation for blocked fields fails for fields that have a large percentage of the area blocked or fields with irregularly shaped blocks. The prime example is the mantle field. Calculational techniques for irregular fields were discussed in Chapter 3. Equation 3–21, as well as modifications suggested by Hallberg et al.[5] and Hanson et al.[6] were proposed for irregular fields.

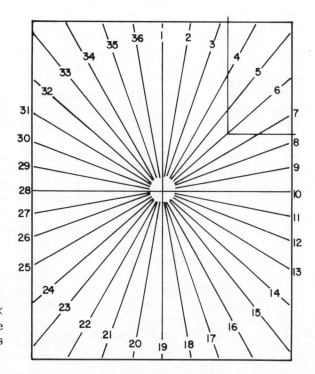

Figure 14–12 Projection to a depth of 5 cm of a cobalt-60 field defined at 80 cm, as 12 cm × 15 cm with a corner block of 3 cm × 5 cm. The radii used to determine the average SAR at the central axis are illustrated.

The method of determining the average scatter air ratio is to add the scatter air ratios along 36 radii centered on the point of calculation and then divide this total by the number of radii used. As an example consider Figure 14–12. This figure represents the projection to a depth of 5 cm of a cobalt-60 field at 80 cm of 12 cm x 15 cm with a corner block of 3 cm x 5 cm. To calculate the scatter dose on the central axis, we measure the distances along the 36 radii indicated. Then we find the corresponding SAR values, add them and divide by 36. We use this average SAR value in Equation 3–21 to calculate the dose rate. Details are given in Table 14–1.

As a more complex example, let's progress to the mantle field illustrated in Figure 14–13. Consider the points 1, 2, and 3 indicated

TABLE 14–1. Details of Calculation of the Dose Delivered by Field Illustrated in Figure 14–12 Performed by Separating Radiation Beam into Primary and Scattered Components

Radius	Distance to edge of field	SAR	Radius	Distance to edge of field	SAR
1	8	0.188	19	8	0.188
2	8	0.188	20	8	0.188
3	8.5	0.193	21	8.5	0.193
4	6	0.165	22	9.5	0.202
5	5	0.151	23	10	0.206
6	4	0.134	24	8.5	0.193
7	5.5	0.158	25	7.5	0.182
8	7	0.177	26	7	0.177
9	6.5	0.171	27	6.5	0.171
10	6.5	0.171	28	6.5	0.171
11	6.5	0.171	29	6.5	0.171
12	7	0.177	30	7	0.177
13	7.5	0.182	31	7.5	0.182
14	8.5	0.193	32	8.5	0.193
15	10	0.206	33	10	0.206
16	9.5	0.202	34	9.5	0.202
17	8.5	0.193	35	8.5	0.193
18	8	0.188	36	8	0.188

$$\text{Average } SAR = \frac{6.591}{36} = 0.183 \qquad\qquad TAR_0 = 0.742$$

$$SSD = 80 \text{ cm}, g = 0 \text{ cm}, d = 5 \text{ cm}, D_p = 100 \text{ cGy/min}, X_{ac} = 80.5 \text{ cm}, T_T = 0.97$$
$$F = 1.03, 0 = 1.00$$

$$D_p = 100 \times 0.97 \times 1.03 \times 1.00 \left[\frac{80.5}{80 + 0 + 5}\right]^2 (0.742 + .183) = 82.9 \text{ cGy/min}$$

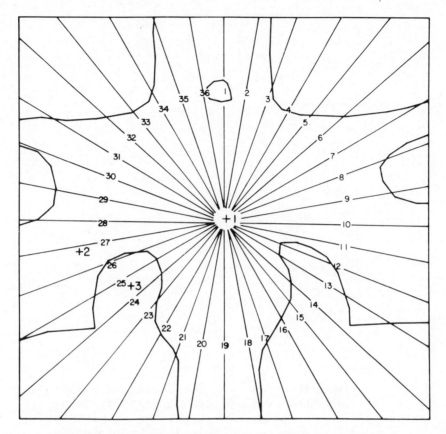

Figure 14–13 Mantle field with radii used in the determination of the average SAR at the central axis.

in the figure. Point 1 is the on central axis at a depth of 8.5 cm, point 2 is at the right axilla at a depth of 8 cm, and point 3 is located under the right lung block at a depth of 8 cm. The 36 radii are shown centered on point 1. The radii for points 2 and 3, are illustrated in Figures 14–14 and 14–15. Note in Tables 14–2 and 14–3, the values of the SARs for areas under a block are listed as negatives. For instance, along radius 1 in Table 14–2, it is 21.5 cm from the central axis to the edge of the beam, the area from 14.5 cm to 12.5 cm along this radius is under the larynx shielding block. The SAR for 21.5 cm, 14.5 cm, and 12.5 cm are 0.311, 0.276, and 0.259 respectively. The total SAR contributing to the dose on the central axis is 0.311 − 0.276 + 0.259 = 0.294. The dose at point 2 illustrated in Figure 14–14 calculated in a similar manner. The details are given in Table 14–3.

To calculate the dose at point 3 under the lung block, we

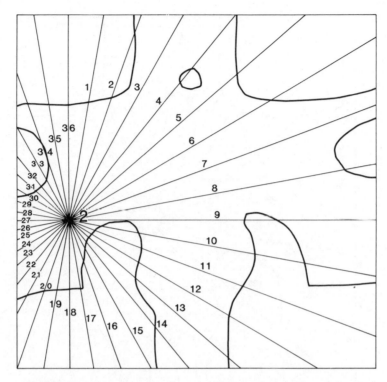

Figure 14–14 Radii used in the determination of the average SAR for the axilla point. The data are listed in Table 14–3.

will use a method proposed by Hanson and Berkley.[7] With this method the dose under a block is calculated as

$$D_{p,b} = D_{ac}\ T_T\ F\ O\ \left(\frac{X_{ac}}{\text{SSD} + g + d}\right)^2 \{T_B\ \text{TAR}_o\ (d,r)$$
$$+\ T_B\ S_{du} + S_{do}\}\quad \textbf{(14–1)}$$

where T_B = transmission through shielding blocks measured in air

S_{du} = average scatter-air ratio at point P from area under the blocks

S_{do} = average scatter-air ratio at point P from unblocked area of field

all other symbols are as defined in Chapter 3

Again we adopt the convention of a negative value to indicate SARs under a block. Accordingly, in Table 14–4, radius 1 is shielded from the edge of the field, a distance of 29 cm, to a position 18 cm from point 3. Radius 1 is in the open beam from 18 cm to a

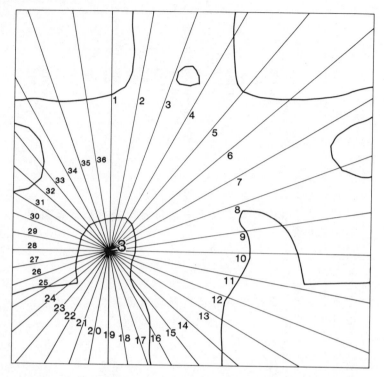

Figure 14–15 Radii used in the determination of the average SAR for the point under the lung block. The data are enumerated in Table 14–4.

point 3.5 cm from the calculation point, and then from 3.5 cm to point 3 radius 1 is under the shielding block. The SARs corresponding to 29, 18, and 3.5 cm are 0.318, 0.293, and 0.126. It follows from this analysis that the SAR is −0.318 + 0.293 − 0.126 = −0.151. Note the minus sign is used to indicate this contribution is from the blocked area of the beam. In order to calculate the dose with Equation 14–1, the absolute value of the average SAR from the blocked portion of the beam will be multiplied by the transmission through the block and added to the other terms. This term is denoted in Equation 14–1 by $T_B S_{du}$.

At this point it should be emphasized that certain approximations are implicit in this procedure. If the point of calculation is within 1 to 1.5 cm of the edge of the patient or the shadow cast by the primary collimator or secondary blocking, there may be significant differences between the calculated and actual doses. In this case it it necessary to know the edge effect caused by the collimator, blocks, or patient; then appropriate corrections may

TABLE 14–2. Calculational Details of the Central Axis Point for the Mantle Field Diagramed in Figure 14–13

$SSD = 95$ cm $g = 0$ cm, $d = 8.5$ cm $D_p = 100$ cGy/min, $X_{ac} = 80.5$ cm, $T_T = .92$
$F = 1.06$, $0 = 1.00$

Radius	Distance to edge of field	SAR	Radius	Distance to edge of field	SAR
1	21.5,14.5,12.5	$0.311 - 0.276 + 0.259$	19	21	0.309
2	21.5	0.311	20	21.5	0.311
3	15	0.281	21	15	0.281
4	13.5	0.268	22	14	0.272
5	14.5	0.276	23	11	0.246
6	17.0	0.291	24	9	0.226
7	23.5	0.316	25	26,16,8.5	$0.321 - 0.286 + 0.220$
8	19.0	0.301	26	23.5	0.316
9	18.5	0.299	27	22.5	0.313
10	22.5	0.313	28	20	0.307
11	22.5	0.313	29	19	0.301
12	23.5,12,7	$0.316 - 0.255 + 0.199$	30	23.5	0.316
13	22,15,7	$0.312 - 0.281 + 0.199$	31	20.5	0.308
14	9.5	0.232	32	17	0.291
15	11.5	0.250	33	15	0.281
16	12.5	0.259	34	16	0.286
17	13.5	0.268	35	23	0.315
18	21.5	0.311	36	22	0.312

$$\text{Average } SAR = \frac{10.319}{36} = 0.287, \; TAR_0 = 0.589$$

$$D_p = 100 \times 0.92 \times 1.06 \times 1.0 \left[\frac{80.5}{95 + 0 + 8.5}\right]^2 (0.589 + 0.287) = 51.7 \text{ cGy/min}$$

TABLE 14-3. Details of Calculation for Point 2 in Figure 14-14

$SSD = 95.0$ cm, $g = -.5$ cm, $d = 8$ cm, $D_{ac} = 100$ cGy/min, $X_{ac} = 80.5$ cm, $T_T = .92$, $F = 1.06$, $0 = .94$

Radius	Distance to edge of field	SAR	Radius	Distance to edge of field	SAR
1	13.5	0.266	19	8	0.213
2	26,23.5,15	$0.314 - 0.310 + 0.278$	20	8.5	0.219
3	28	0.317	21	10	0.236
4	31.5,23,21	$0.319 - 0.310 + 0.304$	22	10	0.236
5	27	0.316	23	8	0.213
6	28.5	0.318	24	7	0.199
7	40	0.330	25	6.5	0.191
8	34	0.323	26	6	0.186
9	38,25,21.5	$0.327 - 0.314 + 0.304$	27	6	0.186
10	38,29,23,9,3.5	$0.327 - 0.318 + 0.309 - 0.227 + 0.131$	28	6	0.186
11	22.5,9,3	$0.308 - 0.227 + 0.116$	29	6.5	0.191
12	22.5,9.5,3	$0.308 - 0.231 + 0.110$	30	5.5	0.176
13	25.5,10,3	$0.314 - 0.239 + 0.110$	31	5	0.165
14	23,16,3	$0.308 - 0.284 + 0.110$	32	5	0.165
15	3.5	0.131	33	5	0.165
16	5	0.165	34	6.5	0.191
17	8	0.213	35	13.5	0.266
18	8	0.213	36	13.5	0.266

Average $SAR = 0.224$ $TAR_0 = 0.608$

$$D_p = 100 \times 0.92 \times 1.06 \times 0.94 \times \left(\frac{80.5}{95 - 0.5 + 8}\right)^2 (0.608 + 0.224) = 47.0 \text{ cGy/min}$$

TABLE 14–4. Details of Calculation for Point 3 in Figure 14–15

$SSD = 95$ cm, $g = 0$ cm, $D_{ac} = 100$ cGy/min, $X_{ac} = 80.5$ cm, $T_T = 0.92$, $T_B = 0.03$, $O = 0.94$, $F = 1.06$, $d = 8$ cm

Radius	Distance to edge of field	SAR	Radius	Distance to edge of field	SAR
1	29,18,3.5	$-0.318 + 0.293 - 0.126$	19	13	-0.263
2	29,3.5	$0.318 - 0.131$	20	13.5	-0.266
3	30,4	$0.319 - 0.142$	21	14	-0.270
4	33,30.5,4	$-0.322 + 0.320 - 0.142$	22	15	-0.278
5	38,25,4	$-0.326 + 0.314 - 0.142$	23	16.5	-0.285
6	42.5,28,3.5	$-0.331 + 0.317 - 0.131$	24	15,6.5	$-0.278 + 0.184 - 0.165$
7	37,3.5	$0.326 - 0.131$	25	13.5,8,4.5	$-0.266 + 0.213 - 0.153$
8	34,29.5,3	$-0.323 + 0.319 - 0.114$	26	12.5,4	$0.257 - 0.142$
9	32.5,21.5,17,3	$0.321 - 0.304 + 0.287 - 0.114$	27	12,3.5	$0.253 - 0.131$
10	32,23,17,3	$0.320 - 0.309 + 0.287 - 0.114$	28	11.5,3.5	$0.249 - 0.131$
11	32.5,16,3	$-0.321 + 0.284 - 0.114$	29	12,3.5	$0.253 - 0.131$
12	34,15,3	$-0.323 + 0.278 - 0.114$	30	12,3.5	$0.253 - 0.131$
13	27,16,3	$-0.319 + 0.281 - 0.114$	31	13.5,3.5	$0.266 - 0.131$
14	20.5,18,3	$-0.301 + 0.292 - 0.114$	32	15,12,3.5	$-0.278 + 0.253 - 0.131$
15	17.5,4	$0.290 - 0.142$	33	18,12,3.5	$-0.292 + 0.253 - 0.131$
16	15,10	$0.278 - 0.236$	34	24.5,20.5,3.5	$-0.312 + 0.302 - 0.131$
17	14	-0.270	35	30.5,18.5,3.5	$-0.319 + 0.294 - 0.131$
18	13	-0.263	36	29,18,3.5	$-0.318 + 0.292 - 0.131$

Average $S_{du} = 0.174$,   Average $S_{do} = 0.119$, $TAR_o = 0.608$

$$D_p = 100 \times 0.92 \times 1.06 \times 0.94 \times \left(\frac{80.5}{95 + 0 + 8}\right)^2 (0.03 \times 0.608 + 0.03 \times 0.174 + 0.119)$$

$$D_p = 8.0 \text{ cGy/min}$$

be made. Another approximation is the use of the vertical depth and vertical distance from the source rather than the depth and distance along a ray line. This approximation usually introduces a small error but it may become significant near the edge of a large treatment field.

14.5 ROTATIONAL THERAPY CALCULATIONS

Tissue-air-ratios were originally formulated to aid in calculating beam-on time for rotational therapy. This technique requires radii spaced 10° apart to be centered on the point of rotation. Then the distance from this point to the skin surface is measured and the TAR or TMR is found along each of these radii. The TARs are added and then divided by the total number of radii to find an average TAR. The value of the average TAR is used to calculate the beam-on time. Reference to Table 14–5 and Figure 14–16 will clarify this procedure. This treatment is for a rectal lesion using an 18 MV X-ray beam rotated through 90°. The TAR along each radius are given in the table with the average TAR computed on the bottom line. This average TAR is used in the calculation sheet in the same manner as the TAR for a single field was used for isocentric treatments.

For this partial rotation, notice the rotation is not centered on the tumor but below it. The reason for this is that the hot spot

TABLE 14–5. Details of Calculation for Arc Therapy Plan Shown in Figure 14–16

Depth (cm)		TAR
14		0.809
13		0.832
12		0.854
11.5		0.865
11		0.876
10		0.895
11		0.876
12		0.854
13		0.832
14		0.809
Σ	=	8.502
Average	=	0.850

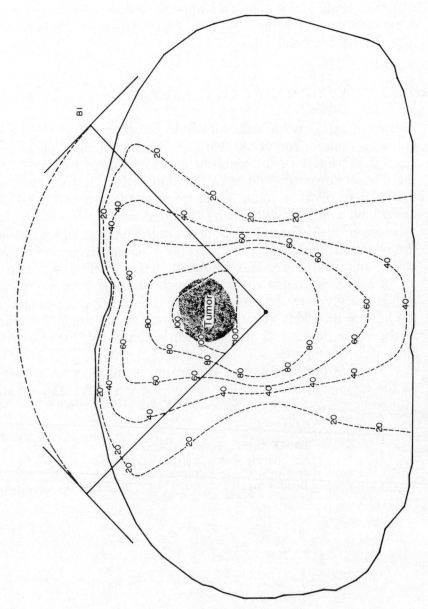

Figure 14–16 Rotational treatment plan with a 90° arc.

of the distribution is above the axis of rotation. This technique of locating the axis of rotation below the tumor is referred to as "past-pointing." Of course, for a full 360° arc the hot spot would be centered on the tumor and past pointing would not be necessary.

14.6 QUALITY ASSURANCE PROGRAM

After the treatment plan has been determined, the patient simulated and beam-on time calculated, a continuing program of quality assurance must be enforced to insure the plan is executed. This task may be separated into two halves. The therapist must see the patient is correctly positioned for the first treatment and a supervisory level technologist should assure all subsequent treatments are performed in an identical manner. The second half of the quality assurance program is the monitoring of the treatment record to guarantee that the correct dose is administered each treatment session. This task is the purview of the physicist or dosimetrist. A program of weekly chart reviews must be adhered to diligently. The physicist or dosimetrist should check that the correct beam-on time is used daily, that all additions of dose are accurate, that appropriate field sizes are employed, that the patient's thickness along the central axis has not changed and all beam modifying devices are being used correctly.

14.7 PROGRAMMABLE CALCULATOR AND PERSONAL COMPUTER PROGRAMS

With the ready availability of programmable calculators and personal computers, much of the routine drudgery may be eliminated from beam-on time calculations. A calculator or computer can be programmed to query a technologist, dosimetrist, or physicist with the same questions as posed on the menus of the calculation sheets presented in this chapter.

The limited memory available on many programmable calculators requires various answers to the questions be parameterized and stored as a few constants. The percent depth dose might have to be calculated using a Glover's[8] constant approach or TAR values with the method of Thomas.[9] Additionally, the field size dependence, output factors and peak scatter factors can usually be fit with a second or third order polynomial. These approaches have been discussed in Chapter 3 and extensive references to other methods are given at the end of the chapter. However, the memory of personal computers permits percent depth dose or TAR values as well as output factors, field size dependence, peak scatter factors, wedge factors, and tray factors to be stored in tabular form.

The programs are fairly straightforward to write and once implemented can relieve much of the tedium and eliminate many careless errors. But like all computerized operations, these programs should be extensively checked before entering clinical service and validated on a continuing basis thereafter.

Notes

1. H. E. Johns, G. F. Whitmore, T. A. Watson, and F. H. Umberg, "A System of Dosimetry for Rotation Therapy with Typical Rotation Distributions," *J. of Canadian Association of Radiologists*, IV(1953), pp. 1–14.

2. J. Garrett Holt, John S. Laughlin, and John P. Moroney, "The Extension of the Concept of Tissue-Air Ratios (TAR) to High-Energy X-ray Beams," *Radiol.*, 96(1970), pp. 437–46.

3. C. J. Karzmark, Angela Deubert, and R. Loevinger, "Tissue-Phantom Ratios—an Aid to Treatment Planning," *Brit. J. Radiol.*, 38(1965), pp. 158–59.

4. *Central Axis Depth Dose Data for Use in Radiotherapy, British Journal of Radiology Supplement 17*, (London: British Institute of Radiology, 1983).

5. Jerome R. Hallberg and others, "Computational Analysis and Dosimetric Evaluation of a Commercial Irregular-Fields Computer Program," *Med. Phys.*, 4(1977), pp. 528–34.

6. W. F. Hanson, L. W. Berkeley, and M. Peterson, "Calculative Technique to Correct for the Change in Linear Accelerator Beam Energy at Off-Axis Points," *Med. Phys.*, 7(1980), pp. 147–50.

7. William F. Hanson and Lawrence W. Berkley, "Reply by Hanson and Berkley to 'A Note on the Formalism for Irregular Field Calculations,'" *Med. Phys.*, 8(1981), pp. 716–17.

8. J. R. Glover, "A System of Three Equations Allowing Calculations of Central Axis Percent Depth Dose and Related Quantities," *Phys. Med. Biol.*, 12(1967), pp. 119–20.

9. Robert L. Thomas, "A General Expression for Megavoltage Central Axis Depth Doses," *Brit. J. Radiol.*, 43(1970), pp. 554–57.

Additional Reading

ANALYTICAL EXPRESSIONS FOR CENTRAL AXIS PERCENT DEPTH DOSE AND TISSUE-AIR RATIO VALUES

CHRISTOS KANELLITSAS AND JUAN V. FAYOS, "Analytical Approach for Depth Dose Calculations (^{60}Co Beams with Fixed Source-Target Distance)," *Radiol.*, 115(1975), pp. 181–85.

PAUL M. PFALZNER, "A General Formula for Axial Depth Dose Derived from an Empirical Power Law for Tumor-Air Ratios," *Radiol.*, 75(1960), pp. 438–45.

THEODOR D. STERLING, HAROLD PERRY, AND LEO KATZ, "Automation of Radiation Treatment Planning IV. Derivation of a Mathematical Expression for the Percent Depth Dose Surface of Cobalt-60 Beams and Visualisation of Multiple Field Dose Distributions," *Brit. J. Radiol.*, 37(1964), pp. 544–50.

JOHN MELSKI, "Tissue-Air Ratio Formulae in ^{60}Co Teletherapy Dosimetry," *Brit. J. Radiol.*, 43(1970), pp. 825–26.

R. O. KORNELSEN AND M. E. J. YOUNG, "Empirical Equations for the Representation of Depth Dose Data for Computerized Treatment Planning," *Brit. J. Radiol.*, 48(1975), pp. 739–48.

R. L. THOMAS AND J. L. HAYBITTLE, "A Widely Applicable Method for Computing Dose Distributions from External Megavoltage Beams," *Brit. J. Radiol.*, 48(1975), pp. 749–54.

M. BENASSI AND R. PAOLUZI, "An Empirical Formula, Continuous in Field Parameters and Depth, for the Axial Dose for ^{60}Co Gamma Radiation," *Brit. J. Radiol.*, 45(1972), p. 475.

JOHN G. FOX AND PAUL G. FOX, "Empirical Formula for ^{60}Co Axial Depth Doses," *Med. Phys.*, 5(1978), pp. 61–62.

FIFTEEN | CLINICAL BRACHYTHERAPY DOSIMETRY

15.1 INTRODUCTION

Brachytherapy dates to the turn of the century when Becquerel observed a skin reaction from carrying a radium source in his waistcoat pocket. Pierre Curie concluded there might be medical applications for radium and loaned some to physician-friends. As workers gained experience, advances were made in brachytherapy dosimetry. In 1921, Sievert[1] published his data on the calculated intensity around linear sources. It was in this article that the Sievert integral discussed in Chapter 3 was introduced. Quimby[2] developed a brachytherapy dosimetry system in 1932 based on various combinations of equal strength linear sources. Paterson and Parker[3] proposed the Manchester system of using combinations of unequal strength radium sources to yield "uniform" dose distributions in 1934. The Quimby and Paterson-Parker systems remained the standard techniques until computer methods, which could give complete dose distributions in a variety of planes, were introduced.

15.2 SPECIFICATION OF BRACHYTHERAPY SOURCES

The strength of a brachytherapy source may be specified by activity, equivalent mass of radium or exposure rate in air at a given distance. Although the National Council on Radiation Protection and Measurements (NCRP)[4] recommends the third method, it is rarely used. The first two methods are more commonly encountered.

The activity of radium is specified in terms of mg while the activity of all other isotopes is in terms of mCi. However, with the implementation of the SI units, activity will be expressed in Becquerel.

The use of mg-Ra equivalent is useful for the therapist with accumulated experience with radium 226 implants. However, depending upon the isotope, the dose distribution in tissue may be quite different between radium and the isotope under consideration. Further problems may arise with different wall attenuations or inadequate knowledge of the Γ-factor.

The conversion from mCi to mg-Ra equivalent is accomplished by taking the ratio of the Γ-constant for the isotope under consideration to the Γ-factor for radium, which is $8.25 \dfrac{\text{R-cm}^2}{\text{mg-hr}}$ for radium filtered by 0.5 mm Pt. For instance, the Γ-factor for cesium-137 is

$$3.226 \frac{\text{R-cm}^2}{\text{mCi-hr}}$$

$$\text{therefore } 1 \text{ mCi } ^{137}\text{Cs} = \frac{3.226}{8.25} \text{ mg Ra eq}$$

$$= 0.39 \text{ mg Ra eq}$$

15.3 THE QUIMBY SYSTEM

The Quimby system is based on the use of equal strength radium sources to yield a non-uniform dose distribution. By combining dose distributions from single needles, she generated dose distribution for implants of various shapes. Typically these implants were designed with 1 cm spacings between sources. For planar implants she tabulated the dose rate at several perpendicular distances from the center of the plane. These values were the stated dose rates that characterized the implant. For planar implants designed according to the Quimby system, this dose rate was the maximum value in that particular plane. She extended her method to volume implants; however, in this case she chose a "minimum" dose rate as representative of the implant. Therefore, if one uses the Quimby system, one must be aware of this significant difference when correlating clinical reactions to dose from planar and volume implants.

15.4 THE MANCHESTER SYSTEM

Paterson and Parker devised a system of radium treatments that achieved a uniform dose distribution by a non-uniform distribution of the radium. This system, referred to as the Manchester System, addressed surface applicators and planar and volume implants of various shapes and sizes. This system required the radium to be distributed in the applicator or implant according to very specific distribution rules. Paterson and Parker published tables of the stated dose as a function of the area of the implant and the perpendicular distance from the implant. This stated dose was within 10% of the maximum or minimum value at the given distance from the plane of the implant.

The original dose rate tables were in terms of milligram-hours per 1000 Roentgen. At the time, these original tables were prepared the exposure rate constant, Γ, for radium filtered by 0.5 mm Pt was taken to be 8.4 $\frac{\text{R-cm}^2}{\text{mg-hr}}$. The currently accepted value is 8.25 $\frac{\text{R-cm}^2}{\text{mg-hr}}$. Shalek and Stovall[5] have commented on three additional corrections required to convert the Paterson-Parker tables to modern computer calculations in cGy per hour. The original tables did not account for the oblique filtration of gamma-rays in the encapsulation material. This correction is included in computer calculations using either the interval method or the Sievert integral. Paterson-Parker made no attempt to correct for tissue absorption and scattering that have been shown to decrease the dose rate from radium approximately 1% per cm up to a distance of 4 cm. Finally, a conversion from Roentgen to cGy must be made. Because of these four corrections, Shalek and Stovall recommend multiplying the Paterson-Parker Roentgen by 0.9 for comparison to computer calculations in cGy.

Shalek and Stovall's values will deliver a 4.4% higher dose than those given in earlier textbooks,[6,7] which have been corrected for the change in Γ-factor and converted to cGy, but have not been corrected for oblique filtration or tissue absorption. However, the values of Shalek and Stovall should be in closer agreement with computer calculations than the previous tables.

15.5 AWAY AND ALONG TABLES

The dose rate at several points from an ideal implant may be calculated by hand using "away and along" tables.[8,9] These tables give the calculated dose rates of radium or cesium needles as a function of the perpendicular distance from the needle, as well as the distance along the axis of the needle. The perpendicular distance from the needle is commonly referred to as the "away" distance and the distance along the axis, the "along" distance, hence the name "away and along" tables. These tables are particularly useful in verifying computer calculations both for individual sources and for several sources in an ideal geometry.

15.6 RADIOGRAPHY OF THE IMPLANT

To determine the position of the sources in the actual implant, either orthogonal or stereo shift radiographs are necessary. For these radiographs, a ring of known diameter is required to determine the implant image magnification. It is important that this ring be in the plane of the sources and the same distance from the film as the implant in both views to ascertain the true magnification. To find the magnification of the implant in a radiograph, the largest outside diameter of the ring presented in the radiograph must be divided by the true outside diameter.

Generally, orthogonal radiographs are most useful if hand calculations are to be done using either Quimby's or Paterson-Parker's tables. In this instance, the radiographs can usually be oriented so the implant is approximately parallel with the central axis of the X-ray beam of the AP or the lateral view. If the plane of the implant is parallel with the central axis of the X-ray beam, the implant will project as a line in the radiograph. The width of the plane can then be determined by measuring the width in the other view and dividing by the magnification factor. It is, of course, important that the views be truly orthogonal and the patient does not move between exposures.

While orienting the implant parallel to the X-ray beam in one orthogonal view simplifies hand calculations, this orientation may make data entry into a computer very difficult. Computer techniques depend upon the physicist or dosimetrist being able to identify both ends of each needle in both views. If the needles are superimposed upon one another, this can become a difficult, if not impossible, task. If a large number of sources are used in a multiplane or volume implant, it may also be difficult to identify each source in the two orthogonal views. The stereo-shift procedure simplifies this chore. With this procedure a radiograph is taken such that the plane of the implant is more or less perpendicular to the central axis of the X-ray beam. Let us refer to this view as the "AP view" for convenience, although it could just as well be a lateral view. Then either the patient or the X-ray tube is shifted a fixed distance perpendicular to the X-ray beam and a second radiograph is taken.

A variation of this technique becomes practical if a treatment simulator is used to obtain the radiographs. In this case stereo-shift films could be taken by rotating the gantry a fixed number of degrees between exposures. In either case with the "AP view" and the "shifted view" it is much easier to identify needles in each view than it is with orthogonal radiographs.

The advantage of the stereo-shift technique is ease in identifying needles and the reduction of errors resulting in possible misidentification. However, this advantage is not without its price. The stereo-shift technique is schematically illustrated in Figure 15–1. If one uses the method of similar triangles in Figure 15–1, it follows that:

$$\frac{h}{\text{TFD} - h} = \frac{i_s}{t_s}$$

where
$$h = \text{point of interest to film distance}$$
$$TFD = \text{target-film-distance}$$
$$t_s = \text{tube shift}$$
$$i_s = \text{image shift}$$

Simple algebraic manipulation yields

$$h = \frac{TFD}{1 + \dfrac{t_s}{i_s}}$$

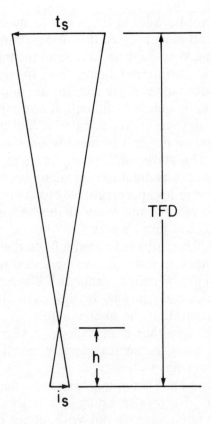

Figure 15–1 Illustration of relationships involved with stereo-shift technique; TFD = target-film-distance, h = distance from point of interest to film, t_s = tube shift, i_s = image shift.

Now h is the z position of the point under consideration. The first derivative of h with respect to i_s gives us the amount of error introduced into the z coordinate by a misidentification in the image. Then

$$\frac{dh}{di_s} = TFD \frac{t_s}{(i_s + t_s)^2}$$

If we take as typical values

$$TFD = 100 \text{ cm}$$

$$t_s = 10 \text{ cm}$$

$$i_s = 2 \text{ cm}$$

then

$$\frac{dh}{di_s} = 6.9$$

we see that a 1 mm error in identification of the end of a needle may result in a 7 mm error in the z coordinate of that needle.

15.7 DOSE RATE DEPENDENCE

The Manchester System devised by Paterson and Parker was based on 6000 R in 168 hours. Later, Paterson[10] published a table correlating clinical response with the dose rate of a radium implant. This table indicated that it was necessary to lower the total dose if the dose rate were higher than 35.7 R/hr (6000 R in 168 hours) and increase the total dose if the dose rate were lower than this value to achieve the same isoeffect as the standard dose rate. Ellis,[11] Orton,[12] and Kirk[13] adopted similar approaches in the development of their brachytherapy time-dose-models. Although further discussion of brachytherapy dose rate effects is not within the scope of this book, one should be careful when adding doses given from external beam to doses given by a brachytherapy application. Because of the different dose rates in these two situations, it is naive to assure that a cGy from one modality has the same biological effect as a cGy from the other modality.

15.8 RADIUM SUBSTITUTES

In recent years many institutions have abandoned the use of radium brachytherapy and have begun using other isotopes. This decision has been made because radium has a complex decay scheme with several high energy gamma rays, has a radiotoxic gas, radon, as a decay product, and is fabricated into bulky inflexible sources. The high-energy gamma rays require a large amount of shielding for personnel protection. The radon and the radium could be released if the source were broken. Finally, the inflexibility of the sources is a definite disadvantage in many applications. Many years of clinical experience with radium, plus the convenience of long half-life must be balanced against the above disadvantages.

Some of the isotopes that are popular radium substitutes are cesium-137, gold-198, iridium-192, and iodine-125. Properties of several radium substitutes are summarized in Table 15–1. Cesium tubes are especially popular for intracavity applications. With a half-life of 30.0 years, source decay is a minimal problem requiring only an annual change in output of 2.3%. Cesium emits a gamma ray of 662 keV, which is easier to shield than the high energy radiations of radium; however, the radiation distribution in tissue of the two isotopes is sufficiently similar that cesium is an acceptable substitute.

Iridium is fabricated as long thin wires or as seeds encapsulated in plastic ribbons. Both the wires and the ribbons have great flexibility and are useful in situations where this is an important requirement. Iridium has a complex decay scheme with a few gamma rays above 1 MeV; however, the principal gamma rays are in the 300 to 600 keV range resulting in shielding requirements that are less than radium. If iridium is to be used more than once or if a department wishes to maintain a large inventory, its short half-life may be a problem. However, if the department is willing to use the iridium only once, it may be ordered in custom lengths for a particular application. This procedure requires some advance planning to determine what lengths are necessary, but this should be done anyway. A further problem might be the storage or disposal of the iridium once it has been used.

Gold seeds have almost universally replaced radon seeds for permanent implants. The short half-life of gold makes it ideal for this situation. Gold has a principal gamma ray of 412 keV and an average energy of 416 keV, which means the HVL in lead is less than the HVL in lead for radium.

TABLE 15–1. Summary of Properties of Isotopes Commonly Used as Radium Substitutes

Radionuclide	Half-life	Gamma photons MeV	Specific gamma ray constant $R\ cm^2h^{-1}\ mCi^{-1}$	Exposure rate constant $R\ m^2h^{-1}\ Ci^{-1}$
Cesium-137	30.0 years	0.6616	3.226	0.3275
Cobalt-60	5.26 years	1.173 − 1.322	13.07	1.307
Gold-198	2.698 days	0.4118 − 1.088	2.327	0.2376
Iodine-125	60.25 days	0.03548	0.04228	0.1326
Iridium-192	74.2 days	0.1363 − 1.062	3.948	0.4002
Tantalum-182	115.0 days	0.0427 − 1.453	7.692	0.7815

Source: "Specification of Gamma-Ray Brachytherapy Sources," *NCRP Report 41*. Used with permission.

As a result of pioneering work by Memorial Hospital in New York, iodine seeds are becoming popular for permanent implants. Iodine emits a 35 keV gamma ray and 27 keV and 31 keV X-rays. At these low energies shielding requirements are minimal but the dosimetry is far from routine. The RBE of iodine is an additional question that must be considered. Institutions contemplating initiating a program with iodine would be well advised to consult the data generated at Memorial.

Other isotopes that have been used as radium substitutes are cobalt-60 and tantalum-182. Tantalum was originally preferred to iridium for applications demanding flexible sources because pure iridium wire is brittle. However, iridium is currently fabricated as a platinum-iridium alloy and these early objections have been overcome. Consequently tantalum, with its high-energy gamma rays requiring greater shielding, has been replaced by iridium.

Cobalt, being relatively easy to produce in a reactor, is inexpensive but the bookkeeping requirements introduced by its short half-life and the shielding necessary because of its high-energy gamma rays have resulted in little application of this isotope. However, remote afterloading machines with high activity sources are one area where cobalt has been used.

15.9 PERMANENT AND TEMPORARY IMPLANTS OF SHORT-LIVED SOURCES

Calculations of the dose delivered by short-lived isotopes must account for the decay of the isotope during the implant. This is done by invoking the concept of "mCi destroyed." As discussed in Section 15.8, gold-198 is frequently used for permanent implants. Gold has a half-life of 2.7 days and a mean life of $2.7 \times 1.44 = 3.89$ days or 93.3 hours. The Γ-factor for gold is $2.33 \ \dfrac{\text{R-cm}^2}{\text{mCi-hr}}$. Then 1 mCi gold destroyed is

$$1 \text{ mCi gold destroyed} = \frac{2.33 \times 93.3}{8.25} = 26.4 \text{ mg-hr}$$

of radium where Γ-factor of radium is $8.25 \ \dfrac{\text{R-cm}^2}{\text{hr-mg}}$

In other words the total "dose" delivered from the complete decay of 1 mCi of gold-198 is equivalent to 26.4 mg-hr of radium-226.

If the gold were used in a surface applicator for a temporary implant the dose could be computed by determining the amount of gold remaining at the end of the implant. By subtracting the amount remaining from the original amount, the mCi destroyed may be found.

Example

Find the equivalent mg-hrs of radium delivered by surface applicator of 10 mCi of gold-198 which was in place for 2 days.

Solution

The half-life of gold-198 is 2.7 days, which means the activity remaining after 2 days is

$$A = 10 \exp\left(-\frac{0.693 \times 2}{2.7}\right) \text{mCi}$$

$$= 5.98 \text{ mCi}$$

or the number of mCi destroyed $= 4.02$ mCi

In terms of equivalent mg-hours of radium that is

$$\text{mg-hrs} = 4.02 \text{ mCi} \times 26.4 \frac{\text{mg-hrs}}{\text{mCi}}$$

$$= 105.9 \text{ mg-hrs}$$

Notes

1. R. M. Sievert, "Die Intensitätsverteilung der Primären Gamma-Strahlung in der Nähe Medizinscher Radiumpräparate," *Acta Radiol.*, 1(1921), pp. 89–128.

2. Edith H. Quimby, "The Grouping of Radium Tubes in Packs or Plaques to Produce the Desired Distribution of Radiation," *Amer. J. Roentgenol. Radium Therapy*, 27(1932), pp. 18–39.

3. Ralston Paterson and H. M. Parker, "A Dosage System for Gamma Ray Therapy, Part I," *Brit. J. Radiol.*, 7(1934), pp. 592–632.

4. *Specification of Gamma-Ray Brachytherapy Sources NCRP Report 41*, (Washington, D. C.: National Council on Radiation Protection and Measurements, 1974).

5. Robert J. Shalek and Marilyn Stovall, *Implant Dosimetry*, (Houston, Texas: M. D. Anderson Hospital, 1967).

6. Harold Elford Johns and John Robert Cunningham, *The Physics of Radiology*, *Third Edition*, (Springfield, Ill.: Charles C. Thomas, 1974).

7. William R. Hendee, *Medical Radiation Physics*, (Chicago, Ill.: Year Book Medical Publishers, 1970).

8. Robert J. Shalek and Marilyn Stovall, "The M. D. Anderson Method for the Computation of Isodose Curves Around Interstitial and Intercavitary Radiation Sources. I. Dose from Linear Sources," *Amer. J. Roentgenol. Radium Ther. Nucl. Med. CII*, (1968), pp. 662–72.

9. V. Krishnaswamy, "Dose Distributions about ^{137}Cs Sources in Tissue," *Radiol.*, 105(1972), pp. 181–84.

10. Ralston Paterson, *The Treatment of Malignant Disease by Radiotherapy*, (Baltimore, Md.: Williams and Wilkins, 1963).

11. Frank Ellis and Arnold Sorenson, "A Method of Estimating Biological Effect of Combined Intracavitary Low Dose Rate Radiation With External Radiation in Carcinoma of the Cervix Uteri," *Radiol.*, 110(1974), pp. 681–86.

12. C. G. Orton, "Time-Dose Factors (TDFs) in Brachytherapy," *Brit. J. Radiol.*, 47(1974), pp. 603–7.

13. J. Kirk, W. M. Gray, and E. R. Watson, "Cumulative Radiation Effect. Part III: Continuous Radiation Therapy—Short-Lived Sources," *Clin. Radiol.*, 24(1973), pp. 1–11.

Index

A